BOWLING GREENS
THEIR HISTORY, CONSTRUCTION AND MAINTENANCE

By

R.D.C. EVANS B.Sc.

Advisory Agronomist

The Sports Turf Research Institute

Published by
THE SPORTS TURF RESEARCH INSTITUTE
BINGLEY, WEST YORKSHIRE, BD16 1AU

First Published 1988 by:

THE SPORTS TURF RESEARCH INSTITUTE, BINGLEY, WEST YORKSHIRE, BD16 1AU, ENGLAND. FIRST EDITION : ISBN: 0-9503647-7-0

SECOND FULLY REVISED EDITION COPYRIGHT © SPORTS TURF RESEARCH INSTITUTE 1992. ISBN: 1-873431-01-5

✿ ✿ ✿ ✿ ✿ ✿ ✿ ✿ ✿ ✿ ✿ ✿ ✿ ✿ ✿ ✿ ✿

NOTE 1: The fact that photographs of particular items of equipment or machinery appear in this text should not be taken to imply that the STRI endorses one firm's products over another. When purchasing equipment for a club it is always wise to obtain details of all rival products and to make a choice based on full on-site demonstrations and on the exact requirements of the particular club, bearing in mind the supply of spare parts, local servicing facilities, etc.

NOTE 2: The application rates given in the following text for pesticides should be regarded as being for guidance only, although every effort has been made to ensure that quoted rates are appropriate. It should be understood that pesticide users are under an obligation to comply with legal requirements governing the usage of such materials and that the instructions included with each product are mandatory, including instructions regarding application rates. Users should be familiar with the Food and Environment Protection Act (1985), Part 3: Control of Pesticides Regulations (1986).

✿ ✿ ✿ ✿ ✿ ✿ ✿ ✿ ✿ ✿ ✿ ✿ ✿ ✿ ✿ ✿ ✿

BY THE SAME AUTHOR:

THE BAYONET : AN EVOLUTION AND HISTORY. Militaria Publications, Milton Keynes 1985 (with F.J. STEPHENS).

BOWLING GREENS : THEIR HISTORY CONSTRUCTION AND MAINTENANCE. Sports Turf Research Institute, Bingley. First Edn. 1988.

CRICKET GROUNDS : THE EVOLUTION CONSTRUCTION AND MAINTENANCE OF NATURAL TURF CRICKET TABLES AND OUTFIELDS. Sports Turf Research Institute, Bingley. 1991.

BRITISH BAYONET LETTERS PATENT. Private Publication, Baildon, Shipley, West Yorkshire. 1991.

THE CARE OF THE GOLF COURSE. Sports Turf Research Institute, Bingley. 1992. (Co-editor with P. Hayes & S.P. Isaac.)

✿ ✿ ✿ ✿ ✿ ✿ ✿ ✿ ✿ ✿ ✿ ✿ ✿ ✿ ✿ ✿ ✿

❋ ❋ ❋ ❋ ❋ ❋ ❋ ❋ ❋ ❋ ❋ ❋ ❋ ❋ ❋

QUEEN: What sport shall we devise to drive away the heavy thought of care?
LADY: Madam, we play at bowls.
QUEEN: 'Twill make me think the world is full of rubs, and that my fortune runs against the bias.

WILLIAM SHAKESPEARE, RICHARD II Act 3 Scene 4 circa 1595

To cure the mind's wrong bias, spleen,
Some recommend the bowling green.

THE SPLEEN - poem by Matthew Green   1696-1737

The bowl runs as our life does, which strong affections sway:
You'll ne'er run right unless you set your bias the right way.
Of Courtiers and of Bowlers the fortune is the same;
Each jostles t' other out of place, and plays a separate game.

ANONYMOUS BALLAD,   17TH CENTURY

If only Hitler and Mussolini could have a good game of bowls once a week at Geneva, I feel that Europe would not be as troubled as it is.

CAPT. R.G. BRISCOW M.P. Speech quoted in the Birmingham Post, 1937.

"When a club is fortunate enough to be served by a competent groundsman, it should never part with him. Like the family doctor, he gets to know the constitution and life-history of his patient, and can treat it better than any committee can."

JAMES A. MANSON in *THE COMPLETE BOWLER*, 1919, p. 148.

ACKNOWLEDGEMENTS

So many people have helped in so many ways during the production of this book that thanking them all adequately is an almost impossible task. However, particular thanks are due to a number of trade firms who contributed photographs and other material.

These are: Sisis Equipment (Macclesfield) Ltd., Cheshire; Ransomes Sims & Jefferies plc, Ipswich; Toro Irrigation Ltd, Ringwood, Hampshire and; H. Pattisson & Co. Ltd, Luton, Bedfordshire

Also to F.K. Sullivan, Divisional Surveyor, Borough of Brecknock for allowing me to photograph greens in his area, and to John W. Holroyd of Shipley, West Yorkshire for the cover artwork. The Secretary of the English Bowling Federation, John Webb, provided valuable information on that particular variant of the game.

By far the greater proportion of my thanks must be reserved for my colleagues past and present at the Sports Turf Research Institute who all made a contribution to this book, either by adding to my background knowledge of the subject or by materially assisting in many invaluable ways.

I am particularly grateful to:

Dr. Peter Hayes, the Institute's Director, who initiated this project and who has provided much advice and encouragement throughout. To Jeff Perris, Senior Advisory Agronomist, for proof-reading my typescript and making many useful suggestions based on his long experience of bowling green advisory work. To James Westwood, for help with photography and for producing the diagrams which illustrate Chapter 5. To David Stansfield, Graham Holmes and Matthew Bell, for allowing me to utilise the work reproduced here as Appendices A and B respectively. To Douglas Joss, now retired, whose long memory of the STRI's early involvement in bowling green construction proved most useful, and to Dewar Wishart for checking and revising the section covering modern constructional techniques. Also to Neil Baldwin, the STRI's Plant Pathologist, for allowing me to plagiarise freely his 1987 publication "Turfgrass Diseases".

Finally I am also most grateful to Ann Bentley and especially Kath Ullah for many hours of sterling work on the Institute's desk-top publishing system.

R.D.C. Evans
STRI, Bingley, 1988

ADDITIONAL ACKNOWLEDGEMENTS : SECOND EDITION

In preparing this new edition, I am further indebted to my colleagues at the STRI for much helpful comment. Gordon C. Macadam in particular must be credited with virtually all of the revision work for the Chapter on green construction. James Westwood and Rob Everett kindly provided CAD print-outs of bowling green levels, and Mike Canaway and Steve Baker allowed me to reprint their article as Appendix C. Neil Baldwin has once again allowed me to draw freely on his disease and pest publications. Additional photographs of equipment and bowling green accessories have been received from Mrs L.J. Hilton (Sisis Equipment Ltd), Mr P.G. Roberts (Toro Irrigation Ltd), Mr R. Horner (Better Methods Europe), Mr Bob Rendle (Ransomes Sims & Jefferies Ltd) and Mr D.J. Lloyd (Sportsmark Group).

I am most grateful to Mr K.W. McAuliffe and particularly Mr W.H. Walmsley of the New Zealand Turf Culture Institute for a much-improved account of that country's unique *Cotula* greens. Mr G.E. Smith of Solihull, Mr P.J.W. Talbot of Saker Leisure Ltd and Mr R.L. Hall of Lodge Sports were most helpful on the subject of artificial outdoor greens.

For contributing the Foreword, Mr R. Holt (Secretary, Crown Green Bowling Assn) and Mr Bob Jack (President, English Bowling Association) deserve warmest thanks, as does Mr D.E. Partridge (National Administrator, EBA Greens Maintenance Advisory Scheme) for facilitating this matter.

Finally, Diane S. Hill deserves all the credit for keyboard work on the desk-top system. Improved presentation of the text is entirely the result of her expertise.

R.D.C. Evans
STRI, Bingley, 1992

CONTENTS

Page

FOREWORD to the newly fully revised Second Edition

On behalf of the British Crown Green Bowling Association it gives me great pleasure to contribute a foreword to the second edition of *Bowling Greens*. In the world of crown green bowls for our sins (or possibly purely out of ignorance) we are blessed with a number of bowling greens which are not of the desired standard and books concerning the maintenance and upkeep of a bowling green are essential. The first edition represented a comprehensive treatment on the subject and I made extensive use of its contents to give authoritative answers to the many questions I received on the construction and maintenance of bowling greens. Quality publications on this particular subject are few and far between and as a reference book it is a must for any greenkeeper worth his salt or in fact to any bowler interested in the upkeep of his club's bowling green. A tremendous amount of additional research and expertise has gone into this second edition and on behalf of the British Crown Green Bowling Association I would like to offer our thanks and appreciation to Roger Evans for the amount of work put into this publication and wish him every success with it. I would have no hesitation in recommending the book to any interested parties.

Ron Holt
Secretary
British Crown Green Bowling Association

❊ ❊ ❊ ❊ ❊ ❊ ❊ ❊ ❊ ❊ ❊ ❊ ❊ ❊ ❊ ❊

The greatest asset of any bowls club is the green upon which the game is played. Maintaining the playing surface to the highest possible standard is of paramount importance to the continuing success and future welfare of the club and therefore should be of great concern and interest to every club member. The bowler will derive the greatest enjoyment from playing the game and demonstrating his own skill, whenever the green is in superb condition.

The English Bowling Association realises that proper and timely maintenance of the green has become more difficult in recent years, owing to both economic and vocational factors and that as a consequence, clubs have needed more expert guidance in this area. With this in mind the EBA introduced Greens Maintenance Advisory Scheme in 1984 and during the period the Scheme has been in operation the support and assistance given by the Sports Turf Research Institute has been greatly appreciated.

The first edition of this book was highly recommended to all bowls clubs and this second version is endorsed by the EBA with equal enthusiasm. We are delighted that the STRI has produced this publication and we are confident that it will give even more bowls clubs the advice and guidance they need, firstly to improve the condition of their green and thereafter to maintain it at a high standard throughout the playing season.

R Jack
President 1992
English Bowling Association

INTRODUCTION

THE HISTORY OF THE GAME

One of the few things which can be said with complete certainty about the origins of the game of bowls is that it is a very ancient game indeed. The often-repeated legend that the game was invented by a certain bloodthirsty medieval king who was wont to pass an idle hour by rolling the severed heads of recently executed prisoners at a convenient target can fortunately be dismissed as purely apocryphal - the game is much more ancient than that.

It is in fact reasonable to assume that some version of the game was played in the dawn of prehistory - tossing or rolling rounded and conveniently-sized pebbles at some kind of marker is after all a fairly obvious way by which the members of some primitive and long-forgotten tribe may have amused themselves. Among the earliest known artefacts relating to the game are a set of nine stones, a larger stone ball and a marble archway (this latter fulfilling a somewhat similar function as a croquet hoop) found in the tomb of an Egyptian child who died about 5,200 B.C. The Polynesian game of Ula Maika, also involving stone markers and balls, is probably almost as old.

In the Europe of 2,000 years ago, prototype forms of the Italian game of Boccie, the Basque Quilles and the French Boule have been detected. Such games largely involved tossing a ball through the air towards the target rather than rolling it along a more-or-less level surface. Bowling a ball along the ground is, however, a feature of the old German game of Kegel, played as early as the 3rd or 4th century A.D. In this case the game took on a markedly religious aspect as the target clubs or skittles were regarded as representing the Heathen and the Christian bowler, in knocking him down, was hence cleansed of sin. The game thus gained full church approval and was, in fact, played along monastic cloisters. The French game of Gettre de Pere is another related sport and involved placing a ball or missile close to a small set object, probably fixed in the ground. This version probably reached England during the course of the Norman Conquest.

In this context, it is interesting to note how the ancestral game developed along divergent lines in France and England. As far as France is concerned, bowls developed into the jeu provençal (the game of Provence) where balls were tossed or rolled down a 25 metre pitch at a tiny jack (cochonnet). At the end of the 19th century the Provencal game evolved into the modern boule or pétanque, played on a shorter 15 metre rink. Now immensly popular throughout France, no visitor to that country could be unfamiliar with the sight of the boule games played casually in every village square at lunch times and early evenings. To the British visitor it seems odd that the game is played on almost any surface, usually grassless, but surface levels are relatively unimportant in the case of a game where the unbiased steel bowls are unusually tossed through the air at the jack, although occasionally a rolling technique is also employed. Boule can claim to be the national game of the French, with over 15,000 clubs and very keen competition in the national championships. Incidentally, a bowls variant survives in Brittany which is more akin to the British game. The Bretons play on a prepared rink of rolled sand 25-30 metres long using spherical 4 inch diameter lignum vitae bowls, biased by means of a lead plug inserted into one side. The rink has boarded sides and the rules allow bouncing the bowl off the boards to reach an otherwise obscured jack. In Brazil, a somewhat similar variant is played using unbiased ceramic bowls, for all the world like giant snooker balls. A curved line is obtained by exploiting the trough-shaped clay rink, its edges being contoured up to meet the side boards.

By 1300, German bowlers were aiming at anything between 3 and 17 target pins. In the period 1400 - 1600 the game had spread into Austria, Switzerland and what is now modern Poland. By this time, playing surfaces were cinders or clay, the latter being sun-baked to concrete-like hardness. Covered, all-weather rinks or courts were also gradually coming into use where the playing surface was commonly of wooden planking.

To the modern British reader, the above account of the game's development may appear a little confusing as it will be obvious that many of the games referred to are not 'Bowls' in the modern English sense of the word, but related games which in this country would be called skittles or perhaps ten-pin bowling. Duckpins, candle-pins, five-pins and nine-pins are other variants of this type of ball-game. On a worldwide scale, this form of game (particularly ten-pin bowling) remains dominant through the whole of the American continent, Scandinavia, Japan and Australia. Even billiards, snooker and pool, also internationally popular, can to

PLATE 1. An early illustration of bowling at a conical marker. From a 14th century M.S.

PLATE 2. A Victorian artist's impression of the famous game on Plymouth Hoe in 1588.

PLATE 3. Bowls in the Netherlands, circa 1650. Note the fixed peg aiming point and the rather primitive bowling surface. (A painting by David Teniers the Younger, Torrie Collection, Edinburgh University.)

PLATE 4a & 4b. English village bowlers. About 1850.

some extent be regarded as a related table-top version of the same family of games. Bar-billiards, for example, even retains a form of the archetypal skittle or pin.

From the Middle Ages onwards, however, British players gradually evolved their own characteristic version of the basic game which we would now commonly refer to as 'Bowls', or, more precisely and correctly, as Lawn Bowls or Bowling on the Green. Under British influence over the last few centuries this game also has spread out on a worldwide scale and today rivals the skittle-type game in popularity on the international scene. The English variety of Lawn Bowling today predominates in the British Isles and in many of the old British Colonies - New Zealand and South Africa in particular. Canada, Australia and the USA also hold many devotees of the lawn-based game.

BRITISH LAWN BOWLING

Although the French may have brought their own version of Bowls across the Channel during the Norman Conquest as mentioned above, it seems more than probable that Saxons and Celts had been amusing themselves with similar games for centuries prior to the Norman invasion. Greco-Roman pottery and tapestries clearly show balls or rounded stones being bowled along the ground rather than tossed, and show that the target was a peg fixed in the ground rather than a set of skittles which had to be knocked over. The Greek and Roman game is therefore clearly related and may be directly ancestral to English lawn bowls in that the object is to bowl one's ball along the ground so that it contacts or lies close to a small marker which served the same purpose as the modern jack. The jack and the skittle are, of course, analogous but do not fulfil quite the same function. The Romans may therefore have brought this form of game to the British Isles after the 55 B.C. invasion, although historical proof of this seems unavailable. Suffice it to say that, by the Middle Ages, lawn bowls had become the preferred activity in England while skittles in its many guises predominated on the Continent of Europe. 13th and 14th Century manuscripts survive which show the game being played along modern lines. One contemporary illustration shows two players with one ball each bowling at a small conical target rather than a spherical jack.

English bowlers soon ran into trouble with the Authorities. Statutes prohibiting the game were issued in the reign of Richard II (1377 - 1399). At the time, the chief worry stemmed from the fact that the effective defence of the realm relied heavily on a citizen militia of expert archers and those in power made repeated attempts to encourage archery amongst the peasantry, regarding all other games and sports as undesirable distractions which interfered with the commoners' required pursuit of expertise with the longbow. Shakespeare is, however, historically correct in portraying Queen Isabella and one of her Ladies in Waiting discussing whether to pass the time with a game of bowls (in Richard II Act 3, Scene 4, written about 1595), as the ban was at that time only applied to the lower classes of society. The prohibition was renewed in the reigns of Henry IV (1399 - 1413) and Edward IV (1461 - 1483) but again only as far as commoners were concerned. In 1511 Henry VIII issued a statute which stated:-

"the game of bowles is an evil because the alleys are in operation in conjunction with saloons or dissolute places and bowling ceased to be a sport, and rather a form of vicious gambling."

This edict was not legally rescinded until 1845 but was only haphazardly enforced and the game hence continued to flourish. Official disapproval seems, however, to have tended to drive the game underground to a certain extent and it gained a rather unsavoury reputation at times due to its association with taverns and gambling. The wealthy, however, continued to play the game respectably with friends and family on secluded private estates. Henry VIII remained a keen player despite his prohibitions, although innkeepers during his reign were fined two pounds per day for allowing bowling and betting on their premises, and bowlers could be, and were, imprisoned. A further statute promulgated by Henry VIII (in 1541) prohibited *"artificers, labourers, apprentices, servants and the like from playing bowls except in their masters' house and presence at Christmas"* - a rather short bowling season.

The famous game played between Sir Francis Drake and Sir John Hawkins in 1588, when even the imminent arrival of the Spanish Armada was not considered sufficient reason for abandoning a game, serves very well to illustrate that legal bans were only patchily applied. In the reign of James I (1603 - 1625) the King was actually advocating the sport - in his Book of Sports published in 1618 he recommended the game to his son. Again, in 1630 the Earl of

Derby was granted a plot of land in Chester on which a bowling alley was constructed, implying official approval.

During the Commonwealth and Civil War period Puritan attitudes and the upheavals of the conflict probably placed severe restrictions on the pursuit of the game, but with the Restoration (1660) bowls became very fashionable and, with royal approbation, grew in popularity. In 1670 a set of twenty formalised Rules of the Game were drawn up which would not seem too foreign to a modern bowler. Through the 17th and 18th centuries bowls continued as a popular recreation and most towns and villages could boast a green, usually attached to the local inn.

Sufficient emphasis has not yet been given to the role played by the Scots in the development of Lawn Bowls. In Scotland, bowls first gained a hold on the populace in the 16th century and for a time assumed the status of a national sport. North of the Border, the game never gained an unsavoury reputation through association with alehouses, drunkenness and gambling, and therefore Scots bowlers escaped the kind of prohibitive legislation imposed by the English monarchs. (Kirk Elders did, however, castigate bowlers from time to time and play on the Sabbath was definitely not approved.) James VI of Scotland (and 1st of England) came down in favour of the game as we have already seen. Curling - that characteristically Scottish form of bowls on ice - can perhaps be regarded as a monument to the Scots bowler's stubborn refusal to allow his recreation to be ruined by a harsh climate! A doctor from Jedburgh, Thomas Somerville, wrote in 1741 that -

"Bowls were then a common amusement. Every country town was provided with a bowling green for the diversion of the inhabitants in the summer evenings. All classes were represented among the players, and it was usual for players of different ranks to take part in the same game. A bowling green usually formed part of the policy or pleasure grounds of country houses. At these private bowling greens ladies also shared in the amusement, thus rendering it greatly more attractive."

In more recent times, Scotland must have the credit for two major steps forward in the evolution of the modern game. Firstly, the Scots pioneered serious attempts at improving the quality of turf bowling surfaces and hence gave birth to the modern art and science of bowling green construction and greenkeeping. Secondly, in 1849 they formulated a code of laws which forms the basis for the game of Flat Green (Association) Bowls as it is played today. Their early contributions to bowling green improvement will be covered in more detail later in this volume.

Today, Lawn Bowling is played in all parts of the British Isles and, with well in excess of a million regular participants of all age groups, qualifies as a major sport. Certainly it cannot be slightingly dismissed as "old man's marbles" as it has sometimes been in the recent past. Incidentally, it is also perhaps worth mentioning that other non-lawn games which share a common ancestry with true bowls still thrive in places. Skittle alleys can still commonly be found in parts of England - indeed many West Country lawn bowling clubs have indoor skittle alleys to provide members with amusement and recreation in the winter months when the outdoor green is closed. Ten-pin bowling enjoyed a renaissance in Britain in the 1950's and 60's when many defunct cinemas were converted to bowling alleys, a craze which developed under influence from the USA. Mention has already been made of Scottish curling on ice - another surviving bowls variant involves bowling or hurling large bowls over considerable distances across moors or wastelands, or along miles of country lane. This form of bowls is still played in Tyneside in England, and in parts of Ireland, the basic idea being to cover the distance in the least number of throws.

British bowling today is, however, dominated by Bowling on the Green, with three variations of the game of Lawn Bowls being played on two basic forms of bowling green. In terms of the geographical area covered and in terms of numbers of players, Association or Flat-green bowling dominates the scene. It is the only form of lawn bowls played in Ireland and Scotland and is also the game which was spread, largely by Scottish emmigrants, to parts of the former British Empire. Association bowls is characteristically played on a green divided into parallel rinks, each rink being between 18 and 19 feet wide. Historically, rink bowling of this kind is a relatively recent development which probably arose to allow more individual players to use a particular green at one time without interfering with each other. It also facilitates team play with

PLATE 5. Studying the state of play. Flat rink (Association) bowls at the EBA Amateur National Championships, Mortlake, August 1966.

four team players acting in concert. Flat-rink bowls is governed by the English Bowling Association, formed in 1903. This English ruling body is pre-dated by the Scottish Bowling Association - formed in 1892. Surprisingly enough, the oldest national flat-rink bowling Associations are those of the Australian states of New South Wales and Victoria formed as early as 1890. The English Women's Bowling Association joined the scene in 1931. U.S. lawn bowlers are catered for by the American Lawn Bowls Association formed in 1915.

Crown green bowls differs significantly from the flat-rink discipline in that it is played all over the green in any direction and not confined to rinks. A biased jack is employed and play is single-handed and not a team game. The game is played on a "crowned green" - in effect a low hill with the centre anything from 6 to 18 ins. higher than the four corners. Today, crown-green bowls is centred on the North of England, extending west into North Wales, Isle of Man and south as far as Worcestershire. Its governing body is the British Crown Green Bowling Association which was founded in 1907. The British Parks Amateur Bowling Association also organises crown green bowls but is not a nationally recognised body.

The third major variety of lawn bowls still played in England is Federation Bowls, governed by the English Bowling Federation (1926) and the English Women's Bowling Federation (1956). As originally played in the Durham and Northumberland (and later Norfolk) areas the Federation game resembled crown green bowls in being played with a roving jack on greens of variable size. It has now, however, developed into a rink game played on flat greens in the eastern counties of England.

As for crown green bowls, ditch requirements are less exacting than for the game played under Association rules.

All forms of lawn bowls are co-ordinated and promoted by the English Bowls Council formed in 1971.

PLATE 6. The crown green game on a typical municipal green in the North of England. Myrtle Park, Bingley, June 1982.

PLATE 7. Indoor flat-rink bowls. The Crystal Palace indoor facility is one of the oldest in the country. Here England and Wales play a Hilton cup match in March 1964.

14

Mention must also be made of indoor bowls. The popularity of flat-rink bowling led to a demand for indoor facilities where the game could continue during the winter off-season. As early as 1909 the Crystal Palace and Alexandra Palace in London commenced indoor bowls, on rather primitive and unsatisfactory surfaces. The popularity of the activity has spread rapidly since that time and indoor bowls is now widespread on a variety of carpet-like surfaces (originally jute but now largely synthetic). Space restrictions have led to the development of short mat bowls in Northern Ireland which requires only a 6 x 45 ft. mat. Indoor crown-green bowls is rarely possible due to the difficulties and expense of providing a suitable slightly-domed surface. The English Indoor Bowling Association appeared in 1933 and the Women's equivalent in 1951.

CHAPTER 1
THE DEVELOPMENT OF GREENS AND GREENKEEPING (PRIOR TO 1945)

Although the evolution of the game of lawn bowls in the British Isles over the last six centuries or so is quite well documented, the same cannot be said for the history of bowling green construction and maintenance.

In the earliest times, it is safe to assume that the game was played on any suitable patch of ground. After all, it is possible to play the basic unrefined game on virtually any reasonably level area of sufficient size - even one lacking any form of grass cover. Actual green construction work, in the sense of the actual altering of natural contours and the preparation of areas of land specifically for bowling purposes, does however date back to a surprisingly early period. Southampton old bowling green for example may have been in existence since 1299, although it is doubtful whether this ancient club is still playing on its original green. The prize for the club which has been continuously playing a single green for the longest period of time, must surely go to Hereford Bowling Club - established in 1484. This late 15th century green, tucked away behind the Bowling Green Inn near the centre of Hereford has seen the town grow up around it to an extent that the green is now at a lower level than surrounding buildings and streets, a fact which has created some drainage difficulties in recent years.

An even older green, dating from just after the Norman Conquest, is that at Lewes in Sussex. Situated just inside the castle gates, this green was formerly the jousting ground of a castle built by William de Warrenne. The Lewes green is just over ¾ acre in extent and is shaped like a square with an additional triangle at one end. The natural downland turf undulates considerably and bowls with a very heavy bias were used. The green is owned by the Marquis of Abergavenny but has been managed since 1753 by the Lewes Bowling Green Society, who still own thirty pairs of 18th century bowls. A biased roving jack was used and the game is therefore similar to today's crown green game.

In subsequent centuries the quality of one's bowling surface depended on one's social status. The mass of the peasantry continued to play on any convenient area of ground which was probably subject to the barest minimum of preparation and maintenance. Bowls was played on commons or village greens, presumably on sheep-grazed turf, until legal prohibitions made overt public bowling a risky activity - playing areas then tended to be more discreetly hidden behind taverns and village inns. It was probably not until the 19th century that the bulk of the population were able to play on prepared surfaces which would come anywhere near satisfying the requirements of the modern game.

For the wealthy or aristocratic bowler, however, the situation was somewhat different. Bowling greens or bowling alleys became a feature of many a gentleman's well-planned garden. Incidentally, in modern usage the term "alley" tends to bring to mind a picture of a plank-surfaced indoor skittle alley. In the past, however, the word seems to have had a wider meaning and many records of the existence of 'bowling alleys' often actually refer to narrow strips of turf analagous to what we would now term a true bowling green and which resembled a single isolated rink on a flat Association bowls green.

The Tudor gentleman's garden is described in detail by Dr. Andrew Borde (*Boke for to lerne a man to be wyse in building of his House* : published circa 1500) who states that the well-planned garden should include an orchard, fish pools, a dovecote, butts for archery and a bowling green. Queen Elizabeth's privy garden at Whitehall included both tennis court and bowling green. At this period lawns and garden walks were often of herbs, particularly camomile, rather than grass turf and there is every reason to suppose that bowling greens were often laid with a similar ground cover. Low and slow-growing herbal lawns could well have helped minimise maintenance problems in the days when grass had to be laboriously mown with scythes, sickles or hand shears. A late 16th century green, surrounded by yew trees, survives at Dirleton Castle, three miles west of North Berwick in East Lothian.

A bill relating to the construction of a bowling green at Windsor Castle actually survives in the Royal Archives. One W. Herbert was paid, by order of Charles II in 1663, as follows:-

PLATE 8. Bowls on a country house alley - Bramshill House, Hampshire, 17th Century.

PLATE 9. 18th century bowls at White Fryers, Gloucester.

"May 11, 1663. To W. Herbert for making ye bowling green and walks £10, and for cutting Turfe for ye green £3 12 s. in all £13 12s. For 8 pairs of bowls and carriage and hampers £4 5s. 6d. Sept. 26. Iron work for ye bowling green door £1 17s. 11d."

The reference to turfing as a method of laying this 17th century green is particularly interesting.

In 1683 one Randle Holme published 'The Academy of Armory', a book on heraldry and other subjects. Apposite to our study are his remarks on bowling surfaces:-

"Several places for Bowling: First, Bowling greens are open wide places made smooth and even, these are generally palled or walled about. Secondly, Bares are open wide places on mores or commons. Thirdly, Bowling-alleys are close places, set apart and made more for privett persons than publick uses. Fourthly, Table Bowling, this is tables of a good length in halls or dineing roomes, on which for exercist and divertisement gentlemen and their associates bowle with little round balls or bullets."

Bowling green surfaces must have been of reasonably good quality by this time as Holme also remarks, in a section entitled *"Orders agreed upon by Gentleman Bowlers"* that *"Noe high heeles enter for spoiling the green, they forfeit 6d."* Another stated rule is that *"all stamping or smoothing is barred."* The ban on high heels surely implies that surfaces, at least on enclosed greens, were uniform and true enough to warrant such a prohibition.

In the reign of Queen Anne (1702 - 1714), private bowling greens continued to be popular. The Duke of Devonshire's Chatsworth house in Derbyshire had a bowling green as a central feature, overlooked by the house so that play could be watched from indoors. At another Queen Anne residence, Cassiobury, the bowling green was in a wood, the approach being via an avenue of trees. In an anonymous early eighteenth century gardening book, translated from the French, entitled "The Solitary or Carthusian Gardener" and dated 1706, the author says there are five ways of making green plots *"namely by Turfs, by Spanish Clover-grass, by Hay-seed, by the Seed of Sanfoin, and by that of Medick Fodder"*. He considers turf (i.e. grass) the best. He also states:-

"A Bowling Green should be incompassed with great Trees such as Elms, Horse-chestnut trees or Acacias accompanied by Yews. They are only proper in spatious Gardens and commonly are drawn in the remotest places to prevent the confining of the prospect by the tall Trees that surround it".

Included in this book is one of the earliest-known plans for a bowling green, surrounded by trees planted at regular intervals - some trimmed in topiary work.

Mention has already been made of a plot of land in Chester being granted to the Earl of Derby in 1630. It was in St. John's Parish near the river Dee and enclosed by high walls of stone. The section of the plot used as a bowling alley was 99 yd. in length and 42 yd. in breadth and survived until the 1830's when it was eventually built over. Very old crown greens still survive in Chester, Chesterfield, Shrewsbury and Penrith. It seems likely that the game of crown green bowls as we know it today evolved as a result of the inadequate construction of these early greens. Difficulties must have been frequently encountered in the skilled task of producing a level and uniform surface. After initial construction, settlement and subsidence problems probably also played a part in producing the characteristically domed North of England green, on which this variant of the game subsequently evolved.

During the period of approximately 1300 - 1700, therefore, there was probably very little real progress made in the improvement or design of playing surfaces. Bowling greens established themselves as desirable and artificially constructed features of the rich man's garden while, initially at least, commoners continued to play on any suitable natural area of ground. Some experimentation took place with alternatives to grass for the actual ground cover plant but constructional methods probably remained very basic and maintenance was carried out by labourers, or at best gardeners, using only hand tools. Simple tools such as garden rakes, weed forks, hand rollers, shears and scythes evolved early and 14th century examples would be recognised easily by a modern greenkeeper. Rollers were in use by the 18th century, as a foreign visitor to England remarked at that time that English greens were *"so even that they bowl upon them as easily as on a great billiard table - they have thick rowling-stones to keep the green smooth"*. Grass cutting must, however, have remained something of a headache and the virtual impossibility of achieving a really accurate and uniform playing surface with shears or scythe probably held back the development of really skilled and expert bowls for a considerable period.

The 18th and 19th century, however, saw the emergence of three factors which revolutionised the quality of bowling surfaces and hence changed the nature of the game itself. The significant innovations were:-

[a]   The use of sea-marsh turf.

[b]   The more organised and scientific approach towards green construction and maintenance pioneered by Scottish bowlers and greenkeepers.

[c]   The invention of the mechanical lawn mower.

The first two factors were in fact intimately inter-related as the Scots seem to have been the first to have advocated and used sea-marsh turf for bowling greens.

To deal first with mechanical grass trimming, we owe the invention of the lawn mower to Edwin Budding, a free-lance engineer of Stroud in Gloucestershire who undoubtedly conceived the idea from his familiarity with a machine used in the local woollen industry for shearing the nap off bolts of cloth. His mower was patented on 25th October 1830 and the specification refers to:-

"a new combination and application of machinery for the purpose of cropping or shearing the vegetable surfaces of lawns, grass-plots and pleasure grounds, constituting a machine which may be used with advantage instead of a scythe for that purpose.............. grass growing in the shade, too weak to stand against the scythe to cut, may be cut by my machine as closely as required, and the eye will never be offended by those circular scars, inequalities and bare places so commonly made by the best mowers with the scythe, and which continues visible for several days."

Budding's criticism of the scythe is particularly interesting with reference to bowls surfaces. Budding's patent was licenced to J.R. and A. Ransome of Ipswich in 1832 and this firm (now Ransomes Sims and Jefferies) is of course still in existence. One satisfied customer was the foreman at Regent's Park Zoo, who commented in 1831 that the machine did the work of 6-8 men with scythes and brooms and produced a far better finish. Other manufacturers gradually appeared - Alexander Shanks of Arbroath in 1841, Thomas Green of Leeds in 1856. The spread of the use of such machines was, however, slow and many bowling greens were still being cut with scythes until the First World War. Cutting a bowling green with a scythe was always a highly skilled business. A late 19th Century article in the magazine "The Field" remarks (rather prematurely) that:-

"the introduction of lawn mowers has effectually done away with the industry of lawn mowing by hand, for it was no ordinary wielder of the scythe who was regarded as good enough to mow a first-class green. Fifty or sixty years ago a man who had established a reputation for this kind of work was always in demand, and in many cases he could command his own price."

Writing in 1912, J.A. Manson records that *"In Scotland greens are mostly mown with the scythe which, in the opinion of many, is the only instrument which should be used on a first class green. But the majority of groundsmen, in other respects well up to their work, cannot handle the scythe and perforce employ the lawnmower, which is a capital substitute."*

The author, during the last 30 years, has talked to a number of elderly greenkeepers who recall using scythes on bowling or putting greens, although latterly they were used more commonly for shaving out undesirable weeds like clover rather than for routine grass cutting.

Turning to the other factors listed above, the influence which Scottish bowlers had on the

BUDDING'S
PATENT GRASS-CUTTING MACHINE.

SOLD BY APPOINTMENT, BY

J. R. & A. RANSOME, IPSWICH.

This Machine is so easy to manage, that persons unpractised in the Art of Mowing, may cut the Grass on Lawns, Pleasure Grounds and Bowling Greens, with ease. It is easily adjusted to cut to any length, and the beauty of its operation is, that it leaves no seam, nor any of the cut grass upon the Lawn. Other advantages of this machine are, that the grass may be cut when dry, and consequently it may be used at such hours as are most convenient to the Gardener or Workman,—while the expence of Mowing is considerably lessened, as more than double the work may be done with the same manual labour that is requisite with the scythe.

PLATE 10. The first lawn mower was Budding's machine. Patented in 1830 and manufactured by Ransomes from 1832. (Advert circa 1840.)

20

development of flat rink bowling greens during a period stretching very roughly from the early 18th century to the First World War cannot be over-estimated. A measure of their influence is that flat rink greens came to be known as "Scotch Greens", to distinguish them from the North of England crown green (crown bowls is not played in Scotland). To quote J.A. Manson again:-

"In Scotland bowls first took root in Glasgow, probably in the latter half of the sixteenth century; for when the Kirk Session in 1595 forbade Sunday play it is fair to suppose the game had already acquired formidable popularity. Some have claimed Edinburgh or Haddington for its birthplace, but Dr. J.G. Wallace-James informs me that the earliest mention he found in Haddington's records is dated 1662, when the frugal grant of £160 was sanctioned for 'the laying out of ane bowling green on the sands'. But Glasgow's right to pride of place is incontestable. In 1695 the Council parted with ground in Candleriggs to Mungo Cochrane solely for the construction of a green. The Willowbank club claims to be the lineal descendant of those who played here from the very first and in that case is much the oldest club in Scotland."

The first known use of sea marsh turf, lifted from its natural seaside environment and relaid as a bowling surface, may be found in the records of the managers of the bowling green at Cowan's Hospital in Stirling. Here, one may read that on 16 January 1738:

"the patrons considering a petition given in by several of the merchants, trades and other inhabitants showing the badness of the Bowling Green, and craving the same might be laid with salt faill, they therefore appoint the masters" of the hospital *"to cause William Dawson, gardener, and keeper of the said Green, to lay the same with salt faill as soon as possible, the expense thereof not exceeding the sum of £10 sterling."* In March, next year, the expense of the improvements was found to be £138 4s. Scots, or £11 16s. 8d. Sterling ; and the patrons ordered *"the bowl meal* (mail, or charge) *to be augmented to one shilling Scots (a penny, Sterling) from each person playing."* On 22 March 1740, *"the patrons appoint the master to provide half-a-dozen pair of byass bowls to the Bowling Green, and to cause make a sufficient lodge for the bowls in a proper part of the garden."* The bowls seem to have served for fourteen years, as on 6 April, 1754, *"the patrons appoint the master to provide six pair of new bowls and an odd one for the use of the Hospital Bowling Green, a great many of those already there being almost useless."* Again, on 5 February 1763, eight pairs of good byass bowls and two jacks were ordered to be purchased for the use of the Green. The price was £3 6s. 10d. Sterling, paid to Robert Home, merchant in Edinburgh.

Improvements in the management of the Green became necessary in 1777. On 16 May that year, *"the managers considering that of late great complaints have been made to them that the Hospital Green, flower garden, and back walk are not kept in the same good order and condition which they used to be in : that people are allowed without distinction not only to make a thoroughfare of the garden, but also to use the Bowling Green contrary to the original intention thereof ; they therefore authorise the Hospital master to give orders to the keeper of the said Green with regard to the proper management and regulation thereof, so as that improper persons may be prevented from taking up the Green ; and appoint the said keeper to obey the orders that may be given him from time to time by the Hospital master thereanent, at his peril ; and authorize the Hospital master to cause build a small brick house for holding the bowls, in such convenient situation as may be pointed out by the managers."* Still there was dissatisfaction, and on 5 July 1779, the magistrates framed a set of Regulations for the Keeper of the Hospital Green, etc., the following being the principal:—*"Not to suffer boys and others to make a common thoroughfare of the garden and terraces, but to keep the garden doors lockt, and to give attendance to let decent people, as well as strangers as town's folk, pass through them. To await regularly on the Bowling Green, to allow none but decent people to play at bowls, and no children or servant-maids, etc., to walk on the Green."*

Attention must be drawn to the use of the term "salt faill" in the above extracts. "Faill" (fail or fàl) is the Gaelic word for turf or sod, salt faill hence being synonymous with the more modern term sea marsh turf.

During the Victorian era the practice of using sea marsh turf as a bowling surface became well established and gradually spread southwards into England and Wales. Such turf occurs naturally around our coasts, the Morecambe Bay area and the Solway Firth being particularly rich natural sources. The Forres marshes in the north of Scotland were also commercially exploited and some in South Wales. The merits and demerits of sea-marsh turf as a bowling surface will be discussed in detail later (see page 34); suffice it to say at this point that, during the eighteenth, nineteenth and the first quarter of the twentieth centuries, it was the best naturally-occurring material available. It could be found in commercially usable quantities and was fairly consistent in quality and could therefore form the basis of what was to become an organised turf-supply industry. Briefly, sea-marsh turf proved attractive as a bowling surface because it tended to have a uniform, natural cover of fine, wiry grasses and areas could be selected which had only a minor broad-leaved weed content. Again, the natural soil is a fine, evenly-textured silt which facilitated turf-lifting and allowed easy trimming to a very uniform thickness. After careful laying on a bowling green, the silt could be rolled down to give a fast, even and highly accurate surface which the bowler found ideal. Sea marsh turf thus gained such an enviable reputation that even today one encounters an older generation of bowlers who still feel that it is mandatory for the best of greens. Unfortunately, it also has many serious drawbacks which are often not immediately apparent when a green is first laid and its popularity has hence rightly declined drastically in more recent years. It is, however, true to say that for a lengthy period of time it was the best material for the purpose and its use represented a major step forward in bowling green improvement.

Besides popularising the use of sea-marsh turf, Scottish bowling green builders had, prior to the First World War, evolved a distinctive method of bowling green construction which, with minor variations, remained in vogue until the Second World War. (One West Sussex contractor, is still advocating the Scottish constructional system today - and still using sea-marsh turf). The most distinctive feature of the Scots method of green construction was that no soil whatsoever was placed beneath the turf. An even subsoil formation surface was first produced, of sufficient area to allow a 42 x 42 yd. playing surface (i.e. six rinks in each direction, allowing the green to accommodate a maximum of 48 players at any one time). A pipe drainage system was then introduced into the subsoil surface consisting of 2 or 3 in. diameter clayware pipes at anything from 9 - 21 foot centres, running into mains placed under the surrounds ditch and thence to a suitable outfall. Drains were sometimes omitted for drier sites. Over the subsoil was then spread some 6 to 12 in. of hard-core variously described as clinker, ash, broken stone or even "brick-bats". Sometimes this would be divided into fine-over-coarse layers but 3 in. gauge clinker seems to have been most often favoured. Next a 1 in. - 3 in. layer of fine ash - 1/4 in. grade is mentioned in one text. Finally, between 1 and 3 in. of sand was spread and the sea-marsh turf laid directly on this sand bed. The turf was cut 1 1/4 - 1 1/2 in. in thickness. This basic constructional method was advocated by the Scottish Bowling Association after its formation in 1892 and during the 1920's and 30's also became a standard English Bowling Association requirement.

This Scottish method of construction had a number of advantages. Greens so made had good underlying drainage - important in wetter areas like the West of Scotland. The stone or clinker foundation is a firm one, could be well consolidated and hence minimised subsidence after the green had been laid. The sand layer beneath the turf was easy to grade to an accurate surface level and, together with accurately cut turf, helped form an almost instant bowling surface of high quality.

The growth of Public Parks as a result of the Public Health Acts of 1875, 1890, 1906 and 1925 and a related increase in the demand for bowling greens led to a spate of green-building following the above constructional methods. Many greens were built by Welfare organisations in the Depression of the inter-war period using volunteer labour drawn from the ranks of the unemployed.

Of course, not all greens were constructed using this standard Scottish method. Sea-marsh turf was expensive, particularly if transported long distances. In 1920 the cost of building a green by the above system was about £120, of which £25 represented the cost of the turf alone - a quite considerable proportion of the total. As a result, impecunious clubs sought cheaper substitutes. Moorland or Mountain turf was sometimes used, but material of the required uniform quality was difficult to find in quantity in natural situations and underlying soils tended

PLATES 11 & 12. Sea marsh turf. Lifting and boxing to uniform thickness.

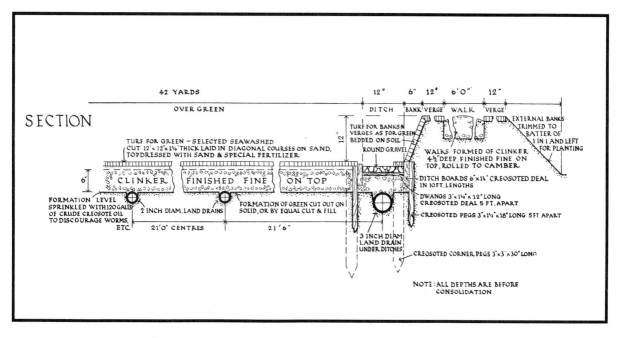

FIGURE 1. Method of green construction evolved in Scotland for sea marsh greens.

to vary more with stones etc. making uniform cutting more difficult. Seeding was, of course, also an alternative method of green establishment but initially it was difficult to obtain seed of suitable quality. Hay loft sweepings were cheap and widely employed where money was short but developing swards tended to contain weed and coarse grasses. Some early advocates of seeded greens insisted that seed should be harvested from moorland pastures, thereby ensuring a higher proportion of the desirable fine grasses. Gradually, of course, seed quality improved and the commercial availability of good seed slowly led to increase in the acceptability of the seeded green. Old-established seed firms like Sutton's of Reading did much to improve seed quality and demonstrate in the face of established prejudice that it was possible to form a perfectly satisfactory bowling green by seeding rather than turfing. Sutton's laid a bowling green at their own recreation ground in Reading in the late 1920s, partly to demonstrate the point. Their green was sown in September and was ready for play the following June. The majority of bowlers, however, continued to regard seeded and non-seamarsh greens as an inferior substitute for the real thing, even in the face of accumulating evidence to the contrary.

For a seeded green, soil had to be used as a surface layer. One early specification details a 4 in. layer of topsoil, ameliorated if necessary with sand, over the standard fine ash/clinker base.

In the case of crown greens, construction was, of course, complicated by the definitive "mushroom top" contours of the finished surface. Such greens vary between 30 and 60 yd. square with 45 x 45 yd. being most usual. Circular greens were sometimes constructed but were always relatively rare. Scottish flat green specifications were adapted for crown green construction. Drains were usually (but not always) omitted beneath the actual bowls surface as the contours shed surface water into the surrounding ditches. The rough shape of the finished surface was first formed by crowning the subsoil formation surface, subsequent layers reflecting the slightly domed effect. For the best crown greens, clinker foundations were again used, topped with fine ash and sand which were carefully spread to pre-set concentric circles of level pegs so that the centre of the finished green was between 6 and 14 in. above the corners. Sea-marsh turf could then be laid. It is normal to turf a flat green working from corner to corner, laying turf in diagonal lines with staggered joints like brickwork. For crown greens, an alternative method was sometimes advocated, starting at the centre on the crown and then laying concentric circles of turf to the level pegs previously placed in position. Some expense could be spared in the case of crown greens in that ditch and bank requirements are not nearly as rigorous as in the case of flat-rink Association greens. (The same is true of flat Federation greens.) Indeed, ditches and banks were sometimes omitted altogether; although not a requirements of the game, it was, however, realised that ditches were useful for drainage purposes. It is interesting to note that Manson (in *The Complete Bowler, 1912*) states that perimeter ditches were virtually unknown around English greens prior to 1870, either flat or crown.

One source gives the cost of a crown green built to modified Scottish specification in 1936 as £470 excluding labour. With crown greens also money could be saved by seeding or by omitting the clinker and ash base layers, but sea-marsh turf and clinker foundations were used whenever funds permitted.

Bowling green maintenance prior to 1930
There seems to have been little attempt made to produce a rational system of bowling green maintenance prior to the late 19th Century. Traditionally the process of bowling green upkeep was probably left to individual greenkeepers working largely on a trial and error basis, aided only by hand tools and a limited range of chemicals - manures and so on which had proved their value in general agricultural and horticultural usage.

As had been mentioned previously, it was the Scottish bowling fraternity who took the first steps towards a more systematic and rational approach towards green maintenance and during the first third of the 20th Century they gained an enviable reputation as the leaders in the field, their influence spreading throughout the British Isles. Developments were, of course, brought virtually to a standstill by the exigencies of the 1914-18 war, but with the cessation of hostilities the Scottish influence on greenkeeping matters became even more marked. It must be stressed that the Scottish approach was by no means a really scientific one - there was no experimental work as such. Strictly pragmatic thinking was the order of the day and greenkeeping techniques were evolved as a result of long practical experience.

Scottish greenkeeping methods were originally specifically developed in connection with flat rink sea-marsh greens laid with soil-less sand and clinker foundations as we have already seen. Their methods soon spread, however, with varying degrees of success, to turfed and seeded greens in general, of both flat and crown types.

One of the most vociferous and influential among Scottish greenkeepers was William Paul of Paisley, an ex-president of the Scottish Bowling Association and for 30 years secretary of the Renfrewshire Bowling Association. He is now probably best remembered as the inventor of the hollow tine fork (still known as a Paul fork in some parts of the country), but during the 1920s he produced a stream of articles and booklets which did much to popularise Scottish greenkeeping practices. A privately published booklet "The Care and Upkeep of Bowling Greens" produced in the 1920-25 period is typical and provides a very good summary of current techniques.

Briefly, Paul's recommendations for the upkeep of a green built in the Scottish manner are as follows:
Commencing in the spring, the green should be brushed with a stiff besom. Repeated rolling was then advised, continuing this operation right through the playing season (1/4 ton rollers were widely used at the time). The importance of harrowing is also stressed, using a heavy wooden harrow with 2 in., nail-like tines, to remove moss and creeping growth. Harrowing should be continued fortnightly through the playing period. Weed should be controlled by close scything of clover and pearlwort etc. in the spring. Commencing in March, fertiliser should be applied - Peruvian guano or sulphate of ammonia. Paul's fertiliser recommendations vary but applications of sulphate of ammonia, sulphate of iron and sandy carrier are usual, given every three weeks through the growing season. Watering is considered vital - the Scottish soil-less construction is very free draining and two weeks' drought was thought dangerous.

PLATE 13.   Association green established by seeding at Sutton's Recreation Club at Reading.   Photographed in 1931.

25

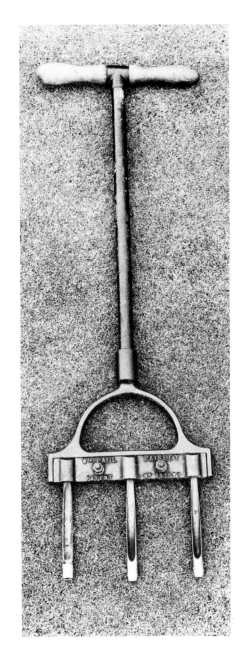

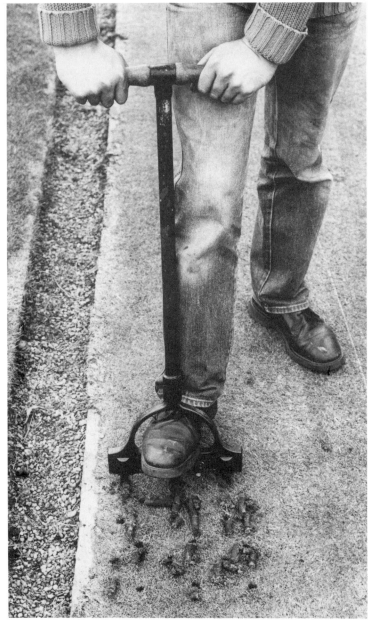

PLATEs 14 & 15. One of William Paul's original hollow tine forks first used in 1919 on the Abercorn bowling green at Paisley, Scotland.

GENERAL DIRECTIONS

— FOR —

"PAUL'S PROCESS" OF TURF TREATMENT.

||||||||||||||||||||||||||||||||||||||||||||||||||||||||||||||||||||||||||||||||||||||||

IF moss exists it shows unhealthy conditions of some kind. Bowling green turf should be of an open, sandy nature. Much of it of recent years is of clay or peat structure, which, under the roller and playing becomes compressed, making life for the grasses very difficult. They die out and moss comes in their place. Older greens also suffer in time from a "skin bound" condition although their subsoil may be of quite a healthy texture. There are others whose subsoil has become caked from various causes—the use of too fine sand perhaps being the most common.

They all want "digging up by Paul's Process." Even where the turf and conditions are good, "Paul's Process" will still further better them.

First of all cut out a small plug from the green and examine it. If it is of this putty-like clay or of peat fibres, the ejected wads of turf from the cutting implement should be taken away.

To begin with the moss must all be broken up and scratched out of existence. If you have a large bowling-green harrow, trail it several times in all directions over the turf; or a little spiked roller machine for extracting the moss is excellent. Where much moss exists it may also be necessary to carefully scarify the moss with fine rakes made by driving 2 rows of wire nails through an 18" narrow flat board. The scarifying must be thorough, crisscrossing it to carefully moulder away the moss—not to tear it out. Considerable grass will also be lost in this operation. (It is not unusual for a full cart load of moss to be taken off a badly infested green). The green must afterwards be clean swept of the loose moss.

Then perforate the turf with the "Paul's Process" Implement every 4" or 5", doing a rink at a time and taking away the wads at completion of rink. If the wads, however, are good healthy material let them lie and roughly break them up with a flat rake to await the final top dressing. After the whole green has been perforated apply the feeding. I recommend 2 or 3 cwts. bone flour, 1 cwt. good grass fertiliser and 1½ cwts. basic slag. A change of feeding is at times beneficial.

This should be scattered on by hand. 3 cwts. dry carbonate of lime is also good for sweetening the ground and liberating potash in the soil. If the wads have been removed, 8 tons of top dressing will be necessary to fill up the holes by the spring. 6 tons good sharp sand put through a ¼" riddle and 2 tons good clean soil. The sand should be as coarse as possible. Even the finer riddlings swept into the bottom of the holes make excellent drainage. If the ejected wads are healthy, break them up roughly and apply about 5 tons good sharp open sand, spreading as evenly as possible. Leave for the rains to act on it, but an occasional rake over will help in its distribution. Before the winter sets in the little turfs of remaining grass roots should be raked off the surface. In satisfactory greens the soil could be omitted or reduced, and it need not be repeated too often in subsequent years on the others.

Many of the holes may still be partly open till the green is swept in the spring. After thorough sweeping in March the roller will complete the closing of them. About the middle of March a cwt. of good grass fertiliser (Ichthemic Guano or other) should be applied to the turf and no cutting done, of course, until it has been washed in to the soil. Throughout the playing season occasional light dressings of 8 lbs. of Ammonium Sulphate mixed with 5 times its own weight of fine sand or clean soil will keep the grass up to concert pitch.

Replacements of cutters 5/- per set of 3.

WILLIAM PAUL, : : : **41 CAUSEYSIDE STREET, PAISLEY.**

FIGURE 2. One of Paul's many leaflets on bowling green maintenance. Circa. 1925.

MOSS EXTRACTOR.

(Illustrated on right.)

This machine is invaluable wherever moss infests the surface of Putting Greens, Bowling Greens, or Lawns, and its use proves it to be a great boon and labour-saver to Greenkeepers and Gardeners. It is very speedy and effective in tearing out the moss, while combing and aerating the grass. Even if there is no moss, its use is very beneficial to the grass, and it is altogether better and quicker in action than a rake. Can be employed during the whole season, and will be found very serviceable when used prior to the application of top dressings.

16 inches wide (with Box) ... ... **£5 5s. net.**

GREEN'S PATENT 'SILENS MESSOR' LAWN MOWER.

The 'Silens Messor' is a very light running machine and produces a fine even surface on the lawn. The cylinder, which is reversible, has eight cutters. *(Illustrated.)*

Complete with Grass Box. Drawing rope and handle supplied with all hand machines from 14-inch size upwards. If required for 12-inch size, 2/6 extra.

	£	s.	d.		£	s.	d.
8-inch cutter	5	15	0	16-inch cutter	11	0	0
10-inch ,,	6	15	0	18-inch ,,	12	10	0
12-inch ,,	8	0	0	20-inch ,,	13	10	0
14-inch ,,	9	10	0	24-inch ,,	16	0	0

This type of machine can be supplied with gear instead of chain drive, if required, at above prices.

Special close-cutting machines for Golf and Bowling Greens, which include one or two additional cutters in cylinder, can be supplied at an extra cost of **7/6** each additional cutter.

RANSOMES' 'CERTES' LAWN MOWER.

Designed to ensure perfect cutting on Golf Greens. The machine-cut gearing is totally enclosed and grease lubricated. Cutting cylinders with eight knives, and thin bottom blades for close cutting. Steel front roller running on ball bearings; screw adjustment to front roller. *(Illustrated.)*

14-inch cutter ... **£10 15s.**
16-inch ,, ... **£11 10s.**

Grass Boxes included.

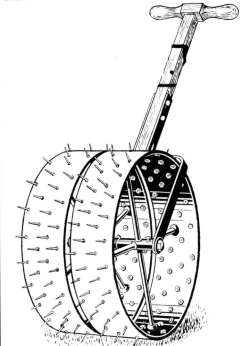

FIGURE 3.   Bowling green maintenance machinery 1920-1939.

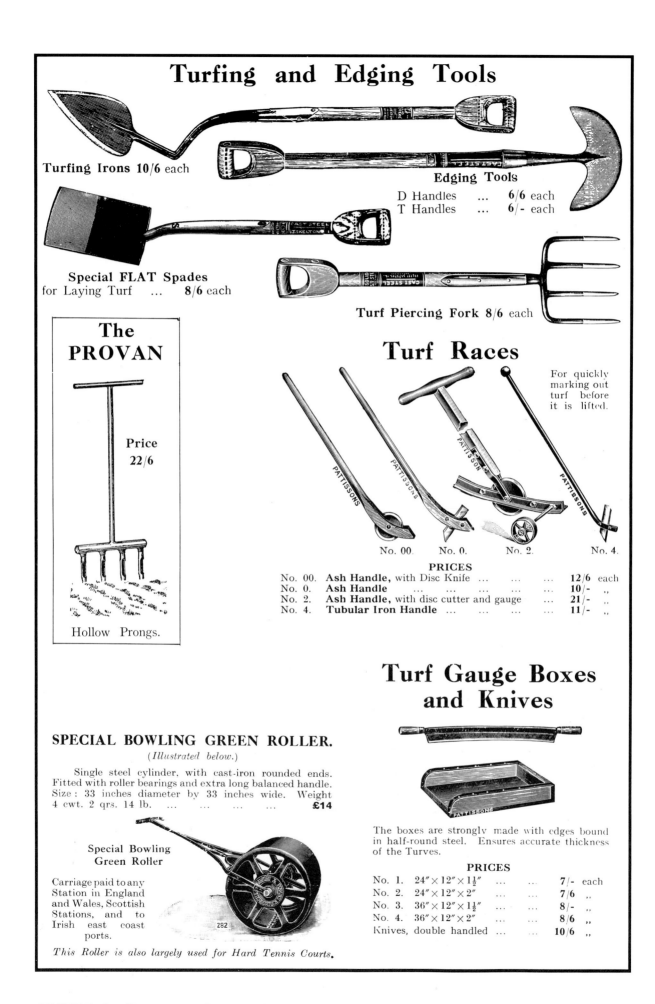

Turfing and Edging Tools

Turfing Irons 10/6 each

Edging Tools

D Handles ... **6/6** each
T Handles ... **6/-** each

Special FLAT Spades
for Laying Turf ... **8/6** each

Turf Piercing Fork 8/6 each

The PROVAN

Price **22/6**

Hollow Prongs.

Turf Races

For quickly marking out turf before it is lifted.

No. 00. No. 0. No. 2. No. 4.

PRICES

No. 00. **Ash Handle**, with Disc Knife	**12/6** each
No. 0. **Ash Handle**	**10/-** ,,
No. 2. **Ash Handle**, with disc cutter and gauge ...	**21/-** ,,
No. 4. **Tubular Iron Handle**	**11/-** ,,

Turf Gauge Boxes and Knives

The boxes are strongly made with edges bound in half-round steel. Ensures accurate thickness of the Turves.

PRICES

No. 1. 24″×12″×1½″	**7/-** each
No. 2. 24″×12″×2″	**7/6** ,,
No. 3. 36″×12″×1½″	**8/-** ,,
No. 4. 36″×12″×2″	**8/6** ,,
Knives, double handled	**10/6** ,,

SPECIAL BOWLING GREEN ROLLER.

(Illustrated below.)

Single steel cylinder, with cast-iron rounded ends. Fitted with roller bearings and extra long balanced handle. Size : 33 inches diameter by 33 inches wide. Weight 4 cwt. 2 qrs. 14 lb. **£14**

Special Bowling Green Roller

Carriage paid to any Station in England and Wales, Scottish Stations, and to Irish east coast ports.

This Roller is also largely used for Hard Tennis Courts.

FIGURE 4. Hand Tools for greenkeepers - about 1930.

Autumn end-of-season work commenced with scarification with a fine sharp rake to remove moss. The green should then be 'graiped', i.e. hand forked using a tool with straight solid tines, this being described as having been in vogue "for generations". In cases where greens are felt to be over-compacted (or "skin-bound"), Paul's own hollow tine fork is strongly advocated. Hollow tine forking was first carried out on greens at Abercorn, Paisley, in 1919, much to the consternation of some more conservative members of the bowling fraternity who thought the operation too severe. After forking, Paul recommended autumn fertiliser (nitrogen, potash and basic slag) followed by top dressing using either 7 ton sharp sand or a 5 ton sand/2 ton compost mix. Top dressing should be worked in with a long rake or straight edge to improve levels. Autumn wormkilling could sometimes also be necessary. (The seed firm, Carters of Raynes Park, London, had introduced the first expellent wormkiller in 1902.)

In the light of modern knowledge, such a system of greenkeeping is open to a number of criticisms. There are, for example, several glaring omissions - there is no mention of the important questions of mowing frequency, mowing heights or mowing patterns. Turf diseases are entirely ignored - admittedly few effective treatments were available but trouble must have been encountered at times with damaging diseases and one might reasonably expect some comment as to possible causes and remedial action. Fusarium patch disease must for instance have occurred periodically, also dollar spot disease to which sea-marsh turf is particularly prone.

By today's standards the amount of rolling advocated is excessive, although one must bear in mind that mowing was predominantly carried out with hand machines which do not have the rolling action of the heavier motor mowers used today - more frequent rolling as a separate operation was therefore justified, although perhaps not with rollers as heavy as the ones then in favour. Fertiliser recommendations are obviously rather arbitrary and understandably not based on any scientific understanding of plant nutritional requirements. The amount of fertiliser used over a twelve month period is excessive but this criticism must be tempered to a certain extent by the fact that Scottish greens were soil-less and free draining and therefore have a higher nutritional requirement than more conventional constructions. Weed, worm and moss control measures were barely adequate but, of course, were limited by the lack of suitable herbicides and other more recently developed chemical treatments.

Whatever their deficiencies, however, Scottish constructional and maintenance techniques provided consistently better bowling surfaces than had been possible previously and helped increase the popularity of lawn bowls in the inter-war period. The upsurge in the number of bowling greens being constructed and the increasing attention being paid to greenkeeping had another beneficial aspect - it stimulated machinery manufacturers to produce and perfect an ever-increasing range of equipment. By the early 1930s a wide range of efficient hand-pushed mowers had been developed from the original Budding machine. Models with extra blades on the cutting cylinder giving a finer cut were introduced for bowling and golf green mowing. Machines such as the Webb Deluxe of 1929, the Ransomes Hand Certes and the Green's Patent Silens Messor were capable of producing an excellent finish and were widely used. Power-driven lawn mowers were very slow to displace the hand machines and many greenkeepers resisted the advent of powered mowers on the grounds that they produced an inferior standard of bowling surface. The first powered lawn mowers were unwieldy and heavy steam driven machines which were briefly used for general sports ground cutting in the 1893-1910 period. They proved far too large and weighty for bowling green usage. Petrol driven machines appeared on the scene with a 1902 Ransomes machine but early models were again large, weighing about 1 ton and hence unsuitable for bowling green cutting. By the 2nd World War, motor mowers suitable for bowling green purposes had been developed but the reactionary attitude of many greenkeepers and bowlers delayed their general acceptance until well after the 1939-45 conflict.

By the 1930s fertiliser distributors, rake scarifiers and spikers were all being produced for the bowling green market. Spinner-type distributors, Sarel spiked rollers, drag brushes and hand-powered rotary scarifiers were all available in catalogues issued in the early 1930s. A notable pioneer was William Hargreaves who invented a mechanical spiker and founded W. Hargreaves & Co. Ltd. in 1932 (now Sisis Equipment Ltd.). Pattissons of Stanmore, Middlesex were also active and originated as far back as 1896.

The scientist and the greenkeeper

The scientific study of turf for lawns and sporting facilities commenced in Connecticut in the USA in 1885 when J.B. Olcott initiated detailed studies aimed at finding the best strains of grass for fine turf. Rhode Island State College of Agriculture was another pioneer, setting up experiments in 1890. Many State Agricultural Colleges in the USA followed suit and in 1920 the U.S. Golf Association established its "Green Section" comprising both research and advisory services.

In the British Isles, turf research began in 1929 when the British Golf Unions' Joint Advisory Council set up the Board of Greenkeeping Research. A research station and experiment ground was set up at the St. Ives Estate in Bingley, West Yorkshire and work commenced under the leadership of the Board's first Director, R.B. Dawson. The Board was reconstituted in September 1951 as the Sports Turf Research Institute, extending its work to formally cover all turf for sport and amenity purposes, but it should not be imaged that the Research Station's sphere of interest was confined to golf course management, even in its earliest years. The bowling fraternity showed a keen interest in research from the start and in February 1930 the London and Southern Counties Bowling Association made a grant of £60 to the Research Station "to allow tests to be carried out during the next twelve months, with a view to explaining in an unbiased fashion better methods of treatment for Cumberland Turf Greens". In response a miniature bowling green was laid down at the Bingley experiment ground, turfing being completed in April 1930. The Scottish pattern of construction was followed with about 10 in. clinker (finer towards the top) underlying 2 in. of sharp Bedford sand on which Silloth sea-marsh turf was laid. Experimental work commenced at once, two important objects being to find out why sea-marsh turf was prone to broad-leaved weed and coarse grass invasion when moved away from its natural coastal environment, and to investigate and possibly prevent the encroachment of annual meadow-grass (*Poa annua*) into the turf. Questions of turf acidity and alkalinity were also investigated and the new green was divided into ten plots each of which was subjected to a different fertiliser regime. A convenient outbreak of fusarium patch disease allowed some fungicide trials to be completed - Bordeaux/Malachite green fungicide was subsequently recommended to many bowling clubs as a result of this investigation work. By 1932, an effective leather-jacket expellant had also been developed (based on a now unapproved chemical, orthodichlorobenzene) and for a time the Research Station sold the material in commercial quantities as St. Ives Leather Jacket Exterminator. In 1934 the Director was able to report on the suitability of New Zealand browntop bentgrass for seeded greens, the importance of mechanical work (particularly aeration) in bowling green maintenance, and on the suitability of mowrah meal and lead arsenate for wormkilling purposes. An improved strain of slender creeping red fescue (cv. Dawson) was also developed.

Significant progress in the scientific management of bowling greens was therefore made at Bingley prior to the Second World War, although this aspect of the Research Station's activities was severely limited by lack of funds during this period. The 1939-45 war, of course, severely curtailed all aspects of turf research but the St. Ives station continued to tick over on a wartime footing until the Armistice.

FIGURE 5. Chemicals for turf maintenance 1920-1935.

PLATE 16. Construction work on the miniature experimental bowling green at the Bingley Research Station. April 1930.

CHAPTER 2
THE SEA-MARSH TURF CONTROVERSY

At this point, it is worthwhile making a digression in this historical survey of bowling green development to consider in detail the merits and demerits of sea-marsh turf as a bowling surface and to assess, with the advantage of hindsight, the successes and failures of the Scottish no-soil method of green construction. These questions have produced major controversies in the past and still cause arguments today. One still commonly encounters bowlers, particularly those of the older generation, who will state, very forcefully, that the only good green is a sea-marsh green and that this material is mandatory if a first class playing surface is to be achieved. It will therefore be of value to attempt to explain how sea-marsh turf achieved its almost legendary reputation in spite of its many serious deficiencies - deficiencies which are still not universally appreciated today.

To consider the Scottish green construction technique first, its advantages during the period when it gained wide acceptance were as follows.

[A] The foundation layers minimised subsidence problems and hence helped towards the provision of an even and true bowls surface. This was particularly important for flat rink bowling, the type of game that the Scots were originally catering for.

[B] The foundation layer also helped provide excellent sub-surface drainage and made for a very quick-drying green. This was particularly advantageous in Scotland itself, in high rainfall areas such as the Glasgow district where clinker construction allowed play very soon after the cessation of all but the heaviest rainstorm.

[C] Clinker and ash were at the time widely available industrial waste products and were obtainable cheaply in most parts of the country. Their use hence helped reduce the cost of a new green.

[D] Forming the turf bed of sand alone eliminated consolidation problems and simplified the process of surface grading. The method could therefore be followed by club members, who often had very limited experience of green construction, with a fair chance of success. The technique also proved popular among professional contractors who also found that it achieved a satisfactory end product with relative ease and economy.

[E] In the years before the development of effective wormkilling chemicals, earthworms were and extremely serious problem for greenkeepers. By eliminating the soil, the Scottish construction minimised worm problems - a more important advantage than it would be nowadays. Absence of soil may also have reduced leatherjacket damage.

Turning to the disadvantages of the system, a further list can be made.

[A] In some situations the free draining nature of the clinker foundation was a positive disadvantage - the turf dried out very quickly unless a reliable and copious water supply was available. Even in Scotland problems were encountered as William Paul made clear - after two weeks of dry summer weather greens of this type begain to show severe drought symptoms unless adequately irrigated.

[B] After the Second World War it gradually became more and more difficult to obtain suitable supplies of ash and particularly clinker. Changes in industrial practices resulted in a drying-up of the supply and by the late 1960s good clinker was virtually unobtainable in many areas. Unfortunately, this led in a few cases to the use of highly unsuitable substitutes. Industrial slag was employed in one or two instances and this in time tended to set into a solid mass which did not drain at all. The fact that recommended materials later became unavailable cannot be regarded as a criticism of the original system, but it is one reason why such construction is no longer as attractive as it once appeared.

[C] The most serious deficiency arose as a result of long-term problems associated with maintaining an adequate grass cover in a no-soil construction. The application of modern

FIGURE 6. Sea-marsh turf advertisements 1935-39.

35

knowledge could well overcome these difficulties, but in the past many greenkeepers encountered serious problems. Apart from being prone to drought, swards in such situations also readily suffered from nutrient deficiency necessitating frequent fertiliser treatment (William Paul advised fertiliser every 3 weeks throughout the growing season, plus an autumn application). Heavy fertilisation in turn fostered problems with fusarium patch disease, reduced desirable fescue grasses in the sward and encouraged annual meadow-grass invasion. Without fertiliser on the other hand, swards tended to be thin, lacking ability to regenerate worn areas. Moss invasion and red thread (Corticium) disease were also common results of inadequate fertiliser supplies. The management of a bowling green built to Scottish specifications was therefore a difficult task and only highly skilled and experienced greenkeepers stood much chance of success. In hindsight, one can say their task could have been made considerably easier given a more adequate constructional method.

We can now turn to the even more problematical question of the use of sea-marsh turf. To explain first exactly what is being considered, sea-marsh turf is a naturally occurring material found on coastal salt marshes as has already been mentioned. It is largely made up of two grass species - creeping bent grass (*Agrostis stolonifera* var. *compacta*) and red fescue (*Festuca rubra* spp. *rubra*). Some weed may also be found, notably common salt marsh grass (*Puccinellia maritima*, formerly *Glyceria maritima*) which does not stand close mowing and is therefore unsuitable for bowling green or lawn purposes. Broad leaved weed may include sea plantain (*Plantago maritima*), buckshorn plantain (*Plantago coronopus*), sea pink (*Armeria maritima*), sea milkwort (*Glaux maritima*) and scurvy grass (*Cochlearia officinalis*). The underlying soil is a fine homogenous deposit laid down by tidal action and is usually a silt (with the majority of particles in the 0.002 - 0.005 mm size range) or occasionally a fine sand (particles 0.050 - 0.250 mm). The sea-marsh soil is alkaline in reaction.

The advantages of sea-marsh turf and the reasons why it was recommended and exploited as a bowling surface were as follows. They depend on the properties of both the indigenous grass cover and those of the underlying silt.

[A] The natural grass cover on sea-marsh turf is dense, wiry and even and hence is a good bowling surface. This is particularly true of turf with a high proportion of red fescue and turf of this kind tended to be preferentially selected for bowls purposes. In the early years of sea-marsh exploitation at least, it was also possible to select areas of natural turf which were relatively free of broad-leaved weed and the undesirable grass *Puccinellia maritima*. As far as natural grass cover was concerned, sea-marsh turf was only rivalled by the downland and moorland turf which was occasionally used as a cheaper substitute. Such upland turf did not, however, naturally occur in the same commercially exploitable quantities as the sea-marsh product and was less uniform and less easy to lift and re-lay. Today, the appearance of improved grass varieties, seed certification schemes, etc. have made seeded greens a more viable alternative to those established by turfing. The slow emergence of a specialised industry growing turf specifically for sports turf purposes has altered the situation totally, but up until recent years sea-marsh turf was simply regarded, with considerable justification, as the best material available for the purpose.

[B] The sea-marsh silt layer harvested with the turf appears, in the short-term at least, to present a number of advantages as far as establishing a bowling surface is concerned. The fact that it facilitates uniform turf lifting has already been remarked upon. It allows an acceptable bowling surface to be established easily and quickly - a green turfed in the autumn could be rolled down to provide a bowling surface of high standard by the late spring or early summer of the following year. This was a marked point in its favour to bowlers anxious to roll the first competitive wood on their new greens. It was also an advantage as far as the specialised contractor was concerned - such firms proliferated during the inter-war period. Contractors could construct sea-marsh greens with relative ease and hand them over quickly to satisfied clients - a sound business advantage!

Against the above must be counter-balanced the many serious problems associated with sea-marsh turf. Unfortunately many of its deficiencies tend to become obvious only after a particular green has been in commission for several years. In such a situation it is all too easy to blame poor maintenance or inexpert greenkeeping for faults which are in fact a direct long-term consequence of the initial use of the sea-marsh turf itself. The problems are:-

36

FIGURE 7. Sea marsh turf advertisements 1935-39.

[A] The sea-marsh bent and fescue grasses exist in their natural environment because they are salt tolerant and are therefore naturally able to withstand both spray-laden winds and periodic inundation by high tides. This action of the sea burns out other grass species and many broad-leaved weeds which cannot tolerate such conditions, and hence maintains the characteristic salt marsh flora indefinitely. Once sea-marsh turf is transported inland and laid as a bowling green, however, a totally different set of environmental factors apply. Salt tolerance is no longer a requirement for survival and the way is open for invasion by other plant species. Colonisation by annual meadow-grass (*Poa annua*) was the most obvious aspect of this problem and within two or three years of initial establishment sea-marsh greens inevitably begin to take on a "spotty" appearance due to the establishment of scattered lighter green annual meadow-grass plants in the darker sea-marsh sward. Very little can be done to counteract this process, short of the greenkeeper spending most of his working life on his knees hand weeding out the annual meadow-grass, and even then he would probably be fighting a losing battle. The annual meadow-grass problem was worsened by the kind of maintenance which has already been discussed as having been necessitated by the Scottish constructional technique. Regular summer watering and frequent fertiliser treatment both favour annual meadow-grass and hence accelerated the deterioration of the traditional sea-marsh green. Such a maintenance regime also has a directly deleterious effect on the red fescue, this grass being the most desirable sward constituent from the bowling point of view as previously mentioned. In the case of the miniature green built at Bingley in 1930 for example, it was found that the red fescue was virtually eliminated after twelve months of then-standard maintenance treatment. Fescue is favoured by conditions of relative poverty and cannot compete in a heavily fertilized sward. When brought inland, sea-marsh turf is also invaded by clover, pearlwort and other common weeds - a serious problem before the advent of selective weedkillers in the late 1940s. Sea-marsh red fescue is also now known to be markedly susceptible to dollar spot disease and this also contributes to the difficulties of maintaining it.

The creeping bent grass constituent of the sea-marsh sward also caused some problems even though it tended to survive more successfully than the red fescue. Being a stoloniferous creeping grass as its name suggests, the bent is inclined to form a soft matted sward with an accumulation of interwoven fibrous stems in the immediate surface. This characteristic tends to result in a slow heavy bowling surface unless mat formation is rigorously controlled by scarification work. This was something of a nuisance but at least the problem could be overcome by good maintenance, in contrast to difficulties with the disappearance of fescue and annual meadow-grass invasion which proved virtually insuperable.

One attempted solution to some of the above problems was to treat inland greens with salt with the idea of reproducing the sea-marsh environment and hence preserving the original sward. Such treatment could prove disastrous in the case of a green with underlying soil as salt deflocculates clay and destroys soil structure, producing compaction, poor grass growth and drainage difficulties. This objection of course did not however apply to greens of Scottish no-soil construction. Salt was applied either by using beach sand, which naturally had a certain salt content, or by using straight salt at a rate of about 1 cwt. to a 42 x 42 yd. green. The practice was never widespread and it is probably fair to say that the treatment was only partially successful. Salt applications delayed the process of turf deterioration but did not overcome the problem entirely. Rain and irrigation water would wash the salt through fairly quickly, leaving the way open again for inland weed and grass invasion.

[B] The silt layer lifted with the sea-marsh turf might form a highly acceptable bowling surface in the short-term, which it undoubtedly did, but in the long-term led to a whole series of headaches for the greenkeeper.

During the first two or three seasons of play, the silt became heavily compacted, both as a result of treading by the players and by the frequent rolling advocated in the days before motor mowers, with their built-in light rolling effect, were employed. After all, rolling with machines weighing 1 ton or more was commonplace on new greens to settle the turf and for all greens in preparation for the start of each playing season. In addition, 4-5 cwt. iron hand rollers were used at frequent intervals throughout the playing season, in some cases supplemented by additional rolling with lighter and broader elm rollers weighing a little less than 1 cwt. With such massive and regular compaction it is little wonder that difficulties in growing grass appeared. As William Paul wrote in 1920:-

ARNOLD'S PATENT WAVELESS BOWLING GREEN ROLLER

Patentee:- ALECK T. ARNOLD, Brick House Farm
KELVEDON, ESSEX. Phone 89

PLATE 17. The use of heavy rollers added to compaction problems on sea-marsh greens. Arnold's machine was available in $^1/_2$ and 1 ton models.

PLATE 18. Early aerating machines did little to relieve the problem. The beneficial spiking effect of this implement was probably counteracted by its rolling factor - the Gibson spiked roller weighed 3 cwt.

"Many greens, unfortunately, have been laid with turf procured from a silt or clay foundation, and while the surface looks splendid in its 'virgin' setting the rolling and playing soon pack it into a putty-like subsoil in which growing healthy grass is impossible."

He pointed out that sea-marsh turf established naturally on a more open substrate with a higher proportion of larger sand particles rather than silt was less prone to problems of over-compaction. Such turf is, however, relatively uncommon on sea marshes and most turf that was used was of a silty nature.

As a green aged, the original silt layer imported with the turf was gradually buried by the top dressing work carried out at the end of each bowling season. Such autumn top dressing was, and still is, essential to fill scars left by play and maintain an even bowling surface. Up to 7 ton of sand (or sandy compost) were routinely used each year and the silt layer was hence gradually buried. Autumn top dressing, plus similar sandy material used periodically as a carrier for fertiliser dressings, might result in about 1/4 in. or so of material being incorporated into the average bowling surface over a 12 month period. If an old established green were to be sampled with a soil auger, corer or similar tool, then the silt layer, originally on the surface, could be found sometimes at a depth of several inches below the sward, its depth of course depending on the age of the green and the quantities and frequency of the top dressing programme. (Out of interest, it is worth mentioning that the author recalls examining a green in South West Scotland a few years ago where the silt layer could be distinctly seen nearly 14 in. below the surface. The green dated back to the late 18th Century but club officials had no knowledge as to whether it had been re-laid at some point subsequent to its original construction. Such a depth of accumulated top dressing must however have represented very many years of maintenance work.)

Such buried silt layers proved to be a menace as far as green maintenance is concerned. Heavily compacted before being buried, the silt acts as a barrier towards water penetration and rooting depth. Poor drainage is therefore encouraged with consequent wet and heavy bowling surfaces, moss and annual meadow-grass increased and finer grasses reduced. Rooting can be very poor indeed, particularly when the silt layer is just an inch or two below the surface. With such shallow rooting depths greens are drought prone in the summer and swards are excessively dependent on frequent fertiliser dressing for their nutritional requirements.

Many of the above points were fully appreciated by the Scottish fraternity. One attempted solution was autumn solid tine forking aimed at penetrating and breaking up the troublesome silt layer - later a bewildering variety of forks and aerating machines were developed to facilitate speedier or more effective aeration. William Paul's hollow tine fork proved one of the best of these innovations as cores of the silt layer were actually physically removed. No tool or machine solved the problem completely, however, and buried silt layers are still a problem on many greens today, of both flat and crown varieties.

It is hoped that the preceding pages will help knock another nail into the coffin of the inflated reputation which sea-marsh turf still possesses for many bowlers. It is worth stressing that even with today's more advanced knowledge of turf culture and with efficient modern equipment, it is virtually impossible to prevent the deterioration of sea-marsh turf transported to inland environments. Silt layers continue to be problematical, as stated above. Hence, when one stands by a particular green today listening to a proud bowler extolling its virtues and attributing these to the fact that it was laid before the War using only the finest Cumberland turf, one may be permitted an ironic smile. Almost invariably, close examination of the sward reveals that not a trace of the original sea-marsh grass remains, the green having been completely colonised by inland grasses - usually annual meadow-grass (*Poa annua*) and browntop bent (*Agrostis tenuis*) in varying proportions. The much-vaunted silt bowling surface is usually several inches below the surface and in that position is nothing but a handicap to the process of maintaining a good green.

Having said this however, one must add a few words in defence of the Scottish green managers who first advocated sea-marsh turf and employed it for so many new greens. In its day it was the most suitable naturally-occurring material available and its employment revolutionised lawn bowling throughout the British Isles, allowing the skills of the modern game to develop by providing better surfaces than had ever been known before. That the material had grave long-term disadvantages proved unfortunate but does not diminish their achievement.

PLATES 19 & 20. Hollow tine forking a sea-marsh green to help break up a buried silt layer. A long and monotonous operation using, in this case, the Sisis version of the fork invented by William Paul.

CHAPTER 3
BOWLING GREEN EVOLUTION: 1945 TO THE PRESENT DAY

POST WAR DEVELOPMENTS IN GREEN CONSTRUCTION

In the years following the Second World War, weaknesses in the traditional Scottish method of green construction gradually led to a preponderance of new greens being built using alternative techniques. Conservative bowlers and contractors kept the Scottish system viable for a long time however - indeed a few flat greens are still being constructed today using the old method - but generally speaking it has rightly fallen out of favour in recent years. Maintenance techniques have also evolved a long way during this period, partly as a result of the abandonment of sea-marsh turf and Scottish construction, but, of course, also as a result of the appearance of vastly improved equipment and new chemical treatments etc.

The main changes which have taken place in bowling green construction are a move away from sea-marsh turf in favour of seeding or alternative types of turf, and the provision of a layer of soil (or sand/soil mix) immediately beneath the sward.

A certain proportion of new greens had in fact always been constructed using soil, even during the heyday of the Scottish system. In the inter-war period the Scottish construction with sea-marsh turf was regarded as the De Luxe system, soil construction being reserved for seeded greens or greens turfed with sea-marsh turf substitutes. Soil greens were cheaper to build and traditionally regarded as very much inferior, particularly during the inter-war years. In the face of much prejudice, however, it was gradually appreciated that in the long-term such "inferior" greens showed a number of significant advantages. The presence of good quality soil beneath the surface made long-term maintenance much easier - greens with this feature were less drought prone and grass growth and vigour were superior. By not using sea-marsh turf the insuperable problem of maintaining maritime grasses under inland conditions was eliminated and troublesome silt layers were no longer present. The decline of sea-marsh turf was accelerated by the over-exploitation of the marshes. After the 1939-45 war it became increasingly difficult to fine turf of top quality and the use of inferior sea-marsh turf containing much broad-leaved weed or the weed grass *Puccinellia*, plus spiralling costs, all contributed to its waning popularity. The pioneer selections of improved strains of turfgrass (like Dawson and New Zealand browntop) available in the 1930s and the beginnings of seed certification made seeded greens a more viable alternative. The very slow but significant appearance of a turf-growing industry producing high quality material specifically for fine sward establishment also made sea-marsh turf a less attractive proposition than it had formerly been.

Initially, where soil was used in green construction only shallow layers 2.5 to 3 in. in depth were used. Where cost considerations permitted the soil was spread over a traditional Scottish foundation of clinker blinded with fine ash. Relatively shallow soil layers were favoured to maintain good water penetration into the underlying clinker and hence produce a fast-drying bowling surface.

By the time that the Research Station at Bingley (now officially The Sports Turf Research Institute) became actively involved in the supervision of bowling green construction projects in the 1950s, thinking on soil depths was changing and deeper layers were being advocated. (As a matter of interest, the first bowling green construction project that the Institute was involved in was a flat green for Rowntrees, the confectionery manufacturers, at York. This was as early as 1949.) As the Institute's then Director, J.R. Escritt, wrote in 1975 (in conjunction with R.B. Gooch of the NPFA in Sports Ground Construction Specifications, 1975 Edition):-

"The depth of 'topsoil' specified is related to the current commercial practice which produces satisfactory bowling greens. There is increasing evidence that a greater depth of specially prepared 'topsoil', say 150 mm (6 in.) or as much as 250 mm (10 in.) would be more satisfactory both for drainage and for moisture retention in dry weather. Obviously, if an increased depth of soil were to be used this would mean increased excavation and deeper drains."

This trend has continued to the present day with a minimum of 4 in. (100 mm) being recommended for a turfed green and 6 in. (150 mm) for a seeded surface.

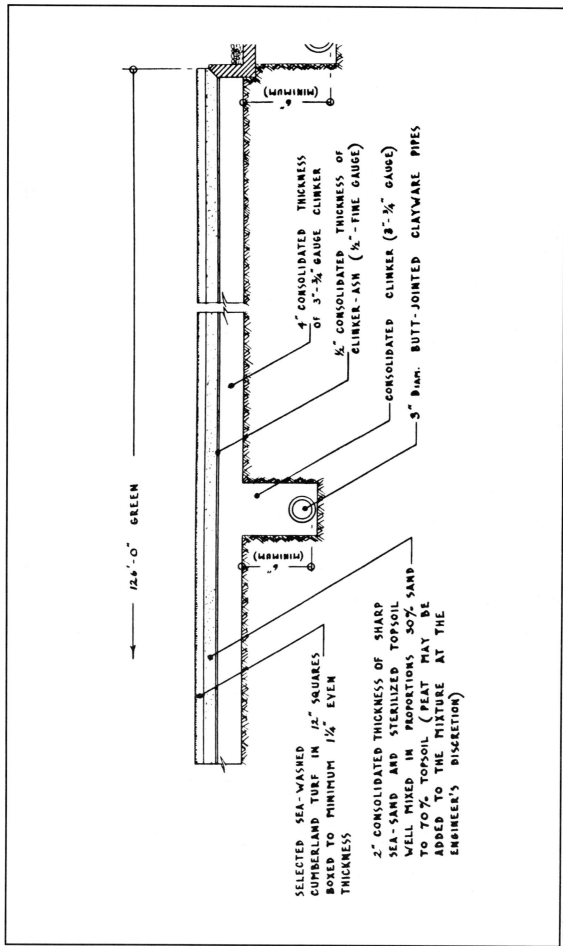

FIGURE 8. Typical bowling green construction of the 1950's. Note the shallow 2 in. layer of soil/sand mix and the continued use of sea-marsh turf.

PLATE 21. The first bowling green construction project in which the STRI was involved. Rowntrees bowling green at York, built in 1949.

Bowling green drainage has evolved to some degree since the Second World War. In the case of flat rink greens a grid system of parallel lateral drains running diagonally beneath the surface has emerged as standard practice, as opposed to the variety of drainage patterns which have been advocated in the past. For crown greens, drains beneath the actual playing surface are generally still considered unnecessary as surface contours shed water effectively into surrounding ditches. For flat and crown greens, perimeter ditch drains should always be included. The traditional clayware pipe drains   (75 mm diameter for flat green laterals and 100 mm for ditch drains) have now been almost completely superceded by plastic pipes of equivalent sizes (60 mm for laterals and 100-110 mm for perimeter ditches).

For the foundation layers, the unavailability of clinker and ash of good quality has led to the use of gravel or broken stone as substitutes, blinded by a suitable grade of coarse sand. Synthetic material such as Lytag is occasionally used for backfilling drain trenches, although not for the foundation layer itself as the even-sized and rounded particles of such materials do not give sufficient stability and lead to difficulties with consolidation.

In recent years the use of standard laboratory techniques has removed much of the guesswork from determining an ideal sand/soil mix for the "top soil" layer. (Rarely the admixture of a small proportion of granulated peat may also sometimes be deemed necessary if the organic matter content of the mix is found to be inadequate.) Such soil analysis work was originally carried out in the late 1950s and early 60s by the United States Golf Association but since the early 1970s has been increasingly used by the Sports Turf Research Institute to determine ideal drainage rates for soils for all sporting purposes, bowling greens included. In recent years there has been a steady tendancy to increase the proportion of sand in the mix and a minimum Hydraulic Conductivity of 50 mm per hour is now insisted upon. Sand of even particle size within strictly defined limits gives best results. Free-draining greens so constructed must have adequate watering systems.

For seeded greens, a seeds mixture made up of browntop bent grass and Chewings fescue is now a standard recommendation. The seeds mix gives a 50-50 sward of the two species but because bent grass seed is a quarter the weight of the fescue seed, four times as much fescue must be included, i.e.

80% by weight Chewings fescue (*Festuca rubra* spp. *commutata*)
20% by weight browntop bent (*Agrostis tenuis* or *castellana*)

Dutch cultivars of browntop are now most widely used such as the long-established Bardot and Tracenta which are finer-leaved, denser, lower-growing and less prone to red thread disease than Highland which is now regarded as a separate species, *Agrostis castellana* (the old Oregon browntop), but are not as green as Highland in winter. The latter point is of course not very significant for a strictly summer game. In summer, appearance depends on age of sward, amount of thatch and watering. Compact Dutch cultivars are likely to be more attractive than Highland unless they develop too much thatch or there is a severe drought. Highland is strongly rhizomatous, unlike the other cultivars. Chewings fescue is fine-leaved, relatively low-growing and disease resistant. Good cultivars are tolerant of close mowing and, for bowls, types with good summer colour are preferred. The STRI now produces an annual booklet covering current grass varieties from which Fig. 14 is taken.

Turfing remains an alternative method of bowling green establishment which, although more costly than seeding, produces a playable surface after a shorter time. If a green is seeded in early autumn, as is usual, then about 18 months must elapse before play can take place. A surface turfed in autumn can usually be played on the following July given a good standard of construction work and adequate initial maintenance. If turf is chosen as an establishment method, then it is essential to use purpose-grown turf from one of the few specialist firms who produce top quality turf in this country. Turf grown from suitable grass cultivars (as would be used for a seeded green) is mandatory and should be free of that ubiquitous weed grass, annual meadow-grass. It is also an advantage to employ turf grown on a substrate which resembles as closely as possible the soil/sand mix used in the construction of a particular green.

There have been several seedling turf products developed in the U.K. during the last 10-20

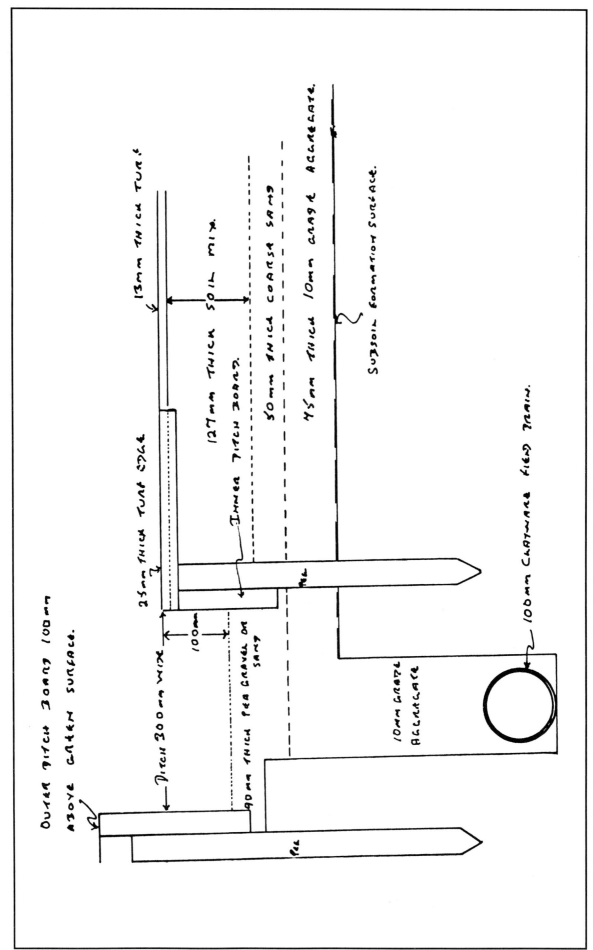

FIGURE 9. Typical bowling green construction in the 1970's. Note the deeper 127 mm (5 in.) soil mix layer.

46

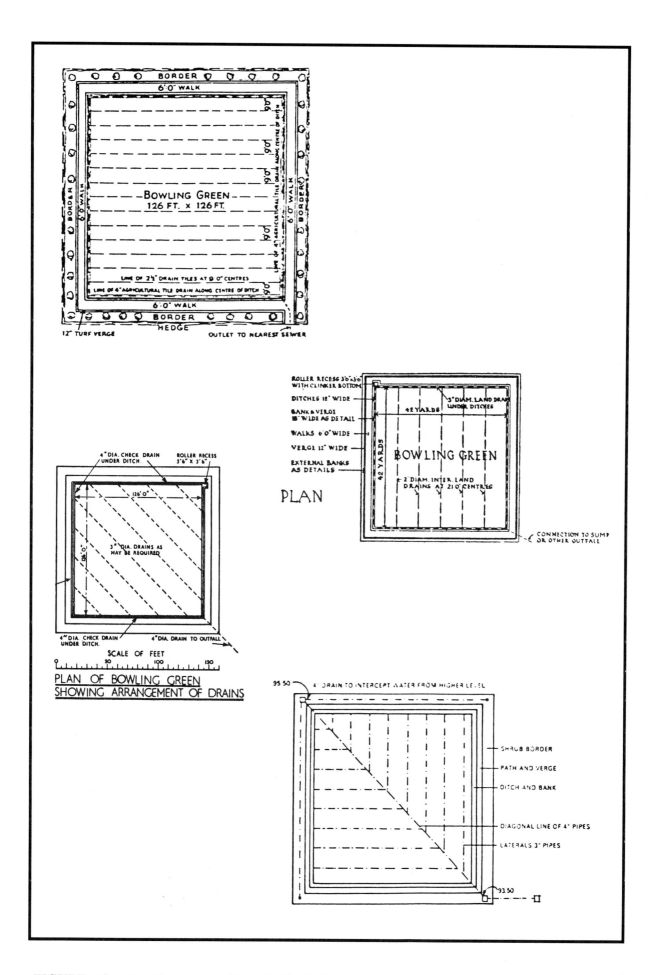

FIGURE 10. Bowling green (flat rink) drain layouts. A variety of patterns have been advocated in the past. Here, four systems from 1931, 1937, 1950 and 1968.

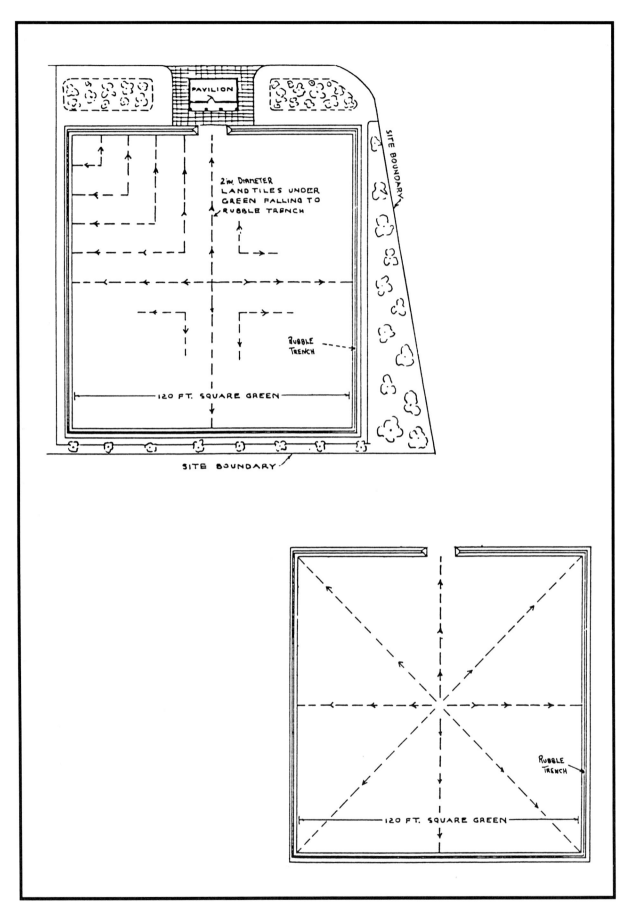

FIGURE 11. The majority of crown greens do not have pipe drains below the playing surface, merely perimeter ditch drains. Drainage systems were, however, sometimes laid beneath the body of a crown green as indicated in these two plans from the 1930's. The possible presence of such systems should therefore be borne in mind when dealing with an old-established crown green.

SAND
SIEVE TEST RESULTS

SAMPLE RE: **DATE:**

ORIGIN OF SAMPLE: **REF. NO.**

CATEGORY	DIAMETER, mm	%
Stones	>8	0
Coarse Gravel	8-4	0
Fine Gravel	4-2	0
V. Coarse Sand	2-1	2
Coarse Sand	1.0-0.5	38
Medium Sand	0.50-0.25	55
Fine Sand	0.250-0.125	5
V. Fine Sand	0.125-0.050	0
Silt + Clay	<0.050	0
Lime Content (as $CaCO_3$)		<0.5

FIGURE 12. A typical laboratory sheet showing a sand with an ideal particle size distribution for inclusion in a soil-sand mix for bowling green construction.

SOIL SAMPLE RE:

BRIEF DESCRIPTION:

DATE:

SOIL REF. NO.

CATEGORY	DIAMETER mm	%	
Stones	>8 mm	-	**SOIL TEXTURE:**
Coarse Gravel	8-4	-	SANDY LOAM
Fine Gravel	4-2	-	
Particle size distribution of mineral matter smaller Than 2 mm			
V. Coarse Sand	2-1	1	**COMMENTS:**
Coarse Sand	1.0-0.5	32	MIX OF ONE PART SOIL TO TWO-THREE PARTS SAND AS PER SAMPLE
Medium Sand	0.50-0.25	44	
Fine Sand	0.250-0.125	9	
V. Fine Sand	0.125-0.050	6	
Silt	0.50-0.002	5	
Clay	<0.002	3	
Loss on Ignition (% of oven-dry fine-earth)		3-5%	
Calcium carbonate (% of air-dry fine-earth)		<0.5	
Water dispersibility of the clay (%)		-	

FIGURE 13. Laboratory analysis of ideal sand-soil mix for bowling green construction.

CULTIVARS OF BENTS (*Agrostis* spp.) AVAILABLE IN 1992

BROWNTOP BENTS (*Agrostis* spp.)

Cultivar	Compactness (shoot density)	Fineness of leaf	Summer greenness	Winter greenness	Freedom from red thread[1]	Short growth
A. tenuis						
Egmont	A	B	B	B	B	B
Bardot	C	B	B	C	B	A
Duchess (LA)	C	B	B	C	B	A
Saboval	D	D	B	B	B	B
Tracenta	D	D	B	C	B	B
Allure	D	D	B	C	–	B
A castellana						
Highland	E	D	D	A	D	E
New cultivars						
Sefton	A	A	–	–	C	A
Heriot (LA)	A	A	–	–	C	A
Lance (LA)	B	B	–	–	B	B
Litenta	–	–	–	–	–	–

[1]*Laetisaria fuciformis*   *Freely available

CHEWINGS FESCUE (*Festuca rubra* ssp. *commutata*)

Cultivar	Tolerance of close mowing	Compactness (shoot density)	Freedom from red thread[1]	Winter greenness	Summer greenness	Short growth
Baruba	A	B	B	DG	DG	C
Frida	A	B	B	MG	MG	B
Center	A	B	B	DG	MG	C
Olivia	A	B	C	MG	DG	B
Lobi	A	B	B	DG	MG	C
Enjoy	B	B	B	DG	MG	C
Waldorf	B	B	B	DG	MG	B
Bingo	A	B	B	DG	MG	D
Wilma	B	B	C	MG	LG	B
Mary	B	B	C	MG	DG	C
Atlanta	B	C	B	DG	MG	C
Alltop (LA)	B	B	B	DG	MG	B
Epsom	B	C	B	DG	DG	C
Beauty	B	C	B	MG	LG	B
Agram	B	C	B	DG	MG	B
Bellamy	B	C	B	DG	MG	C
Tamara	B	C	B	DG	MG	C
Menuet	B	C	B	DG	DG	D
Lustre	B	C	B	DG	MG	C
Weekend	B	C	C	DG	MG	B
Lifalla	B	C	B	DG	MG	D
Scarlet	B	C	B	DG	DG	C
Capitol	B	C	C	DG	MG	B
Koket	B	C	B	DG	LG	C
Tatjana	C	D	C	DG	LG	E
Barnica	C	D	B	DG	LG	D
Banner	C	C	B	MG	MG	D
Ivalo	C	D	B	DG	MG	D
New cultivars						
Nimrod (LA)	B	B	D	DG	MG	C
Bargreen (LA)	B	B	B	DG	DG	B
Rainbow (LA)	B	B	B	DG	DG	B

[1]*Laetisaria fuciformis*

In the tables describing the cultivars of the major turf-type grasses, merit for different attributes are described on an A to E scale, where A is best and E is worst. In some cases, where differences between cultivars are not great, only A to C or A to D are used. These ratings are only for comparison within columns, not between columns nor between tables except where stated. In general, diff-erences between adjacent scores, e.g. between A and B or between B and C are small and statistical significance cannot be guaranteed. A hyphen (-) signifies insufficient data to derive a score. Often there will be several cultivars of similar merit for the use in question and the final choice can be made according to price and/or other commercial factors.

Columns for colour in summer and winter have been changed where possible, to describe actual greenness. The new ratings are not merit ratings. Users should select grasses according to personal preferences. The ratings given are: LG = light green; MG = mid green and; DG = dark green.

Seed of all cultivars named should be available in the UK in 1992, but in smaller amounts where shown as LA (limited availability).

FIGURE 14.   STRI ratings for browntop bent and Chewings fescue cultivars.

years. Some of them have incorporated some sort of light netting or other plastic reinforcement to avoid damage in handling, the seedling sod usually being lifted and sold about 2-3 months after seeding, but others have just relied on the binding of intermingled roots.

Seedling sod is light and easy to handle, and comes in large pieces which facilitate laying, e.g. approximately 0.8 x 3.2 m (c.30 x 130 in.). Among professional users it mainly appeals to the person laying down a new sports facility who will pay a premium for quick delivery of the exact cultivars and speices of grasses required, free of weeds and perhaps even grown on a specified "soil" mixture, growing vigorously so that the interval between site preparation and start of play is cut to the absolute minimum. Any light netting or plastic reinforcement in the sod is only for strength in handling, and should not be expected to do anything to improve wear tolerance of the turf in use. According to their age, thickness, firmness and amount of incorporated nutrients, all seedling materials are likely to require more attention than mature turf, especially with regard to watering immediately after laying and perhaps regularly for several days afterwards, nutrition in the early months, and top dressing or other operations aimed at creating a level playing surface.

Considerable progress has been made since the War in the construction of bowling green perimeter ditches. Traditionally for flat greens, preservative-treated wood boards and stakes have been used but modern difficulties in obtaining suitably-seasoned high-quality timber have encouraged the use of alternative ditch formation methods. Pre-cast concrete kerb units were the first alternative to wood, the outer taller kerb being faced with a softwood striking board to avoid damage to the bowls. (Artificial turf is an attractive alternative to a wood striking board, glued to the kerb face.) Subsequently, purpose-made pre-cast concrete ditch units have been produced to EBA-approved patterns, complete with mitred corner units. The latest development is a high or low backed gulley manufactured from glass reinforced cement. Such units are much lighter than the concrete ditch sections and can hence be made as relatively long sections (2 metres long as opposed to 60 cm for concrete). Some of the above units could well be used for crown green construction although crown green ditch requirements are far less rigorous than for the flat rink game and such refinements might therefore be considered unnecessarily expensive for the average crown green.

ARTIFICIAL OUTDOOR GREENS
Natural grass bowling greens are the subject of the present text, but some mention of artificial outdoor greens is an obvious requirement as there are now a number of such installations up and down the country, both flat-rink and crown artificial greens having been constructed. The attitudes of the various bowling organisations towards such greens are somewhat confused at the present time, for example, the EBA accepts the decision of the county concerned as to whether an artificial green is acceptable for county matches, and eight county Associations have agreed to their use. Some have refused and in other counties the problem has not arisen. The Scottish Bowling Association does not permit their use, the English County Women's BA has only very recently agreed to accept them, whilst the Welsh BA also finds artificial greens acceptable.

As far as crown green bowls is concerned, two artificial greens were recently constructed by the Local Authority on Anglesey and this led to a modification of the BCGBA rules. Law 1 now reads *"The game shall be played on grass, or on an artificial surface as approved by the B.C.G.B.A."*. Whilst the Association have approved the particular surface in Anglesey they have stated that the County of Wales will not receive permission to play county matches on any of the artificial greens because the home advantage will be too great. This highlights one of the problems with both flat and crown artificial greens at the present time - the fact that there are relatively few of them. This means that in inter-club competitions, players whose home green is artificial are used to playing away on grass, but clubs with natural greens are at a distinct disadvantage when they have to play away competitions at one of the few clubs which have an artificial outdoor surface.

As far as installation costs are concerned, current figures of £60-65,000 are comparable to those for grass greens. Day to day maintenance costs are on average less, although artificial surfaces are not maintenance-free as they require cleaning, moss or algae control etc. However, this saving must be offset against the fact that carpets do not last forever and have to be replaced after a few years at relatively high cost. The playing surfaces of artificial greens may also deteriorate progressively with time, the surface becoming faster and faster as the carpet pile wears down, although this seems an arguable and contentious point as far as our present knowledge of such greens is concerned.

The advantages claimed by manufacturers of artificial greens can be listed as follows:

• True, flat playing surface for flat-rink bowls.
• Completely porous system and therefore minimal drainage difficulties.
• High usage level.
• Potential evening and winter usage.
• No specialist maintenance procedures.
• Multi-directional pile carpet.
• Continual usage of same lanes.
• Easily repairable vandalised areas.

The counter-argument might be that winter or poor-weather usage is not a real advantage for flat-rink bowlers as they would prefer to play on one of the many indoor facilities under such inclement weather conditions. Also, that a well-maintained grass green should be largely self-repairing and that wear can be significantly reduced by correct rink-changing policies. A purist might also argue that British lawn bowling should by definition be played on a lawn, i.e. a natural grass surface. Let us leave the subject at this point, as to cover the question fully would probably double the length of this book, with unfortunate results on the cost of its purchase!

POST WAR DEVELOPMENTS IN GREEN MAINTENANCE

Progress in bowling green maintenance techniques since 1945 has been a result of the commercial introduction of a wide variety of effective chemicals for various greenkeeping purposes, the development of vastly more efficient mechanical equipment and a better scientific understanding of the management of turf.

The development of selective herbicides in the late 1940s, and the pioneer studies in the application of these materials to turf which were carried out at Bingley, represented a major breakthrough in greenkeeping. Lawnsands and other early weedkilling materials have now been almost entirely surplanted by 2,4-D and other growth-regulating chemicals. The traditional lawnsand (a mixture of sulphate of ammonia and sulphate of iron) is still used to some extent for mosskilling purposes but for moss control also, new products have appeared. Mercurised turf sands and mercurised mosskillers proved effective and popular for a period until the health hazards of mercury use became apparent and the use of mercury banned by a more environmentally responsible society. The prohibition on mercury has encouraged the use of safer alternatives for mosskilling work, dichlorophen being the most popular today with phenol as an alternative. Unfortunately, research has not yet provided us with an effective selective grass killer - one which will eliminate undesirable weed grasses and leave the required grasses unaffected.

Progress in the identification and scientific description of a number of damaging turf diseases has been paralleled by the introduction of a wide range of fungicides. The pre-war use of such materials as Bordeaux mixture, sulphate of iron, copper sulphate and mercuric chloride gave way initially to the use of both organic and inorganic mercury products, together with cadmium-based materials. Increased safety-consciousness in recent years has again led to legislation against the use of such chemicals on amenity turf but alternatives have fortunately appeared. A wide range of effective fungicides are now available including systemic materials which are actually taken up by the growing plant to give longer-term protection than the contact fungicides which simply coat the plant surface. Non-systemic contact materials are still in use during the winter season however as they give more effective control when grass growth is not actually occurring. More recently, effective chemical treatments for the control of severe (Grade 1) fairy rings have appeared on the market, obviating the necessity for the lengthy digging-out and soil sterilising procedure which was previously necessary to combat this stubborn problem. The recognition of fungal conditions such as thatch fungi (Superficial Basidiomycetes) and dry patch has resulted in further testing of possible control chemicals, so far without complete success.

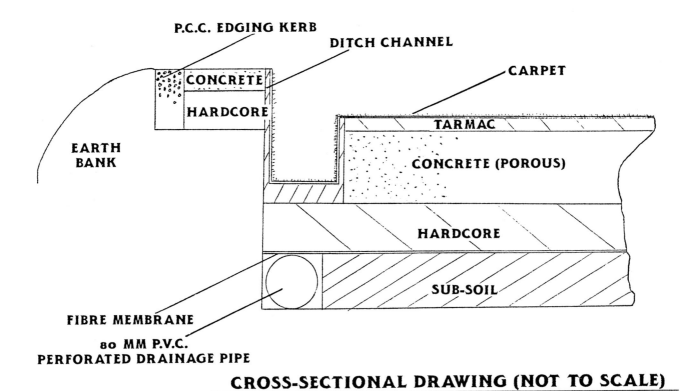

P.C.C. EDGING KERB

DITCH CHANNEL

CARPET

CONCRETE

HARDCORE

EARTH BANK

TARMAC

CONCRETE (POROUS)

HARDCORE

SUB-SOIL

FIBRE MEMBRANE

80 MM P.V.C. PERFORATED DRAINAGE PIPE

CROSS-SECTIONAL DRAWING (NOT TO SCALE)

FIGURE 15. Typical artificial outdoor green construction. (Courtesy Saker Leisure Ltd.)

PLATE 22. Artificial outdoor installation. (Courtesy Lodge Sports Bowls Surfaces & Services Ltd, Lincoln.)

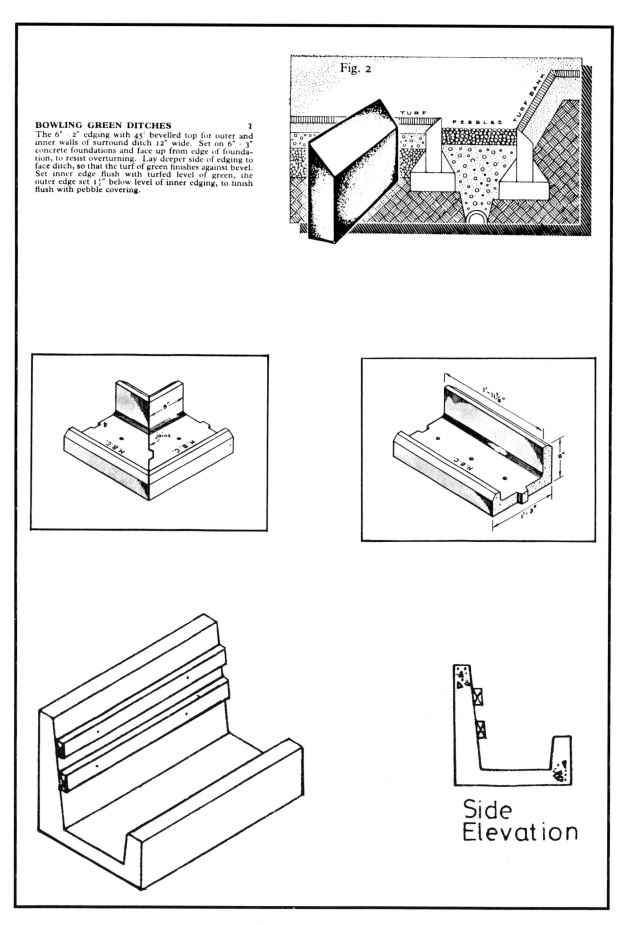

BOWLING GREEN DITCHES   2

The 6" × 2" edging with 45° bevelled top for outer and inner walls of surround ditch 12" wide. Set on 6" × 3" concrete foundations and face up from edge of foundation, to resist overturning. Lay deeper side of edging to face ditch, so that the turf of green finishes against bevel. Set inner edge flush with turfed level of green, the outer edge set 1¼" below level of inner edging, to finish flush with pebble covering.

FIGURE 16.   Bowling green ditch units.
        Top   :   concrete kerb (H.B. Concrete Co Ltd);
        Centre   :   concrete ditch unit (H.B. Concrete & Brierkrete);
        Bottom   :   concrete ditch unit (Roberts).

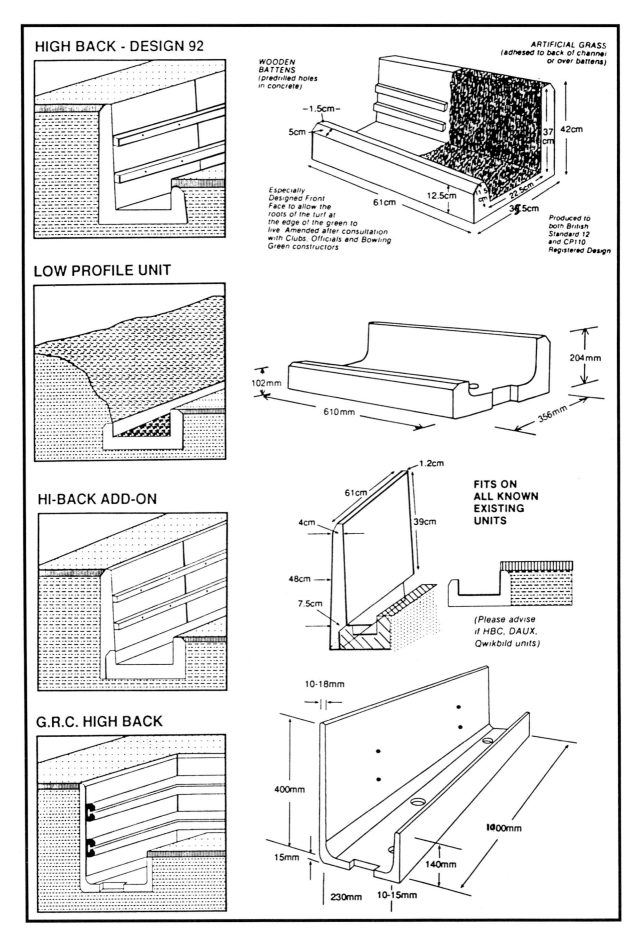

FIGURE 17. Bowling green ditch units. High-back, low-back, conversion and glass reinforced concrete units from Sportsmark Group Ltd.

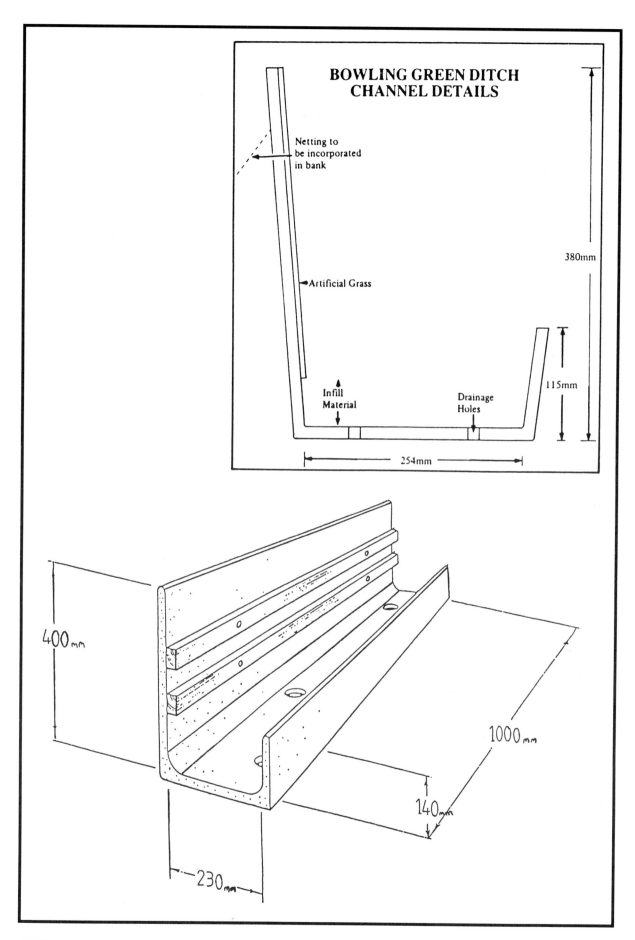

FIGURE 18. Bowling green ditch channel units. Top: Wener Amenity Landscape's grass reinforced concrete design and Bottom: the Kwik-Fit K.R.C. unit from J.K.H. Drainage Units Ltd.

Turning to pest control, worm control methods have also improved. The chemicals originally developed for worm eradication were all expellants - in other words they brought worms to the surface without necessarily killing them and large numbers of worms hence had to be swept up and disposed of. Such chemicals were short-term in their action and treatment at quite frequent intervals was therefore necessary. Materials like potassium permanganate, derris dust and mowrah meal were employed for this purpose but have gradually been replaced by more toxic substances which actually kill worms below the surface. After the War lead arsenate, and to a lesser extent calcium arsenate, were used which gave very long-term control. The very toxic (i.e. to humans) nature of arsenical compounds, plus their now extremely high cost, has now made them obsolete (and illegal) for the purpose. Until very recently, the most effective wormkiller available was chlordane which gave very good control for up to five years. Safety and environmental-protection considerations have, however, led to a progressive ban on its use, which will become total and legally binding at the end of 1992. Sevin (or carbaryl) is a less dangerous alternative which only gives some 6-12 months effective control, but which is nevertheless the most effective material which can be currently recommended. A more recent introduction are wormkillers which give some degree of selectivity, killing troublesome casting earthworm species whilst leaving relatively unscathed the harmless non-casting worms.

The main insect pest of turf in the UK, the leatherjacket, caused headaches for years until the development at Bingley of the "St. Ives leatherjacket Exterminator", an expellant material based on orthodichlorobenzene - a substance since banned as carcinogenic. DDT enjoyed a relatively brief period as a popular insecticide but public concern regarding health factors led to it gradually falling from favour, leaving Gamma-HCH and chlorpyrifos as today's most widely used insecticides. The wormkilling poisons also have an insecticidal action and have in the past been recommended for both purposes.

References above to legal bans and prohibitions on the use of more toxic materials are a reflection of changes in general attitudes to the use of hazardous materials. The trend towards greater safety conciousness will continue in future as the Food and Environment Protection Act (1985), Part 3: Control of Pesticides Regulations (1986) legislation is publicised and fully enforced.

Fertiliser usage on bowling greens since the war has involved fewer basic changes than is the case with pesticides and fungicides, but significant changes in thinking have taken place. It was appreciated early that the fine turf grasses, browntop bent and Chewings fescue, are favoured by acidic soil conditions and this encouraged the use of materials like sulphate of ammonia and sulphate of iron which have an acidifying effect, so helping to reduce worm activity, broad-leaved weeds and some coarser grasses. (Sea-marsh turf has a naturally alkaline soil and the use of acidic fertilisers on greens built with this material contributed to the gradual deterioration of the sea-marsh sward.) Sulphate of ammonia has been used for a long period as an acidic inorganic nitrogen source, supplemented by the use of longer-lasting, slower-acting organic nitrogen sources such as dried blood or hoof & horn meal. Sulphate of iron remains popular for its acidifying effect, the pleasing dark green grass colour which it produces, and its useful moss and disease controlling properties. For several decades after 1945 it was considered necessary to fertilize bowling greens with nitrogenous materials every 5-6 weeks through the playing season, so maintaining good growth and counteracting wear. In addition, spring use of fertilisers containing phosphate and potash (usually in the form of powdered superphosphate, bone meal and sulphate of potash) as well as nitrogen was advocated, with perhaps additional potash in the early autumn. Most greenkeepers made up such dressings to individual requirements out of basic ingredients. Pioneer early work at Bingley quickly established that the late or excessive use of nitrogen in the autumn was undesirable, mainly because it was a major factor in the encouragement of damaging fusarium patch disease and because rank growth late in the year is unnecessarily wasteful, particularly for a summer game surface.

By modern standards the kind of fertiliser regime described above is excessive. It is now appreciated more fully that the heavy use of nitrogen not only encourages fusarium patch disease but also favours undesirable annual meadow-grass at the expense of browntop bent and particularly fescue - the better grasses occur naturally under conditions of relative soil poverty and survive best where fertiliser is not overdone. The results of a most revealing and interesting survey of bowling green soils published by the Sports Turf Research Institute in 1985 (see Appendix A), involved an assessment of soil samples from 225 bowling greens nation-wide and showed extremely high phosphate and potash levels for the majority of greens surveyed. Phosphate in particular is a major factor in encouraging the weed, annual meadow-grass. The excessive use of fertiliser is also undesirable from the bowler's point of view - over-fed greens tend to be lush, slow and heavy and better, faster surfaces result from a reduction in feeding. Unfortunately, it is probably true to say that many greenkeepers, as a point of pride, try to maintain greens of attractive appearance and nitrogenous fertiliser does help provide a good-looking turf. Playing quality should, however, never be sacrificed for the sake of sward appearance - a bowling green is not an ornamental lawn!

Over the last 20 years there has been a steady decline in the use of fertiliser dressings made up of basic ingredients - most greenkeepers now find it more convenient (if rather more costly) to use ready-made fertilisers available from commercial manufacturers. A wide range of proprietary fertilisers are now available which give excellent results in practice. Mini-granular preparations are often easier to distribute evenly using modern fertiliser spreaders than more traditional powdered mixtures bulked with sand or compost carriers. Several commercial fertilisers now contain slow-release nitrogen formulations or nitrification inhibitors which tend to give slower, but more sustained and hence more uniform, growth through the playing season.

More spectacular than the gradual improvement in the chemical weapons in the greenkeeper's armoury has been the evolution of new mechanical equipment. By 1960 most British bowling greens were being cut using petrol-driven motor mowers (electric mowers were tried but never proved successful). Older and more reactionary greenkeepers still swore by the old hand machines but powered machines were faster and hence made better use of increasingly costly labour resources, allowing greens to be cut more quickly and perhaps more often. Refinements in the design of powered mowers ultimately ensured that the finish which they produced was in no way inferior to that produced by the hand-pushed models. An extremely useful development has been the provision on some professional mowers of a small rake or comb which can be fitted between the small front roller and the cutting cylinder. Such combs rake the surface lightly at each cut and can in themselves produce a marked improvement in playing quality - they deserve to be more widely used, as do the rotary verticutting attachments now available for some models of bowling green mower.

The universal use of motor mowers has resulted in a marked decline in the need for rolling as a separate operation. Motor mowers are heavy enough to have a significant rolling action and have made frequent rolling unnecessary. Increasing appreciation of the damaging effects of heavy rolling, producing poor surface drainage, excessive soil compaction, poor grass growth and moss invasion, has fortunately led to a decline in the use of the more weighty rollers. It is after all possible to produce uniformly fast and true bowling surfaces without resorting to road-rollers, vibrating rollers or other similar juggernauts.

Spiking equipment developed between the two wars as we have already seen, with pedestrian-pushed machines appearing first as alternatives to the humble hand fork. Experiments commenced in 1934 by William Hargreaves were particularly significant in the subsequent development of such machines. After the 2nd World War spikers remained basically similar to pre-war versions until the advent of motorisation in the 1950's. The Pattisson S.P. spiker of 1953 proved a popular machine as did the 1963 Sisis Auto Turfman and 1964 Auto-Outfield spiker. Some machines of this type could be fitted with alternative tine patterns - flat knife, round solid or hollow coring. Earlier machines were basically of drum-type with the tines pushed into the ground by the rolling action of a horizontally-revolving drum. A later development was the cam-action or punch-type machine with tines actually driven into the ground by powered cams, giving better penetration into compacted ground, particularly with hollow tines. The Ryan Greensaire, an American design, typifies this class of machine.

To counteract the very deep-seated compaction found on some greens as a result of faulty construction, or repeated heavy rolling over a long period, machines which penetrate more deeply than the 150 mm (6 in.) or so, which is about the maximum achievable with smaller spikers, have been developed. These depend on mole-plough shares or vibrating subsoiler-

FIGURE 19. A selection of advertisements 1947-1950. Note the introduction of selective weedkillers and the continuing use of hand mowers and sea-marsh turf.

type shares for their effect, or in the case of the Charterhouse Verti-Drain, on long heavy tines power-driven into the ground with an accompanying prising action. Other machines shatter compaction by means of long tines down which high pressure air is forced, or achieve the same result using jets of water directed down from the surface.

Rotary scarifiers represent another invaluable advance, using rapidly revolving vertical blades as a far more effective alternative to the hand or two-wheeled wire or rigid-tined rake. The earliest machine of this type which has been traced is the Soutar Moss Extractor illustrated here in Fig. 3 (advert taken from a 1929 catalogue). The post-war Ransomes Gazelle was, however, the first British powered machine, economically built from a modified motor mower by removing the sole-plate and welding nail-like scarifying tines onto the blades of a conventional mower cutting reel. Purpose-designed powered scarifiers followed with an American import, the Rose Verticut appearing in 1956 and the Sisis Rotorake in spring 1957.

As for other equipment, spinner and belt-type fertiliser distributors appeared pre-war and have not changed fundamentally since. Sprayers have, however, developed beyond the old knapsack type - the Drake and Fletcher 'Groundsman' constant-pressure machine of 1959 proving particularly successful. The recent development of C.D.A (Controlled Droplet Application) sprayers is likely to revolutionise spray application in the future, using low-volume pre-packaged herbicides, fungicides etc. which require no dilution and which simplify accuracy in application rates.

In the years after the war most bowling clubs could boast adequate irrigation equipment, using rotary or oscillating sprinklers, spray-lines or perforated hose. Since 1965 automatic watering using pop-up sprinklers has become a possibility, but cost factors have so far ensured that this refinement is only possible for the more affluent bowling clubs.

In the face of all this engineering, however, the basic hand tools have survived and still occupy a vital place in the greenkeeper's toolshed. The drag-mat, drag-brush, switch, daisy grubber and spiked Sarel roller still have a role to play, as does the Scottish greenkeeper's "graip" or solid-tine fork and William Paul's hollow-tined variant. Another necessity which has, of course, not changed over the years are the services of a knowledgeable and dedicated greenkeeper!

The alert reader, when perusing the above account of progress since 1945, may have noticed a distinct lack of detailed references to any basic scientific research directed specifically towards the problems of bowling green upkeep. The omission is a reflection of the fact that funds for research into bowling green problems have been woefully inadequate to date. A rare exception to this state of affairs was a detailed investigation carried out by the STRI into the quality of bowling surfaces and reported on in 1986 (see Appendix B), made possible by a Sports Council grant. Fortunately, much basic scientific work into turf culture generally has been carried out and many advances are applicable to bowls surfaces. Much research primarily directed towards other sports (golf green studies in particular) has also proved invaluable when applied to bowling green work. A need for specialised bowling green research still remains, however, and it is to be hoped that this will one day be practicable. There are after all an estimated 5,200 outdoor flat greens and 3,500 crown greens in the United Kingdom (Sports Council Statistics, 1981), representing a very considerable investment in both initial construction costs and maintenance budgets. Any research which could make green building and upkeep more cost-effective would, therefore, be highly advantageous.

CHAPTER 4
THE *COTULA* GREENS OF NEW ZEALAND

• INTRODUCTION
In Canada and the USA, Australia and South Africa, and other countries where lawn bowls is a popular game, the development of greens and greenkeeping has followed along much the same lines as in the British Isles with modifications dictated by climatic differences, the need for turfgrasses able to withstand hotter conditions, a differing population of native pests etc.

New Zealand is, however, unique in that a high proportion of that country's numerous bowling greens (all exclusively flat rink) have surfaces made up of one of a number of low-growing, broad-leaved plant species rather than grass. New Zealand bowling greens, therefore, resemble the herbal lawns which were a popular feature of English gardens in Tudor times. This widespread use of non-grass species for bowls surfaces is most unusual and any survey of bowling green development would not be complete if it omitted this interesting development.

• CLASSIFICATION
Although more than 20 dwarf prostrate species of *Leptinella* are native to New Zealand only *Leptinella dioica* (= *Cotula dioica*) and *Leptinella maniototo* (= *Cotula maniototo*) are used extensively for bowling greens. Both are tiny white flowered members of the *Asteraceae* family and greens sown with either species are known as "*Cotula*" greens. As they have only recently been re-classified as *Leptinella* sp. for simplicity we will refer to them by their long standing names of *Cotula dioica* and *Cotula maniototo*.

• SEED AND BULBILS
Both plants flower even under close mowing in summer but *C. maniototo* appears to be sterile whilst *C. dioica* can produce viable seeds if left unmown, but seed is difficult to harvest and seedlings are not often true to type.

C. maniototo produces seed-like bulbils of vegetative origin in winter which can be harvested from greens following heavy rain. Yields up to 70 kg per green have been recorded. Bulbils need to be dried slightly until free-flowing and then be sown in the same way as seed. Careful treatment is required if they are to be stored.

• HISTORY OF *COTULA*
The first plant species used for these bowling greens in New Zealand was *Cotula dioica*. It was first recorded in the green at the Caledonian Bowling Club in Dunedin, NZ, in 1913. Attempts to remove it from the original grass green by scarifying actually helped spread the *Cotula* and after some years it covered most of the green's surface. Many players found it a superior and faster surface for play than the conventional grass green and the Caledonian green became a popular competition venue. From about 1923 onwards, other clubs sought to copy this development and natural sources of the plant were located. A considerable area of *Cotula dioica* was subsequently found at Pahia near Invercargill. Many clubs used this material to renovate existing greens and the Pahia plants were found in time to dominate both the existing grass cover and any other "weed" species which might be present. It was once the most common constituent of *Cotula* greens throughout New Zealand. Its popularity within New Zealand received an initial boost in 1953 when the National Bowling Championships were held in Dunedin under extremely wet weather conditions. It was felt by visiting players that the *Cotula* greens had held up under heavy play when waterlogged far better than grass greens would have done and plant material was hence spread throughout the country. Plantings in the northern part of the North Island were largely unsuccessful and many greens reverted to grass until it was appreciated that *Cotula* required rather different management than a conventional sward.

• *COTULA* - ADVANTAGES AND DISADVANTAGES
Cotula greens are preferred to grass by New Zealand bowlers because the speed of the surface is little affected by rain. Under local conditions it is also easier to achieve a satisfactory green speed (14-18 seconds) early in the season than it is using grass. *Cotula* is quicker to establish on a new green than grass and it can be harder wearing if correctly managed with fewer bare patches on rink ends. It is found to give a very uniform surface and renovation costs are low - seed does not have to be purchased as material from other parts of the green can be used to

patch bare areas. Annual meadow-grass invasion can be a problem in a *Cotula* sward, but this species along with other grass species can be eliminated with selective weedkiller.

On the other hand, *Cotula* does have some disadvantages. Because no seed is available for establishment or renovation, vegetative material has to be used. This can be inconvenient although it is satisfactory. *Cotula maniototo* bulbils which germinate and grow readily are unavailable at the normal time for renovation. The far more serious aspect of this lack of seed is that moving large quantities of vegetative material from natural sources and from club to club has introduced most weeds, insects and nematodes to virtually every green.

• SPECIES COMPOSITION OF *COTULA* GREENS
Cotula greens in the southern South Island often resemble herb lawns, often comprising species naturally found on the coast in association with *Cotula dioica*. Starweed (*Plantago triandra*), *Colobanthus* sp., *Pratia angulata*, *Tillaea (Crassula* sp.) and *Hydrocotyle* sp. often form a mixed sward with *Cotula maniototo* and *Cotula squalida*.

North of Dunedin *Pratia angulata* in particular becomes too aggressive and is considered a weed so monostands of *Cotula maniototo* are dominant, with only a few *Cotula dioica* dominant greens remaining.

In some areas starweed is encouraged whilst in others it is eliminated. A number of starweed dominated greens exist.

• RENOVATION OF *COTULA* GREENS
Proper autumn renovation is critical to the survival and maintenance of quality *Cotula* greens because autumn is the best opportunity to restore coverage on bare areas.

Greens are usually heavily grooved (as scarifying is termed in New Zealand) at renovation, not only to prevent the development of an organic layer but also to rejuvenate the *Cotula*. Often at this time greens are treated to relieve compaction. A layer of soil is then applied to level the surface. Shortly before the season opens, a slurry of soil and water may be screeded across the greens to fill in any surface imperfections. Less drastic corrective treatments may also be carried out during the season. If greens are used during winter when they would normally be recovering from renovation, such treatments would be scheduled for some other time of the year.

Cotula has a low requirement for the major nutrients. In particular, the requirement for nitrogen is much lower than that for grass. The standard recommendation is about 50 kg sulphate of ammonia (or equivalent) annually for each green. Much of the early problem with disease in greens in the North Island arose through the mistaken belief that nitrogen was required during the playing season. Fertiliser is now applied only between renovation and opening day. Starving throughout the summer gives a hard wearing surface. Fertiliser may be applied at a low rate to encourage growth on worn ends.

• IRRIGATION
A *Cotula* green will retain its appearance longer in dry conditions than a grass green, especially if *Poa annua* is present, but it will not recover from complete drying as will browntop and other bent grasses. Therefore, over most of New Zealand an irrigation system which can apply at least 25 mm of water a week must be provided. On many greens water is applied by flooding from a central point. Such a procedure often supplies insufficient water to the ends and so some form of spray irrigation is preferred. Because water tends to sit on the leaves of *Cotula* scalding may occur in hot, sunny weather. Irrigation in the evening is therefore preferred. In hot weather the surface may dry out to the extent that the tracks of the bowls and the players footprints show. When they do the green must be watered lightly to cool it down and avoid plant death. Some clubs now use an automatic system with permanent sprinklers around the perimeter of the green and a moveable one in the centre.

Cotula greens definitely require more water than grass greens and perform best when watered lightly but frequently.

PLATES 23, 24 & 25. Top: *Cotula maniototo*; Centre: *Cotula dioica*; Bottom: planing a New Zealand green (Courtesy W.H. Walmsley).

PLATES 26, 27 & 28. Levelling a New Zealand *Cotula* green with taut wires. Photos show wire strainer in position in ditch, wire supported where it bridges a hollow and luting top dressing using the wires as a guide (Courtesy W.H. Walmsley).

• DISEASES, INSECTS AND NEMATODES

Both *Cotula dioica* and *Cotula maniototo* are attacked by a number of damaging diseases, often requiring regular fungicide applications. Careful management can prevent many diseases, for example, it was once considered that *Sclerotium rolfsii* would prevent *Cotula* from surviving north of the central North Island, but now it survives comfortably in the far north. *Cotula* is attacked by many of the usual turf insects as well as a *Cotula* weevil and a root feeding mealy bug.

Nematodes can devastate *Cotula* greens and need to be promptly treated when diagnosed.

• MOWING *COTULA* GREENS

The leaves of the *Cotula* tend to lie flat on the ground so that a complete ground cover can be maintained under closer mowing than for grass. Also, because of leaf orientation the base plate of the mower is often set further back in relation to the reel than is customary for grass mowing. The reel can then sweep the leaves up on to the edge of the plate. One can recommend a reel height of 0.4-.8 mm for a satisfactory running speed. The height can be set with feeler gauges.

In winter, mowing height is increased and mowing frequency reduced, but care must be taken not to let growth become too thick because mowing will then be difficult at the start of the next season. Even though good, early season speed can be achieved more easily with *Cotula* than with grass, player pressure is still great for the surface to be mown closely from the start. As with grass, bare ends are then likely before the end of the season.

Rolling to increase speed was widely advised in the early years of *Cotula* as it was for grass, but when the significance of compaction to plant health was understood, rolling was discouraged. Rolling is again becoming popular because a self-propelled ride-on dual roller machine is available.

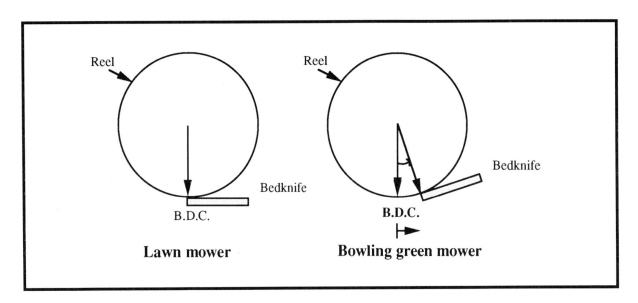

FIGURE 20. Mowers for New Zealand *Cotula* greens have the sole plate (bedknife) set to the rear of the bottom dead centre of the cutting cylinder. This gives a threshing action and allows a very low cut, so increasing green speed (N.Z. Turf Culture Institute).

• WEEDS

Because *Cotula* is in the daisy family (*Asteraceae*) many of the herbicides used in grass greens will damage *Cotula*, so only a small range of herbicides can remove other broad-leaved weeds from *Cotula*. These generally require careful, even application at the time of year least damaging to the *Cotula*.

A number of selective grass killers are safe to use on *Cotula* as are most moss killers.

The best weed control in *Cotula* greens is regular close mowing, which remove most weeds apart from a small range of tolerant weeds. *Hyrocotyle* sp.are most troublesome in New Zealand.

Hand weeding is recommended occasionally for troublesome weeds, especially in new greens.

• LEVELLING *COTULA* GREENS

Cotula greens can be levelled by either adding soil to fill hollows up to the level of high spots or alternatively by shaving the entire surface off the green to a depth of 30-35 mm using a planing machine.

The need for planing the green can be based on the results of a level survey carried out on a 2 m grid. If the difference between the highest and lowest spots is over 30 mm, excluding spots within 2 m of the green edge, then the green is probably best planed. If the difference is less than 20 mm then levelling by adding soil is recommended. Between the two, make the decision based on the shape of the surface and the practicality of the corrective measures. Greens planed in early autumn can be sown with groovings whilst those planed in winter can be sown with bulbils.

There are two means of adding soil to low spots: [i] laser levelling; [ii] use of wires.

With laser levelling a small horticultural tractor has a screeding blade attached beneath it which is actively controlled by the hydraulic system through a laser sensing system so the blade is always perfectly level. Soil is added to the surface and then screeded until it is graded evenly over the surface. It is recommended to set the level at 12 mm above the lowest spot each time.

With the use of wires, a similar height is chosen but wires set 3 m apart are set to level every 300 mm or closer by packing underneath or inserting the wire into a slice made in the surface.

Levelling with wires can level greens to a difference of 8 mm between highest and lowest spots whilst planing results in a 10-15 mm difference.

• ESTABLISHMENT OF *COTULA*

Both *Cotula dioica* and *Cotula maniototo* can be propagated by stolon fragments removed by scarifying using special thick blades (called grooving in New Zealand). All the groovings from three greens (approximately 250 kg) are required to sow a single green. Groovings are spread over the surface covered with a fine layer of soil then rolled and kept moist until roots have formed.

Bare spots in greens are generally sown with groovings at autumn renovation and remaining thin areas are oversown with bulbils of *Cotula maniototo* in late winter or early spring.

Bulbils sown over the prepared surface of a new green will produce a playable surface in about six months if sown at 5 g/m^2. Sowing in July (i.e. winter in New Zealand) at 20 g/m^{-2} can in fact produce a surface by October. In some areas *Cotula maniototo* dominates whilst in other greens it forms only a small proportion of the sward. Its ability to rapidly re-establish a ground cover over worn areas in the winter is regarded as particularly useful.

• CONVERSION TO *COTULA*

Grass greens can be slowly converted to *Cotula* over 2-3 years by heavily liming to pH 6.0 and introducing *Cotula* groovings in autumn or alternatively, they can be killed off or planed and resown with *Cotula*.

Where the green is planed or completely resown, clubs should not count on using the green before November and there is the risk that even more playing time could be lost if *Cotula* establishment is poor. In favourable conditions light play can often commence in mid-October.

• DEVELOPMENTS IN THE UK

New Zealand bowlers seem to be satisfied that *Cotula* is the best surface for play in their country, although its differing playing characteristics make it difficult for New Zealand players to perform well in international matches abroad when they have to try and read slower grass greens.

Interest in New Zealand's unique greens was stimulated in Britain as a result of the 1974 Commonwealth Games (held in New Zealand) and the 1986 World Bowls competition which took place in Auckland. Following the 1974 games the STRI at Bingley contacted the New Zealand Turf Culture Institute and obtained some 16 lbs of *Cotula dioica* (then called *C. pulchella*) material for study. These were sown in 1974 at the Institute's experiment ground on an area of some 10 m^2 (24 sq. yd). Good establishment was obtained but very regular hand weeding was found necessary to keep the plot free of annual meadow-grass and pearlwort. The *Cotula* developed a good ground cover in 1974 and retained it when cut at 3 mm in spring 1975, but thinned out considerably later when subjected to even closer, i.e. very close, cutting. Weed invasion subsequently proved troublesome and the same poor winter colour was observed as in New Zealand. Progress in 1976 was not good and on the advice of the English Bowling Association, further investigations were abandoned. However, at the time of writing, fresh moves are being made to carry out further trials on *Cotula* bowls surfaces in the UK. With support from the EBA, the STRI research staff in 1992 are carrying out experimental work on trial plots of both *Cotula dioica* and *Cotula maniototo* and will be producing data on establishment, ground cover and green speed. This may be regarded as symptomatic of the continuing interest in New Zealand's greens in the UK and a reflection of the high reputation enjoyed by their bowling surfaces. At least two British clubs, one in England and one in Wales, have recently expressed interest in using *Cotula* on their greens - such a project could probably be regarded as premature and unwise at the moment, as we have insufficient data on the performance of *Cotula* under UK climatic conditions and no practical experience of the specialised maintenance techniques which are required. (One green in the Channel Islands has already been deliberately infected with *Cotula*, so far with rather patchy results.) The point should also be made that the excellent reputation of New Zealand greens is in part as a result of factors other than the obvious one, that they are established with *Cotula* rather than grass. New Zealand greenkeepers, for example, pay far more attention to the question of accurate surface levels than we do generally in this country. We could therefore learn from their example by producing truer and more uniform flat greens without taking the more drastic step of attempting to switch from grass to *Cotula* as a ground cover species.

• ACKNOWLEDGEMENT
The Author most gratefully acknowledges the fact that the greater part of the above account of New Zealand's *Cotula* greens was contributed by W.H. Walmsley, a sports turf agronomist at the New Zealand Turf Culture Institute, Palmerston North, NZ. His most valuable and interesting contribution to this chapter is included with the Author's sincere thanks.

CHAPTER 5
MODERN BOWLING GREEN CONSTRUCTION

The following method of construction for flat and crown bowling greens is based on some 30 years of experience in supervisory work accumulated at the Sports Turf Research Institute and makes full use of all relevant scientific research.

Advance planning

An early start to planning is essential for construction work since timeliness for many of the necessary operations has a great bearing on the final result. Several approaches may have to be considered depending on site characteristics. The aggregate drainage layer could possibly, for example, be omitted for a site which was exceptionally free-draining - perhaps on a gravel subsoil. Again, in the case of a very sandy topsoil, there might be a lessened requirement for amelioration of the upper layer. The approach to construction ultimately adopted may also depend to a certain extent on available finance. A penny-pinching approach to bowling green construction should, however, be avoided if at all possible as carrying out the job correctly in the first place saves money in the long-term.

A 16 week contract period should be offered in documentation, culminating in sowing or turfing and allowing for some initial maintenance work to be completed by the Contractor. Timing is important as it is usual to sow in late summer or early autumn or to aim for autumn turfing. Spring or summer seeding and turfing need not, however, be entirely ruled out if an adequate water supply is available so that drought damage can be prevented during early establishment. It will also be necessary to obtain planning consent from the Local Authority before work is intended to commence.

Advice should be sought, therefore, at an early stage from the Sports Turf Research Institute on the particular aspects of site, viz. the general construction procedure appropriate to the type of green (flat or crown) required, design of drainage system in relation to outfall and suitability of existing topsoil.

At the outset, a survey drawing is required showing existing levels, site features, including underground services or overhead, if any, and drain outlets, e.g. ditches or public surface water drains. If the latter are to be used permission will have to be obtained from the Local Authority.

The existing levels are used to establish finished levels related to the surrounds, and to establish the relationship of the pipe drainage system to finished levels. While it is preferred that bowling greens are constructed on unfilled land, a certain amount of cut and fill or importation of suitable fill to give required finished levels is sometimes inevitable. The levels provided on the survey drawing in conjunction with calculated finished levels are used to determine quantities relating to excavation, materials required and all other operations specified for the construction of the green and any ancillary works which may be required.

Grading

Following site clearance as required, grading to provide the required subsoil formation surface is carried out with specialised equipment operated by skilled personnel. The work should be carried out when the ground conditions are dry. Firstly, topsoil clean from any subsoil is scraped off the bowling green area, ditch, path, surround and working width all round and if it is to be replaced it should be stacked in an approved position near the proposed soil mixing area. Any surplus topsoil should be disposed of as directed by the engineer or architect. The exposed subsoil is then accurately graded to the required levels of the green, ditches, banks, verges and paths, allowing for the appropriate build-up of the drainage layer and special soil mix over the green, and topsoil over the surrounds.

On a flat rink green grading is completed bearing in mind that the top of the bank all round the green should be a minimum of 229 mm higher than the finished green surface, the bank being at an angle of not more than 35° from the perpendicular on completion if turfed, or upright in other materials, like concrete slabs, etc.

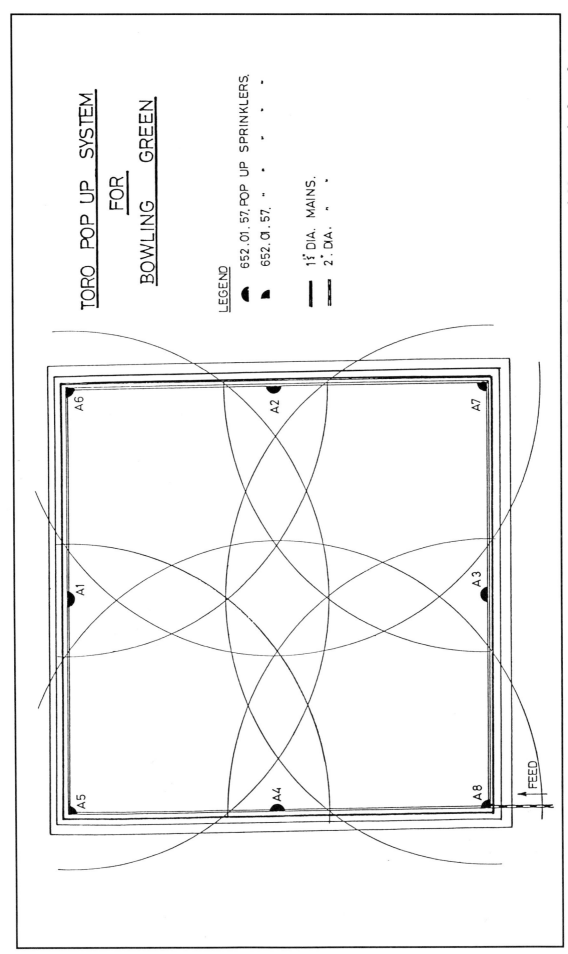

FIGURE 21. Pop-up watering system for a bowling green (courtesy Toro Irrigation Ltd). The four corner sprinklers are in fact often omitted on grounds of economy, except where they are necessitated by an exposed windy green site.

On a crown green adjustment to subsoil levels is completed bearing in mind that the level at the centre of the green can be 254 mm, 305 mm or 380 mm above the corner levels. 380 mm is now the Crown Green Bowling Association's recommended height for a 40 x 40 yd. crown green, and pro rata for greens of other sizes. Crown greens may vary between 30 x 30 yd. to a maximum of 60 x 60 yd. The top of the outer ditch board should be a minimum of 100 mm higher than the green surface on completion of a crown green.

On a site where filling has to be accepted as a means to obtain the required subsoil formation surface, it is essential that the filling be completed in no more than 150 mm deep consecutive layers, each layer being thoroughly consolidated to avoid subsequent settlement. Surplus subsoil should be disposed of as directed by the engineer or architect.

Pegs should be set at the correct levels and the subsoil graded to conform to them using boning rods to obtain the true and even formation surface required. In the case of a crown green, the subsoil formation surface is crowned to conform to the contours of the finished bowling surface.

Water supply
A water supply is necessary. This can consist of a system which provides one or two water hydrants. Alternatively spraylines or a pop-up watering system can be introduced. A specialist irrigation contractor should be engaged if this last-named type of irrigation is to be included in the specification.

Drainage
Good drainage is essential and this is normally provided on a flat green by installing emptying drains through the formation surface of the green, drains within the ditches and over both spreading a drainage layer of suitable aggregate. The ditch drains should connect to a positive outfall.

On a crown green emptying drains are introduced in the ditches but are generally omitted in the body of the green as the contouring of the formation carried through to the surface permits for speedy run-off of surface and sub-surface water.

The drainage introduced on both the flat and crown greens is connected to a 100-110 mm outlet drain of unperforated plastic pipe to British Standard 4962:1982. Alternatively jointed vitrified clay pipes to BS65 and 540:1966 can be used but plastic piping is now usual.

Ditch drains for both flat and crown greens are then introduced with appropriate fall using perforated plastic drain pipes of 100-110 mm outside diameter to BS 4962:1982. Approved plastic bends are used at the corners except at the lowest corner where an appropriate plastic junction is introduced to connect the ditch drains to the outlet drain referred to above.

Normally for a flat green 80 mm outside diameter perforated plastic drain pipes are introduced with appropriate falls at anything between 4.5 metre to 7 metre intervals, the spacing depending on individual site characteristics. Drain trenches are excavated into the subsoil formation surface. Each drain is accurately boned in to connect with the ditch drains, and forms part of a grid system of parallel drains.

Pipes are laid to true line and steady fall on a firm foundation and backfilling is then completed carefully up to subsoil formation surface using approved predominantly single sized hard aggregate, e.g. angular gravel or broken stone of 6-10 mm gauge. Backfilling is then adequately firmed.

As an alternative to plastic drain pipes, clayware field drain pipes to BS 1196:1971 can be used for both ditch drains and drains beneath the playing surface. In this case 100 mm clayware pipes would be used for ditch drains and 75 mm pipes for the grid system.

Depending on the ultimate location of the drainage outlet which may, by permission, be on neighbouring land or a local authority surface water system, it might be necessary to provide a silt pit on the line of the outlet drain.

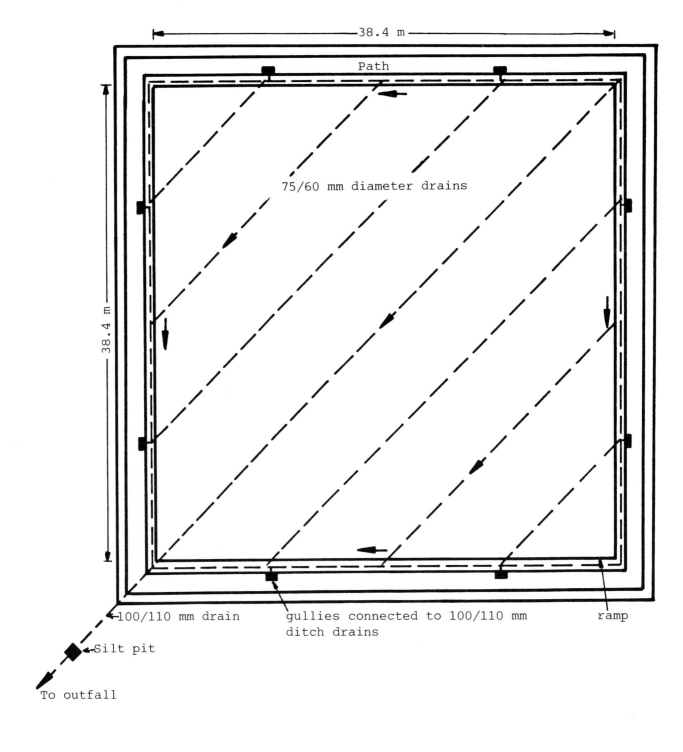

FIGURE 22. Flat green with drainage system.

72

Commonly, silt pits are built with purpose made reinforced precast concrete units to BS 5911:1981, each unit being set in cement mortar. The silt pit is fitted with a removable cast iron cover for inspection and cleaning purposes.

Application of herbicide to subsoil formation surface
An approved total residual herbicide is applied to the whole of the green, ditch and path subsoil formation surfaces in the manner recommended by the maker.

Ditch formation - flat green
For flat rink Association bowling greens, ditches should be not less than 203 mm nor more than 381 mm wide. Traditionally on flat greens preservative treated wooden boards and stakes have been used but as fully seasoned timber is difficult to obtain these days many new flat greens are constructed by alternative methods. The alternatives are:-

[a] Traditional wooden boards with turf bank.

[b] Precast concrete kerb edging on inner side with turf bank.

[c] Purpose-made concrete ditch units with turf bank.

[d] Low-backed glass reinforced purpose-made ditch units with turf bank.

[e] Traditional wooden boards on the inner edge with a vertical wall replacing the sloping turf bank. The wall may be of brick or of concrete paving slab, on any other preferred type.

[f] Precast concrete kerb edging on the inner edge, with a vertical wall replacing the sloping turf bank.

[g] Purpose-made high-backed concrete ditch units.

[h] High-backed glass reinforced purpose-made ditch units.

When the conventional turf bank is dispensed with, the vertical outer face of the ditch, whether a wall or formed as part of a purpose-made ditch unit, must be faced with a striking surface to protect the bowls from damage. 75 mm x 25 mm timber slats treated with preservative may for example be plugged to a wall face with a 38 mm space between them. Alternatively synthetic grass may be used, glued to the vertical face using a suitable adhesive.

If purpose-made ditch units are employed then they should be bedded on cement mortar beds (1-3 mix) and set to an accurate level.

If kerb edging is employed, 150 mm x 50 mm precast concrete kerbs should be chosen. Bevelled top kerbs are no longer advocated as the sharp edge of the bevel can damage woods as they topple over into the ditch. Kerbs should be set on concrete foundations and haunched up 75 mm on both sides. The space between ditch kerb foundations must allow passage of water.

When using traditional ditch boards, concrete kerbs, or purpose-made ditch units, the top edge of the inner side of the ditch support should finish 25 mm below the finished green level. This allows for a double thickness of turf (cut about 12 mm thick) to be laid around the edge of the green, over the top of the inner ditch support. This minimises subsequent maintenance problems with the extreme edge of the turf - if only a single thickness of turf is laid over the edging then the grass, having only a 12 mm rooting depth, tends to dry out rapidly and be prone to weak growth and moss invasion. Even for seeded greens it is normal to lay turf around the perimeter as difficulty is otherwise experienced in stabilising the extreme edge until seed is established. Here also a double thickness of edging turf is to be preferred.

In the final stages of construction pea gravel, rounded pebbles or other suitable material is spread in clean ditch beds to 50 mm depth. Its surface should be not less than 51 mm or more than 203 mm below the grass level, according to EBA requirements. Other materials may be used for this purpose provided they are non-injurious to the woods, and in some cases ingenuity has been demonstrated in choice of some materials, which range from discarded wine bottle corks to rubber ends for badminton shuttlecocks. A recent innovation is "ditchfill", a dimpled rubber infill material as supplied by Wener Amenity Landscaping of Barnet, Hertfordshire.

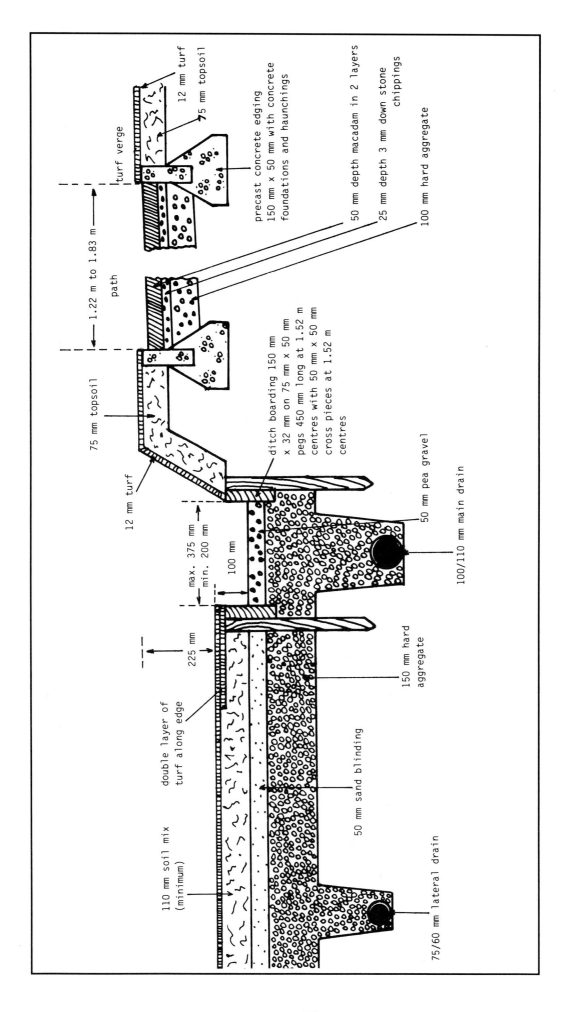

FIGURE 23. Detail on flat bowling green (with traditional ditch and bank boards.

74

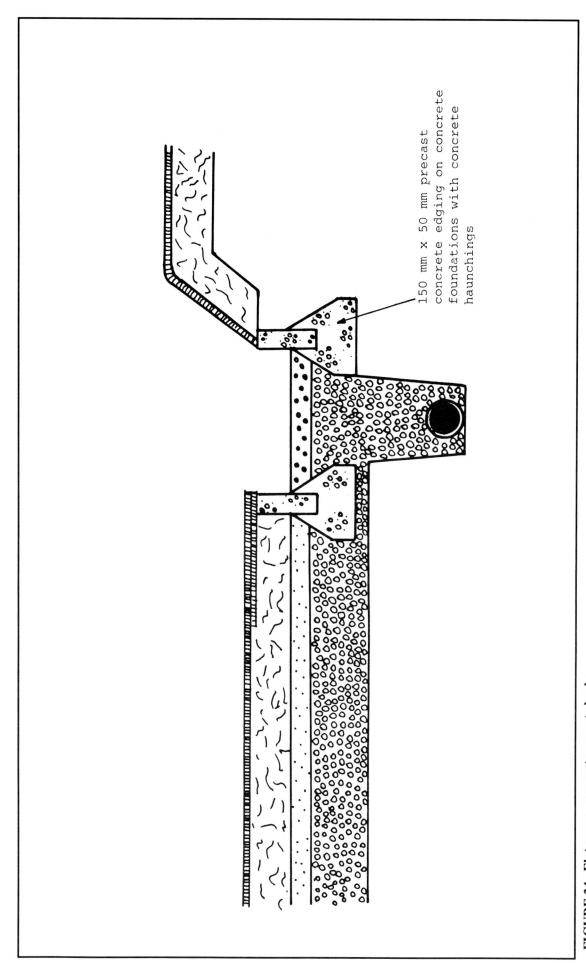

150 mm x 50 mm precast concrete edging on concrete foundations with concrete haunchings

FIGURE 24. Flat green - precast concrete kerbs.

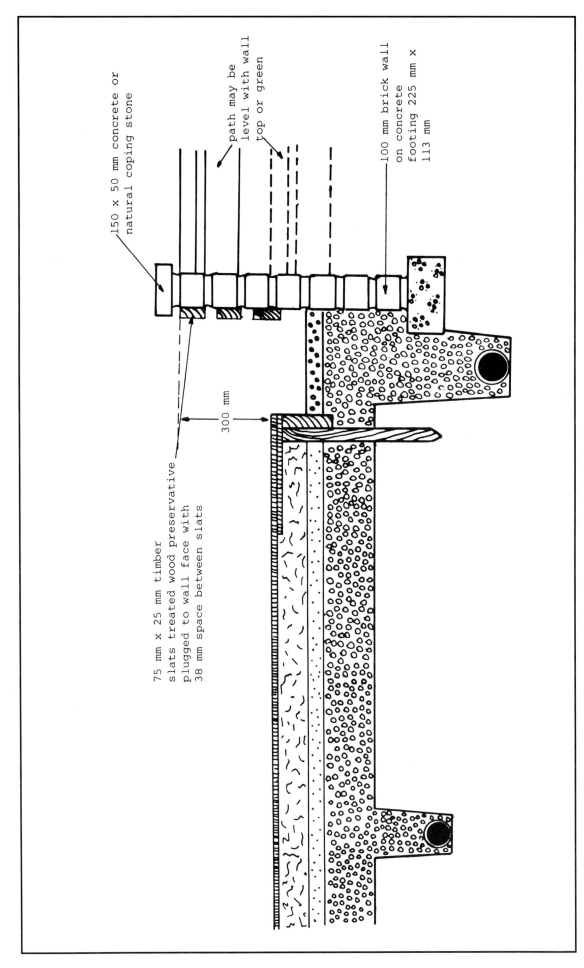

150 x 50 mm concrete or
natural coping stone

path may be
level with wall
top or green

100 mm brick wall
on concrete
footing 225 mm x
113 mm

75 mm x 25 mm timber
slats treated wood preservative
plugged to wall face with
38 mm space between slats

300 mm

FIGURE 25. Flat green - detail for brick surround with wooden board inner edge.

Ditch formation - crown green

For crown greens where ditch requirements are rather less rigid, traditional timber edging or precast concrete kerbs are usually employed. Kerbs are set either side of the ditch to the required height.

Flat top precast inner edging kerbs of 150 mm x 50 mm dimension are set in position to true line and 25 mm below the finished level of the green on concrete foundations and haunched up 75 mm on both sides. The outer edging kerb is set up as above but using 300 mm x 50 mm edgings set 125 mm above the inner kerb level and well haunched up particularly along the ditch side. The space between the ditch kerb foundations must allow the passage of water. Drainage aggregate is then introduced to a level that will allow for 50 mm depth of approved pea gravel or rounded pebbles to finish 100 mm below the green level.

An added item for the crown green is provision of striking boards along the outer ditch kerb. These are composed of 3.5 mm x 175 mm x 31 mm tanalised seasoned soft wood, reasonably free of knots, cut to profile at ends of each board to allow close butting. Painting striking boards white can be very helpful to players bowling in poor light. Each board is fitted with three galvanised mild steel brackets to fit over the tops of the kerbs forming the outer edge of the ditch. Alternatively synthetic grass may be used.

Drainage layer

When the ditches have been formed spread over the green formation surface a 150 mm firmed depth of approved hard aggregate (8-12 mm gauge). The aggregate is carefully transported on to the green area with machinery no heavier than mechanical dumpers. The drains must be protected with, for instance, metal sheets. The drainage layer is then adequately rolled to produce an even firmness with accurate levels being maintained throughout. In some situations the 150 mm firmed depth of aggregate could be reduced to 100 mm firmed depth. In conjunction with this an approved constructional membrane could be laid over the subsoil formation surface (but not over the backfilled drain trenches) in order to maintain the integrity of the full depth of aggregate as laid. Such a membrane prevents the admixture of subsoil and aggregate.

The layer is then blinded with a 50 mm firmed depth of approved coarse sand which will rest on the surface of the drainage aggregate without migrating downwards and causing consequent blockage and which will support the rooting medium without itself becoming contaminated.

The surface of the blinding layer on a flat green is left smooth and level, and on the crown green it is left smooth but maintaining the required contours.

During the later stages of grading, drainage, formation of ditches and spreading of the drainage layer, work can proceed with the preparation of the rooting medium.

Preparation and spreading of special soil mix

The rooting medium for bowling greens, i.e. the topsoil in which the grass will establish, should be of a particularly free-draining nature and yet contain sufficient clay fraction and organic material to sustain reasonably healthy grwoth and prevent over-susceptibility to drought. The majority of the bulk material should therefore comprise sand, which might fall within the medium to coarse category, and should comprise approximately 75-80% of the total. The soil should not contain much more than 5% of clay and a total of 20% of the clay, silt and very fine sand fraction aggregated together. Only very rarely would the natural soil available on the site conform to this sort of specification, but sometimes the available soil might be improved considerably by mixing with a suitable sand to produce a suitable mixture. Laboratory tests are often necessary to identify the optimum proportion of sand and soil to mix together, to obtain a formula which conforms to these design criteria.

Off-site preparation of the soil and sand is best, sufficient of it being prepared to provide a minimum of 110-125 mm firmed depth over a green where turfing is to be completed, but preferably 150 mm where seeding is to be the means of establishing the grass cover. A tractor and bucket loader is used to produce a rough mix in the correct proportions by volume, turning the heaps several times. Final mixing to obtain a satisfactory, even mix should be done through

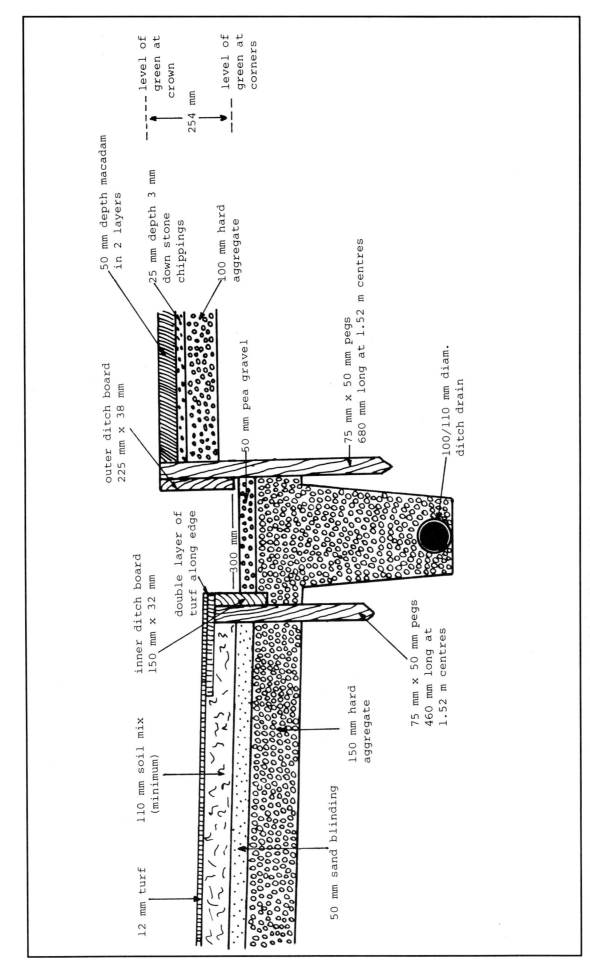

FIGURE 26. Detail on crown bowling green with traditional ditch and bank boards.

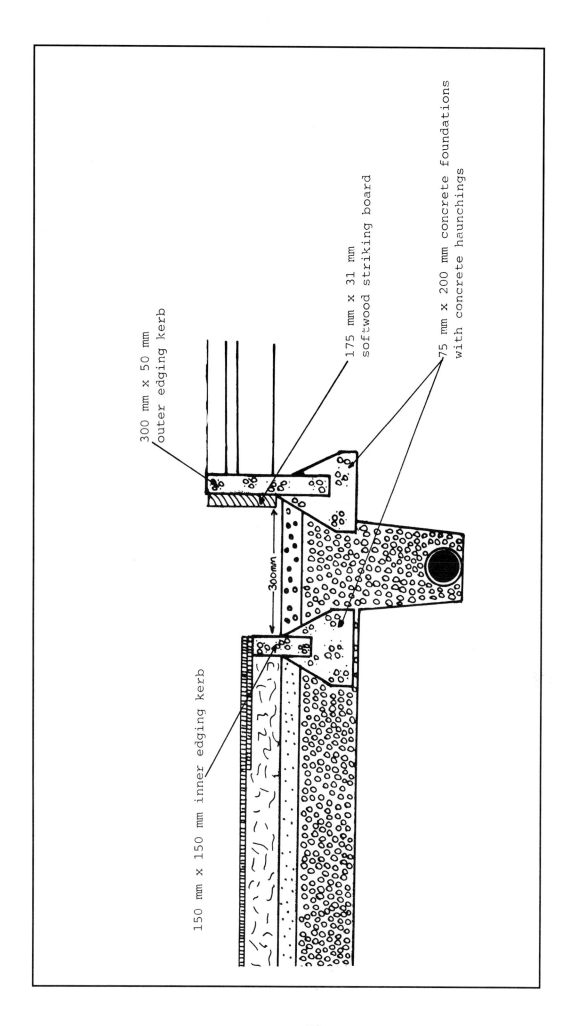

FIGURE 27. Crown green with precast concrete kerbs.

300 mm x 50 mm
outer edging kerb

175 mm x 31 mm
softwood striking board

75 mm x 200 mm concrete foundations
with concrete haunchings

150 mm x 150 mm inner edging kerb

300mm

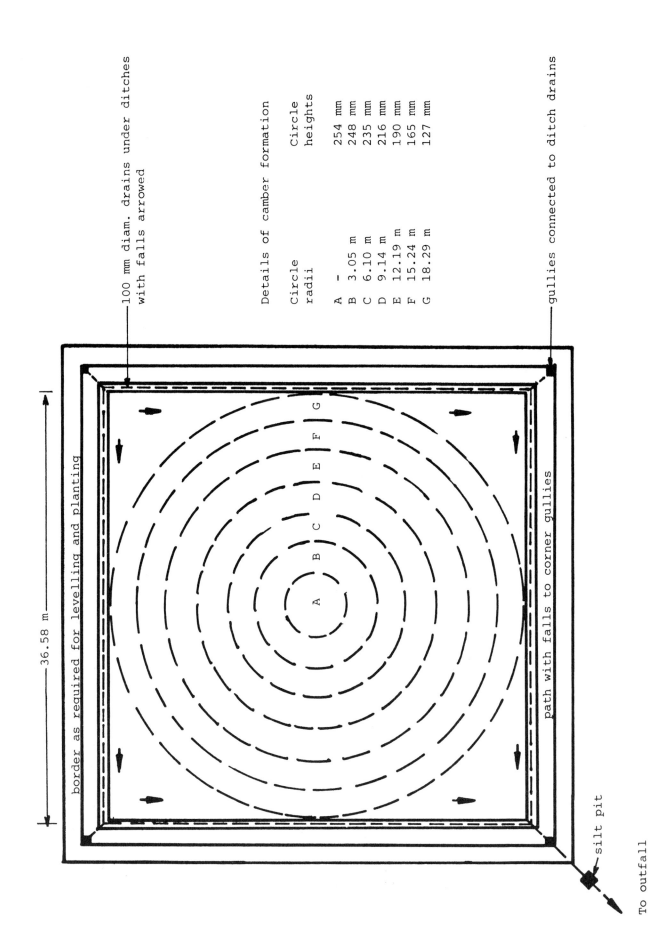

FIGURE 28. Crown green showing contours and ditch drain

80

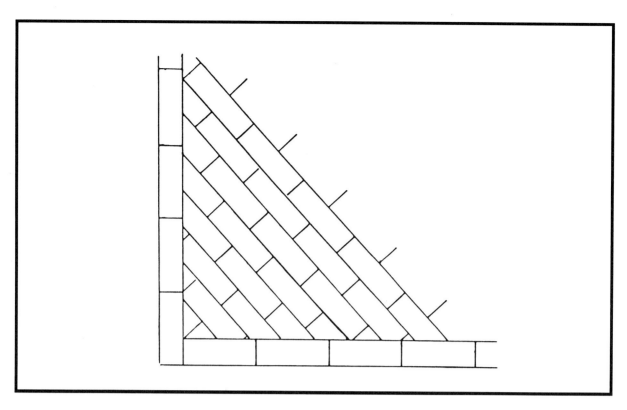

FIGURE 29. Diagram showing diagonal method of turf laying.

PLATE 29. Turfers should work from boards on turf already laid, not off the unprotected turfbed as shown.

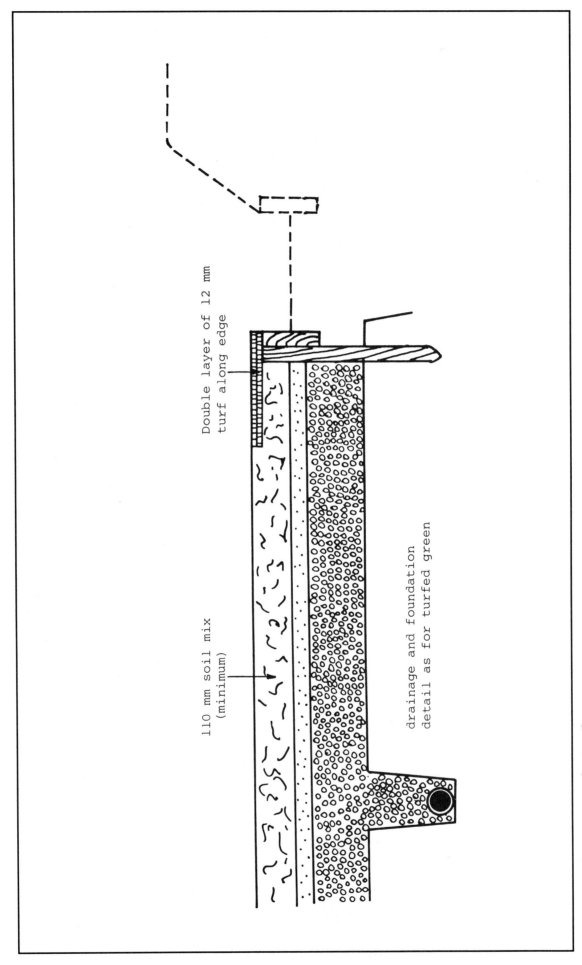

Double layer of 12 mm turf along edge

110 mm soil mix (minimum)

drainage and foundation detail as for turfed green

FIGURE 30. Detail on sown flat bowling green.

a compost shredder or screen, which has the added advantage of removing any sizeable stones. Mixing and spreading must be done with dry materials during the contract period and adequate covering with pastic sheet or canvas should be allowed for, should adverse weather be encountered.

If the quality of the existing topsoil is very poor, it might not respond to amelioration with sand, and in cases such as this alternative sources may have to be sought.

In many cases there is simply not sufficient space available within the contract area to stockpile or carry out any form of mixing and it is often found to be far more cost-effective to purchase a ready-mixed compost from a proprietary source.

Spreading of the special mix over the surface of the green is done by transporting with small mechanical dumpers or wheelbarrows, disturbance of the drainage layer being avoided by running the vehicles or barrows over planks or suitable protective sheets. The mix is then hand raked out to give the even depth required.

Extra material should be allowed for over and above the quantity required for the actual construction. This can then be used for top dressing purposes on completion of turfing or seeding and repeated as necessary during the first 12 months of maintenance, to provide a true and uniform surface. This also ensures that the top dressing used matches the underlying soil mix - a marked advantage. Top dressing prepared in advance should be adequately protected from the weather.

If there is a lime requirement then even application of the required amount of ground limestone can be done at this stage of the works.

Cultivations
Generally deep cultivation is not necessary after the special mix has been spread and levelled but if required it is done with a hand operated mechanical cultivator, care being taken to avoid disturbance of the blinding and drainage layers.

Turf/seed bed preparation
The special soil mix is evenly firmed by alternate hand raking and heeling to provide a fine, smooth turf/seed bed.

On the flat green the production of a level surface is imperative and this is done by setting up accurate level pegs on a 3 m grid or alternatively accurately boned-in, screeding battens being used.

On the crown green it is important to maintain correct contours and levels and this is done by accurately setting in level pegs at 3 m centres on each contour line, the top of the peg representing the finished level of the turf.

During the course of turf/seed bed preparation work all stones having one dimension of 12 mm or more are raked up and removed off site.

In the final stages of turf/seed bed preparation the required pre-turfing or pre-seeding fertiliser (determined by previous soil analysis) is evenly spread and lightly raked into the immediate surface maintaining true levels.

Establishment of grass cover and initial maintenance
The method chosen, turfing or seeding, affects both timing and cost. Turfing is now the most usual method of establishing a grass cover although seeded greens are not unknown. As mentioned earlier, seeded greens usually have a turfed perimeter to ensure stability of the extreme edges.

Where turfing is to be adopted as the means of establishing the grass cover this is best done in the autumn. The turf used should consist of clean fescue/bent free of weeds and weed grass and have a grass cover no longer than 12 mm. It should be cut to convenient size and to a uniform thickness.

Turf is normally delivered to site in convenient loads as laying proceeds and it should not be kept stacked or in rolls longer than seven days. It is laid only when ground conditions are favourable commencing with a band of turf around the perimeter of the green, two turves wide. Laying then proceeds diagonally commencing from one corner and working progressively to the opposite corner. The turves are laid with broken joints, each turf being closely butted to the adjoining.

Turfers work from boards placed on the turf already laid so that the prepared surface is not disturbed and all necessary materials are transported over boards so that the newly laid turf is not subjected to any direct traffic. Following turfing the green surface is rolled with a 250 kg hand roller, two passes only being made and then the green is top dressed with an approved sand at the rate of 4.0 kg/m^2, the sand being evenly applied and drag brushed into the surface.

With seeding the work should be geared to sowing in late August, though sowing in spring or summer is permissible if a reliable water supply is available.

Advance ordering of seed is required, suitable cultivars of bent and fescue being used. The total quantity of seed to be sown at 35 g/m^2 is divided in half, each half being sown evenly in transverse directions by hand and then lightly raked in.

Good initial maintenance is required and this involves - when the young grass is about 25 mm in height removal of all surface stones having one dimension of 12 mm or more; rolling under suitable conditions, with a 250 kg hand roller; carrying out a first mowing when the grass is, say, 40 mm in height (a Flymo type of machine can be used for this) no more than 12 mm of the grass foliage being removed; any excess clippings should be raked off; a second mowing is carried out as previous. If growth remains vigorous the height of cut is gradually reduced to 12 mm before growth ceases for the year.

In the following year special attention is required to fertiliser treatment, which must be adequate, and top dressing with good sandy friable compost matching the special soil mix spread on the green. Several applications of top dressing will be necessary to help perfect the bowling surface.

Returning to the turfed green, good initial maintenance is again essential, top dressing being the main item to help seal the joints between turves and create a smooth surface. Several applications of a good, sandy, friable compost matching the special soil mix are, therefore, necessary. Other items of importance such as mowing and fertiliser treatment are carried out as required.

Surround bank and verge
On a flat green it is useful to turf the surround, bank and verge, if conventional grass banks are being provided. The top of the turf bank is 225 mm above the finished level of the green with the face normally inclined 35° from the vertical. The verge is formed level between the bank and the path, the finished level being 25 mm above the kerb top adjoining the path.

The minimum 75 mm firmed depth of topsoil is spread on the prepared subsoil formation surface, the topsoil being raked to provide a satisfactory tilth. Pre-turfing fertiliser is then applied and turfing carefully completed. As laying proceeds the bank turves are pegged down with wooden pegs or by other approved means until the turves are established. On completion top dress with approved sand and brush in as on the surface of the bowling green.

Construction of surrounding path (1.22-1.83 m wide)
The formation level of the path is properly consolidated and trimmed to the required levels and with a cross fall of 50 mm towards the bowling green.

For a macadam surfaced path a foundation of approved hard aggregate is then laid to a consolidated depth of 100 mm, blinded with 3 mm down stone chippings to 25 mm depth. (For a paved surface path the foundation is to 75 mm consolidated depth and this is blinded with 25 mm firmed depth of coarse sand). In both cases rolling is carefully completed with a 2.5 tonne roller.

Approved 150 mm x 50 mm bull-nosed precast concrete kerbs are laid and light type gulleys to BS 539:1968 complete with appropriate galvanised gratings are then introduced. The gulleys are connected to the 100 mm ditch drains.

The macadam surfacing is then laid in two layers to a depth of 55 mm (alternatively only one course may be laid). For a paved path approved paving slabs are set on cement mortar pads to true line and flat with 6 mm gaps between; the gaps are grouted with cement mortar.

Ancillary works
These are completed as required. This can involve formation of a concrete ramp, external banks for seeding or planting, catchwater drains, roller recess, seat recess, litter bin recess, borders, turf nursery (usually 50 m²) and fencing.

Footnote
Although gravel or broken stone is recommended as a foundation layer in the above account, successful results can be obtained using alternative materials. The Lyon's Bowling Club green at Sudbury Hill has a foundation drainage layer entirely made up of smashed crockery collected from Lyon's Tea Shops and Cafes which apparently gives excellent drainage characteristics. It seems unlikely, however, that this material will replace hard aggregate as the standard recommendation for the purpose!

PLATE 30. Ditch formation using Wener Amenity Landscaping's glass reinforced cement units.

CHAPTER 6
MODERN BOWLING GREEN MAINTENANCE:
the assessment of a green and the calendar of required work

Let us imagine for a moment that we are in the position of a newly-appointed, inexperienced greenkeeper, green ranger or chairman of green committee who is faced with the task of maintaining, and if possible, improving a particular bowling green.

The first point which should be considered is the advisability of obtaining the services of a competent consultant agronomist to assess the present condition of a green, and who could then lay down a detailed maintenance programme for future treatment. An experienced adviser can pinpoint weaknesses and suggest appropriate remedial measures which may save the club much expenditure in the long-term, so justifying in financial terms any fee that he might charge. Without wishing to be in any way disparaging of the very praiseworthy efforts made by amateur committee members up and down the country, one should always bear in mind that bowling green maintenance is a complex and skilled task and a high level of scientific and technical skill is required to achieve a consistently first-class playing surface. Although it is hoped that the present text will be helpful to greenkeepers and club members in the time-consuming and sometimes frustrating task of achieving the perfect bowls surface, expert advice should always be sought if at all possible. Mistakes can after all take a long time to correct and can occasionally be disastrous. A text book can be an indispensable guide to a subject, but ultimately no amount of reading can compensate entirely for the absence of experience and practical skill.

It is also essential to bear in mind that it takes about three years to achieve the full benefit of any maintenance programme. Unfortunately, the rapid turn over of committee members at some clubs, plus the fact that all clubs are full of self-styled expert greenkeepers all too ready to say in loud voices exactly what is needed to transform the quality of a green overnight, tends to work against consistency of maintenance. Once a sound basic maintenance programme has been decided upon it should be adhered to for at least the three year period mentioned above. It is therefore worth repeating again - CONSISTENCY IS VITAL. Obviously there may be a need on occasions for unplanned extra work, as for example the fungicidal treatment of a disease attack, but every bowling green requires a series of seasonal primary maintenance operations which must be followed each year if a good green is to be achieved and preserved.

Before planning an appropriate maintenance programme for a particular green, it is essential (for beginners, experienced greenkeepers and consultant agronomists alike) to make a detailed assessment of the condition of the green. The existing features which should be fully investigated are as follows.

[1] PLAYING CHARACTERISTICS AND SURFACE LEVELS
Anyone who discusses the general quality of British bowling greens with expert bowlers or who has experience of advisory work in this field will soon reach the conclusion that the two commonest problems on both crown and flat greens are excessively slow bowling surfaces and poor surface levels. In the case of flat bowling greens, both features have been scientifically investigated and a report on the survey carried out is reprinted here as Appendix B. This investigation supports the view that deficiencies in both the pace of bowling greens and uniformity of surface levels are commonplace, so when planning the future maintenance of a particular green it is worthwhile to try and assess these two aspects of its surface in some detail.

As far as the question of surface pace is concerned, club members and particularly the more expert bowlers should be consulted in order to determine whether the speed of the green is adequate or excessively slow. Opinions should be gathered regarding the playing qualities of the green at all times during the bowling season - spring, summer and early autumn. Remember, however, that bowlers frequently complain unjustifiably of the lack of pace of outdoor grass greens in the spring. This often is merely a reflection of the fact that they have spent the winter bowling on artificial, indoor surfaces, which are often fast (sometimes excessively so) and therefore take time to readjust to the natural green. Obviously, the pace of a particular green will vary according to weather conditions - most greens are relatively slow after heavy rain, while in some instances one finds that a green will show an increase in pace after light drizzle as compared to its performance when completely dry. Ignoring such day to day variations however, it should be possible to gain a general impression of the performance of a green and to then slant future maintenance towards producing a necessary improvement in pace.

Alternatively, a more objective method of assessing green speed may be employed. There are two ways of doing this on a particular green. The first method simply involves bowling a wood straight across the green, standing as near as possible to the ditch and aiming to stop the wood just short of, or having it just topple into, the ditch on the opposite side. The time taken for the wood to travel across the green should be determined, preferably with a stop-watch. This procedure should be repeated several times in opposite directions and at right angles and an average time obtained. In the case of flat greens, the process should be carried out on several rinks as different rinks on the same green can vary quite significantly in pace. For a crown green, repeat the process in different positions near the edge or over the middle of the green to cancel out, as far as this is possible, the effect of sloping surfaces. No test allows one crown green to be reliably compared with another. They may, however, allow objective comparison of a single green's performance under different weather conditions or at varying times of year. If the wood takes 18 seconds to travel ditch to ditch the green would be very fast by average club standards. A time of 14 seconds is generally considered satisfactory while a travel time of 12 seconds would make the green too slow for most players. The fact that the rate of travel of a wood over a slow green is more rapid than on a green with good surface pace may seem confusing, but it should be realised that for a slow green a wood must be bowled much harder and faster to reach the opposite ditch. Although a bowl decelerates more rapidly on a slow green it leaves the bowler's hand at a much greater speed and hence crosses the green more rapidly.

The above figures were worked out for a standard 42 x 42 yd. flat green - a second or two should be added to the times quoted above if one is dealing with larger crown greens.

Since the size of a particular green influences the figure obtained by the above method, and even EBA-approved flat greens can vary quite considerably in size, a second method of determining green speed has been proposed with a view to allowing more reliable comparisons between greens. This second procedure is advocated by the EBA, and involves placing a jack exactly 30 yd. in front of the mat and timing the travel of the wood from the time it leaves the bowler's hand to a point when it stops within about 8 in. of the jack. Again, this should be repeated on various rinks and in different directions and an average obtained. According to the EBA, 12-13 seconds indicates an acceptable surface pace, and a time of 10 seconds or less is very definitely unacceptably slow. It is doubtful whether this EBA speed test has any value in the case of crown greens where results are complicated by the effects of surface gradients. A third speed test, involving the rolling of unbiased woods onto the green down an inclined plane is described in Appendix B. Speed tests of these kinds cannot be regarded as totally reliable, particularly for crown greens, but they do give some objective indication of the pace of a particular green and can usefully show how its speed varies from season to season and under differing weather conditions.

At this point it is worth stressing that those bowlers who feel that deficiencies in green speed can be overcome by closer mowing or by the use of a heavier roller are usually totally in error. Although it is true that a temporarily faster surface can be obtained in the short-term by rolling or close mowing in preparation for a particular game, neither rolling or close mowing do anything to influence the causes of long-term problems with the pace of a green. Both operations can also have deleterious side effects as we shall see. Long experience indicates that the most common causes of excessive slowness are the dominance of annual meadow-grass in the sward and the presence of a sub-surface thatch or fibre layer. It is these faults which must be eliminated if a faster green is to be obtained and neither rolling or close mowing has any effect apart from possibly making these problems worse in the long run. Annual meadow-grass and thatch will be more fully dealt with a little later in the present chaper.

The second point which should be considered when assessing the condition and future maintenance needs of a bowling green is the question of surface levels. Here of course there is considerable divergence between the needs of flat rink and crown green bowlers. For the rink game, the ideal is a perfectly level surface although this is something which is seldom if ever entirely achieved in practice. Most flat greens show some degree of surface undulation as a result of either imperfections in initial construction or level changes over years of use. Land subsidence over long periods of time is a common problem and can be particularly severe in the case of the many Miner's Welfare greens build in coal mining areas. In time, the rink game itself can also result in surface irregularities. This is particularly true where players bowl continuously on popular rinks without changing strings regularly to utilise other rink positions, and always in one direction across the green. Where particular rink positions are over used, the green gradually develops a "ridge and furrow" surface with the troughs coinciding with the centre of each rink and the ridges with the string positions. Ultimately such a surface has a marked and deleterious effect on bias and skilled and accurate bowls becomes unacceptably difficult, if not impossible. Uneven or inadequate top dressing can also contribute to surface irregularities.

There are a number of methods available for attempting to gain a picture of the surface contours of a flat green. Habitual bowlers can of course be consulted and the rink strings can also give a valuable indication - if pulled taught they rest on the high spots and bridge the relatively low areas. Heavy rain leaving standing water on a green also usefully indicates low areas as puddles lie in the hollows. Alternatively, a long straight edge can be used - a 12 to 14 foot plank is often employed fitted with convenient D-shaped handles on its upper edge. By far the best method is however to have the green surveyed - a specialist surveyor is not required, as most local general surveyors would be perfectly capable of carrying out the task. The results of a typical survey are shown in Fig. 27 and high and low areas can clearly be seen. This is of course invaluable if attempts are to be made to improve surface uniformity. Survey levels should be taken at 2 metre centres. Levels taken along the top of surrounding banks should be included as these are a useful check on whether bank heights conform to EBA requirements in the case of flat greens. Levels taken along inner ditch kerbs are also useful to determine if kerb sinkage has occurred. All levels should be related to a fixed bench-mark.

Modern computer-aided design and drafting systems (CAD's), if fed with the level figures from a particular green, can produce three-dimensional representations of surface contours or grid gradient maps, which give a very clear visual representation of surface levels. Some surveyors may have equipment of this kind, and produce print-outs which are very helpful in clarifying the irregularities which an individual green may show.

It is extremely difficult to lay down guidelines as to what degree of irregularity is acceptable in a flat green. It is of course not only a question of differences in height between high and low spots, but also where these irregularities occur within the body of the green, and how abrupt the changes in contour are. It has been said that new flat greens should be constructed within plus or minus 6 mm of the desired level but few old-established greens would meet such an exacting standard. Variations of up to plus or minus 18 mm can be regarded as capable of correction by maintenance work, i.e. by selective top dressing of low areas. Variations of more than this figure could probably only be corrected in practice by removing turf, adjusting soil contours and then returfing. In the case of a very severely uneven green, this could involve returfing the entire surface. Such work requires skilled and careful turfing and is best regarded as beyond the scope of all but very experienced greenkeepers or specialist contractors.

In the case of crown green bowls, it is even more difficult to put exact figures on what degree of departure from a true surface is acceptable or what is not. Very few crown greens conform to the theoretical requirement of a uniform mushroom-top contour - indeed many show quite considerable humps and hollows apart from the actual crown itself. Crown bowlers are generally happy with this situation, as level variations add interest to the game and give some advantage to the Home Team familiar with the runs and irregularities of their own green. Even for crown green bowls, however, some greens show level variations which are unacceptable and a green survey can be of considerable help in pinpointing the problem and allowing remedial measures to be undertaken.

[2] SWARD COMPOSITION
If a green is to be efficiently maintained, then it is vital that those responsible have some idea of sward composition - the species of grasses present and the approximate proportion of each. Unfortunately, grass identification can be quite difficult - it is certainly not as easy to

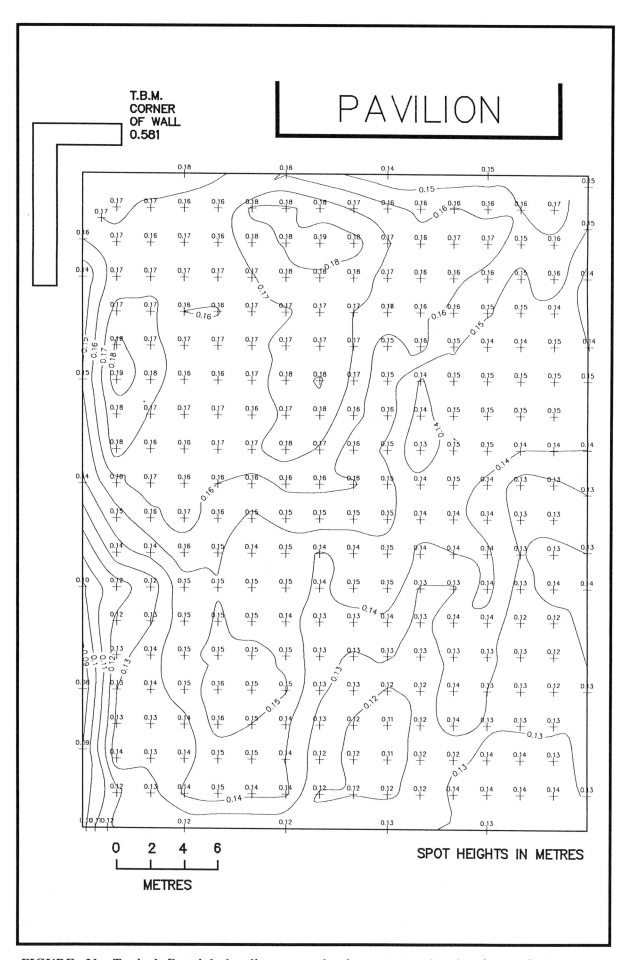

FIGURE 31. Typical flat-rink bowling green level survey produced using a CAD system. Note: the very low left hand corner. Contour lines have been drawn in.

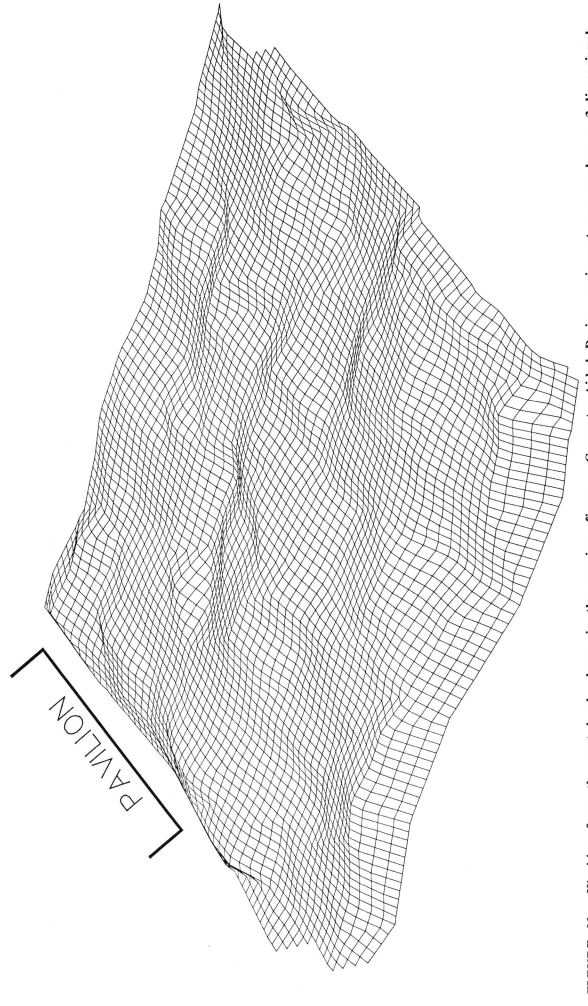

PAVILION

FIGURE 32. Working from the spot levels shown in the previous figure, Computer-Aided Design equipment can produce a 3-dimensional representation of a green (vertical scale exaggerated 60 times), which gives a clear picture of level variations.

distinguish two grass species as it is to correctly name a daisy or a dandelion! Close mowing makes grass identification doubly difficult - correctly naming a grass species in its natural flowering condition is one thing, identifying it in turf cut regularly at 5 mm (3/16 in.) is quite another matter. For the amateur inexperienced in such activities, by far the easiest solution to the problem is to enlist the help of a competent greenkeeper, groundsman or other turf specialist who should, if he is worth his salt, be able to give a reasonably accurate estimate as to sward composition after ten minutes examination of the average green. If a co-operative expert is not readily to hand, however, then the following guidelines may be of value and should allow anyone of reasonable commonsense to reach some idea of the kind of sward he is dealing with.

There are about 27 species of grasses which are commonly encountered in amenity or agricultural grassland in this country, but as far as bowling greens are concerned the majority are likely to be of very little significance.

Let us deal first with the special situation found on relatively new bowling greens laid with sea-marsh turf, as unfortunately there are still some of these around. As has already been pointed out in detail in Chapter 3, sea-marsh turf should be composed basically of two grass species, the sea-marsh red fescue (*Festuca rubra* spp. *rubra*) which has very fine bristle-like leaves and the rather broader-leaved creeping bent grass (*Agrostis stolonifera* var. *compacta*). Neither of these species, especially the fescue, is likely to survive very long under inland conditions and invasion of the turf by inland grass species, particularly annual meadow-grass (*Poa annua*), is virtually inevitable. It is therefore true to say that a 5 to 10 year old sea-marsh green which has been subjected to an average maintenance regime is unlikely to contain a significant proportion of the above grasses. Inland species as described below will tend therefore to dominate on older sea-marsh greens.

New sea-marsh greens apart, there are only three grass species which are likely to be of much significance in fine bowling green turf. These are:

[a] Chewings Fescue (*Festuca rubra* spp. *commutata*)
Chewings fescue is to all intents and purposes identical to the sea-marsh fescue mentioned above. Botanically, the two are merely sub-species of the same grass species and the differences between them are small. The most obvious characteristic of these fine fescues is the fact that the leaves are bristle-like and appear virtually circular in cross-section to anything but an extremely close examination. Fescue produces a tough wiry type of turf and a fast bowling surface. Theoretically fescue should form about 50% of the sward and this is often true of newly-sown greens or greens recently established using high quality turf from a specialised turf grower. The traditional seeds mixture for the finest turf, still standard today, is designed to produce a sward containing 50% Chewings fescue and 50% browntop bent. Unfortunately mis-management of many greens in the past has resulted in a reduction in the proportion of this valuable grass species and sadly most older greens now contain very little or none at all. Fescue can only be preserved in a sward by maintaining conditions of relative poverty - avoiding over-fertilising, over-watering, etc.

[b] Browntop bentgrass (*Agrostis tenuis* or *A. castellana*)
Bent grasses have rather dull green leaves which taper uniformly along their length to a fine point. It is much more common in bowling green turf than fescue and most greens contain at least some. A proportion of the better greens contain a very high percentage of browntop bent indeed. Bent is rather better at withstanding the effects of poor maintenance than the fescues and has hence tended to survive more successfully even in very old greens. In many other situations however it has tended to suffer from competition from far less desirable annual meadow-grass.

[c] Annual meadow-grass (*Poa annua*)
Annual meadow-grass occupies a very paradoxical position as far as fine turf is concerned. It is never sown deliberately and has a number of major disadvantages as a turf grass and is hence best regarded as a weed. On the other hand, it is probably the most common grass is bowling greens in this country. Indeed it is probably no exaggeration to say that if annual meadow-grass became extinct overnight, most British bowling greens would, on the following morning, be seen to consist largely of bare ground.

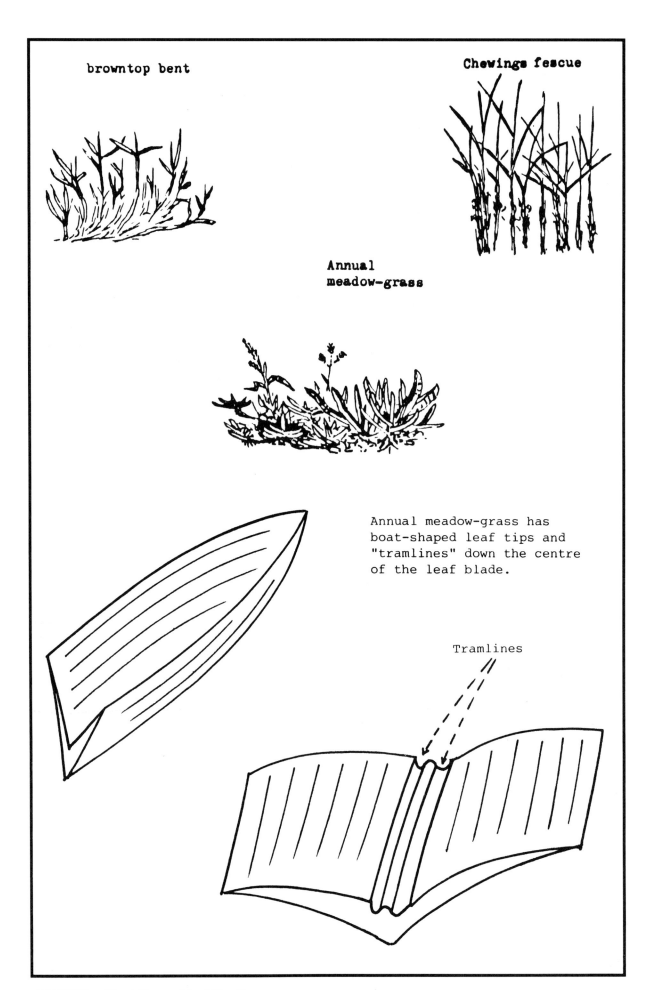

browntop bent

Chewings fescue

Annual
meadow-grass

Annual meadow-grass has
boat-shaped leaf tips and
"tramlines" down the centre
of the leaf blade.

Tramlines

FIGURE 33. Grass identification.

Annual meadow-grass is quite easy to identify. It is a light delicate green, and commonly produces silver-white seed heads at any time during the growing season but particularly in late May-June. Its leaves have distinctive tips shaped like the prow of a boat and there are two distinct grooves, commonly called 'tramlines' running down each side of the mid-rib of each leaf. The tramlines are most easily seen if the leaf is bent back over a finger and are quite translucent if the leaf is held up to the light.

In the past it has been argued that annual meadow-grass fulfils a useful function on the grounds that any grass cover is better than bare ground. There is an element of truth in this but a more sensible attitude is that the disadvantages of annual meadow-grass far outweigh any possible advantages. The single botanical name and the work "annual" are misleading. Annual meadow-grass covers a wide range of plant types, ranging from true annuals, through various biennial and short-lived perennial forms (perhaps with creeping stolons that root at the nodes), to longer-lived perennials (small-leaved, and forming very low dense rosettes which spread only slowly). The perennial forms are hard-wearing and tolerant of close mowing. They can produce viable seed which has a long dormancy at all heights of cut, and the abundant seed, and the ease with which plant fragments take root, help these forms of annual meadow-grass to colonize new areas or re-establish after wear. Growth rate is fast, and plants can flourish in spite of soil compaction (and the shallow rooting which it enforces) in a way which other grass species cannot. Annual meadow-grass is not necessarily a shallow-rooting species but it is better able than other species to tolerate compacted soil.

In fine turf, annual meadow-grass may occur either as isolated patches in the sward, that look unsightly and spoil the playing surface's uniformity (in texture and height of growth), or as a more or less complete cover that has supplanted the sown species. Its main drawbacks are susceptibility to fusarium patch disease, poor performance in drought and in winter, and the seed heads which are unsightly and may affect playing surfaces on fine turf. It is often associated with thatch problems, partly because it produces thatch quickly and partly because it is then well adapted to survive in thatchy conditions. The poor colour in drought is associated with this: if annual meadow-grass is the only grass able to survive on a thick layer of thatch, it will inevitably be the only one to show effects when deep thatch and dry weather combine to cause drought stress. Sub-surface thatch will be described in detail a little later in this chapter.

In established fine turf areas where annual meadow-grass has become dominant because it is better adapted to prevailing conditions than anything else it will not be possible to eliminate the annual meadow-grass unless those conditions are changed. Even if, in future, herbicide treatments are developed which can be recommended for selective control of annual meadow-grass in swards of fescue and bent, the treatments would need to be backed up by appropriate management. It would also be necessary to ensure that the change-over of species could be accomplished gradually, without unsightly treatment effects, and without adversely affecting the playing qualities of the surface in the short-term.

There have in fact been two approaches so far in herbicide research - the application of soil-residual herbicides to swards free of annual meadow-grass, to prevent its establishment from seeds blown or brought onto the area, and the elimination of established plants from a sward by single or repeated doses of a selective herbicide, as indicted in the previous paragraph. Both kinds of treatment have so far shown unacceptable risks of turfgrass damage.

A careful programme of seed bed preparation and subsequent management may succeed in keeping annual meadow-grass out of a bowling green or at least limiting or delaying its spread. This would involve:

[A] Providing a really clean seed bed, in which clean seed of good turfgrass cultivars can produce a dense weed-excluding sward before seeds of annual meadow-grass arrive. Soil sterilisation which kills dormant seeds in the soil, e.g. with methyl bromide or dazomet, is the only effective method at present.

[B] Purchasing seed which is free of annual meadow-grass, asking for seedsmen to have a special examination made by a testing station for the content of annual meadow-grass.

[C] Irrigating sensibly: annual meadow-grass thrives in moist conditions.

[D] Using fertiliser correctly: in particular avoiding excess phosphate, especially organic and

93

alkaline types (bonemeal is both): phosphate assists seedling establishment, rooting and seed production - three essential stages in take-over by annual meadow-grass.

[E] Maintaining a fairly low pH for inland fescue/bent turf (about 5.0 - 5.5).

[F] Giving adequate aeration, to get rid of compaction and surface water.

[G] Scarifying frequently enough to avoid having to be too severe, i.e. using a suitable mechanical scarifier every 3 weeks or so in good growing conditions, thus preventing deep scars and bare areas where annual meadow-grass can establish.

[H] Making sure top dressings are not too heavy, i.e. that they contain a high percentage of a suitable sand, and are worked in well to avoid providing a seed bed for annual meadow-grass.

[I] Sterilising the compost used in top dressing whenever practicable.

[J] Avoiding worm casts which provide a seed bed for the weed and bring dormant seed to the surface.

[K] Removing clippings, and hence seedheads.

[L] Avoiding, if possible, carrying seed in from heavily infested areas on mowers, other equipment and boots.

[M] Avoid continuous mowing at very low levels.

Annual meadow-grass has been covered at some length because it is one of the major problems encountered on British bowling greens. The fact that it produces soft lush growth, particularly if heavily fertilized or watered, means that it tends to produce excessively slow bowling surfaces. Its association with sub-surface thatch layers tends to intensify this undesirable characteristic as thatch itself also makes for a slow green. It also tends to lose growth and colour rapidly in the autumn, remaining weak all winter and recovering only slowly in the spring. This tends to make an annual meadow-grass green weak at the end and again at the start of the bowling season. Springs have been late in recent years and this has tended to worsen early season problems with annual meadow-grass. Its weakness in the autumn when the weather starts deteriorating is more of a problem for crown green bowlers who tend to continue play later in the year than the flat rink fraternity. The management of greens containing a high percentage of annual meadow-grass should therefore be slanted towards the reduction of this undesirable species, and towards the corresponding encouragement of better grasses, particularly browntop bent. Annual meadow-grass reduction (if not total elimination) is certainly possible for the majority of greens, although it is a gradual process and involves following a consistent policy for a period of several years.

Before leaving this brief guide to the identification of bowling green grasses, two other grass species should be mentioned, namely perennial ryegrass (*Lolium perenne*) and Yorkshire fog (*Holcus lanatus*). These are coarse grass species which occur in bowling greens as distinct and obviously undesirable patches of coarse growth rather than being intermingled evenly with other more desirable grasses over a green as a whole. Perennial ryegrass is the most desirable species as far as football fields and other coarse turf areas are concerned and is sometimes found in bowling greens as a result of a careless greenkeeper, for example, overseeding worn rink ends on a flat green with the wrong seeds mixture or re-turfing with coarse turf. Alternatively plants may seed naturally in a green from surrounding agricultural land. Ryegrass is a very tough species with flat leaves which are very shiny on the underside, and its shoot bases are often purple in colour. Yorkshire fog is on the other hand a weed in all turf situations and is never deliberately sown, although it is a very common plant of hedgerows and waste places. It has soft grey-green leaves with distinct narrow pink stripes on shoot bases, and patches usually have a very distinctly grey colour against the greener background of the rest of the bowling surface. Both species may be removed and replaced with turves containing more suitable grasses or discouraged by correct management practices, particularly raking and scarification.

Given some practice with grass identification, it should be possible to undertake a rough estimate of the proportions of the above grasses in the sward of a given bowling green. In practice the commonest situation which emerges is that a green will be basically composed of browntop bent and annual meadow-grass in varying proportions, with smaller and usually relatively insignificant quantities of fescue or the coarse weed grasses. (For newly established greens there is usually a reasonable quantity of fescue with correspondingly less annual meadow-grass.) If the amount of annual meadow-grass present is less than that of the bents and fescues one may congratulate oneself in having a green with an above-average botanical composition. Higher levels of annual meadow-grass make maintenance and the continuous provision of an acceptable bowling surface doubly difficult and in such circumstances future maintenance should incorporate measures aimed at gradually reducing annual meadow-grass and at encouraging the more desirable grasses.

The estimation of sward composition may be complicated by the fact that the green may not show an even mixture of grasses over its entire surface. In the case of flat greens for example, annual meadow-grass is often more common on rink ends, and on heavily used rink ends may frequently form 100% of the grass cover. Localised improvement of sward composition would obviously be beneficial in such a situation. Patches of annual meadow-grass colonising rink ends are often very easy to spot early or late in the year when the poor off-season colour of this species makes it appear very yellow against the greener background of the rest of the surface. A patchy distribution of annual meadow-grass on a green is a greater handicap than an even mixture of it with other grasses, as patches of different grasses tend to destroy uniformity, with woods travelling at different speeds over patches of one grass as compared to another as well as bobbling up and down.

[3] OTHER SURFACE FEATURES

The remaining surface features which need to be noted when a green is being assessed for future maintenance requirements are fortunately less problematical than the question of sward composition. The presence or absence of a broad-leaved weed population should prove fairly easy to establish. (The term broad-leaved is used to distinguish such weed from the weed grasses already mentioned.) Weed identification is again something which is made easier by experience, but at least most weeds are easier to tell one from the other than the grasses. Identifying the weed species which may be present is useful as weeds vary in their susceptibility to the range of selective weedkillers available today and the product appropriate for use on a particular green should be chosen on the basis of what weeds need to be eliminated. The variety and extent of the weeds present should be noted so that appropriate control measures may be taken at an appropriate time of year. One of the commonest of bowling greens weeds, pearlwort, is easily mistaken for moss so particular care should be taken to ensure that this species is correctly named.

Moss itself is a particular class of weed which is frequently troublesome in the bowling green situation. It is necessary to determine whether moss is a persistent problem, obvious at all times of the year and lingering from year to year, in which case it may be an indicator of some other fundamental weakness in the condition of the green. On the other hand, moss can be merely a seasonal problem, appearing in the winter or during a prolonged spell of wet weather: such points should be decided upon so that appropriate remedial work can be planned.

The efficient greenkeeper should also be familiar with the symptoms of a range of fungal diseases of the turfgrasses, or at the very least should be able to diagnose the more serious and common ones such as fusarium and red thread. If disease symptoms do appear then very prompt treatment may be required if significant damage to the quality of the bowling surface is to be averted - under the right conditions disease can spread very rapidly indeed.

The industrious and almost ubiquitous earthworm is another cause of an obvious problem on bowling surfaces. Worm casts if present in sufficient numbers can reduce the quality of a playing surface very significantly, particularly during mild, moist weather when the worms tend to be most active. It is worth remembering that just because a green is free of casts during the dry summer weather or during winter frost does not mean that there are no worms present, it just means that they are inactive under such conditions. Spring and autumn are therefore usually the best times for deciding whether worm control work is needed. Leatherjackets and other insect grubs are again pests which sometimes attack bowling green turf and should not be forgotten as a possible cause of turf weakness.

Other questions which a new greenkeeper, summing up the condition of a green, might ask himself are perhaps whether the sward is showing signs of chemical damage - uneven distribution of a past fertiliser application, weedkiller scorch etc. Or does it show signs of mechanical damage - marks left by a poorly set mower or scarring from excessively severe scarification, and so on? Once all surface features have been adequately investigated, the next stage of assessment can be undertaken - this involves a look below the surface.

[4] THE SOIL PROFILE
In a high proportion of cases, the key to the improvement of a particular green and the source of lasting difficulties with playing quality lies beneath the actual bowling surface in the underlying soil profile. This must always be borne in mind when assessing the condition of a green and an appropriate investigation of soil conditions undertaken. Fortunately for the peace of mind of all concerned, such an investigation of soil conditions need not involve anything as drastic as attacking a green with a spade or hiring a mechanical digger to cut an exploratory trench across from ditch to ditch! All that is needed is either a sheath knife with a blade about five inches or so in length, or preferably a purpose-made soil sampling tool.

If a knife is employed, the technique involves simply cutting, as deeply as possible, a V-shaped slice into the turf and levering it up (without necessarily detaching it entirely) so that the superficial soil profile may be viewed. As far as it goes, this can be very useful, but to carry out the task really thoroughly one must look rather more deeply below the surface and to do this requires a soil-core sampling tool. Such devices usually consist of a T-shaped handle on a probe of semi-circular section which can be pushed into the turf surface and then revolved, allowing a core of soil up to about 12 in. long to be extracted. (Similar devices, on a smaller scale, are used to sample cheeses.) Golf type hole cutters may also be used for shallow sampling. In the case of most bowling greens such sampling tools allow the full soil profile down to the original foundation layer to be examined - this is ideal. Repeating the sampling process here and there over the surface will give an idea of any variations in soil structure which may exist beneath the green. In the case of a newly constructed green, the situation below-surface is usually straightforward and an extracted core might just show, from top to bottom, the soil imported with the turf (if, that is, the green was turfed not seeded), the homogeneous soil-sand mix on which the turf was laid and the sand blinding layer on top of the broken stone foundation.

In the case of an old-established green the situation is often much more complex with the soil profile showing stratified layers which are as distinct as the growth rings in a tree trunk. These layers can almost be regarded as representing the archeology of a particular green and can often give a clear indication of the history of that green, at least as far as showing what original construction method was followed and what top dressing materials were used over the years. Examination of a soil core should give information on the following points:-

[a] Rooting depth
Ideally the grass roots beneath a green should extend 5-6 in. (125-150 mm) below the surface. With older greens this ideal seldom exists as soil compaction, rootbreak layers and the presence of a surface thatch layer all tend to limit rooting depth. Some greens, particularly those showing a distinct thatch layer over a compacted soil, may show less than 1 in. (25 mm) of root and the majority of greens show a rather inadequate 2-3 in. (50-75 mm). Very shallow rooting makes for a weak sward, too dependent on artificial fertiliser for its survival. Shallow rooted swards are also prone to drought damage, suffering very quickly from water loss as the superficial layers of the green dry out. Pulling a soil core apart can often indicate rooting depth quite clearly as the roots hold the top part of the core together, whereas the core breaks apart at the limit of rooting depth. Very often the limit of root growth coincides with some obvious feature of the profile, such as a distinct layer of sand, a dark peat layer, or the remains of the sea-marsh silt layer brought in with the original turf in the case of a Cumberland green.

Excessively shallow root indicates a need for more frequent or deeper aeration work in future maintenance. It should be realised that roots grow in air spaces between the soil particles - the root itself needs air to develop. Soil compaction or waterlogging obviously limits the amount of air present in the soil and limits root growth, and hence top growth and the standard of the bowls surface. Spiking or aerating allows more air to penetrate the soil and hence encourages healthy root growth. Using spiking equipment can also help break up layers of sand or peat, as described above, which form "rootbreaks" and limit the depth of root penetration.

[b] Thatch or fibre layers
It is most important to decide whether or not there is a layer of organic material between the sward itself and the actual soil surface. Spongy thatch is the most frequent cause of excessively slow bowling surfaces and can also encourage surface waterlogging, moss growth, the spread of annual meadow-grass and other problems. The accumulation of a layer of fibrous material is a natural feature of turf development and cannot be entirely prevented. Total prevention would in fact be most undesirable as a surface with no underlying fibre would lack resiliency and could easily become thin in wet weather. However, when fibre builds up to an excessive degree it becomes a problem. About ¼ in. (6 mm) of matted material would be acceptable on bowling greens while a ½ in. (15 mm) layer would begin to prove troublesome. The 4-6 in. (100-150 mm) layers which are not infrequently seen make turf maintenance and the formation of good playing surfaces extremely difficult.

Most people who are experienced in turf management will realise that there is more than one form of thatch or fibre. In the past, words like mat, thatch or fibre have been used very loosely and more precise definition of terms would therefore be of value. The following classification could be a guide:

Litter
A loose and fluffy accumulation of grass clippings and decaying leaf bases and sheaths in between the grass stems at the base of the sward. Litter is not usually seen on intensively used or well managed turf but is more characteristic of old and neglected lawns which are perhaps cut weekly without boxing off clippings and which receive very little additional treatment. It would never be found on a bowling green unless it had been neglected and probably not played on for a number of years.

PLATE NO. 31. Soil sampling tools.

Fibre
Fibre resembles coconut-matting in being tough and wiry in texture and brown in colour and consists of old roots and other organic debris. Fibre usually overlies dry soil, the turf

97

becoming very dry indeed and difficult to re-wet under drought conditions. Fibre is most commonly found under acidic conditions where the sward is bent and fescue with a tendency to invasion by acid loving weeds like sheep's sorrel, bedstraw and woodrush.

Thatch
Thatch can be waterlogged throughout most of the year and often smells strongly of decay and stagnation. It is yellow/brown in colour, sometimes with black streaks showing the activity of anaerobic bacteria. The underlying soil is usually wet, compacted and perhaps of clay with restricted drainage. Annual meadow-grass usually predominates in the sward with perhaps some surviving bent. Thatch can accumulate to layers several inches thick particularly in water-collecting hollows on heavily played parts of a green. Over-watering and over-fertilising are also major factors in the process of encouraging thatch build-up.

As with many other problems, the prevention of fibre or thatch formation is more satisfactory and much less laborious than curing an established problem. If one is starting with a young and fibre-free sward, regular scarification using a rotary scarifier can do much to prevent serious accumulation of material. The use of a comb attachment on the mower is a useful supplement, raising horizontal stems into the cutting mechanism and so preventing build up.

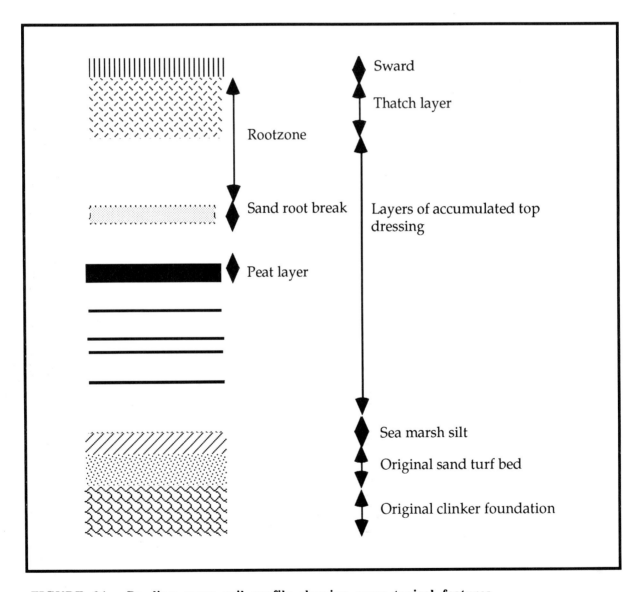

FIGURE 34. Bowling green soil profile showing some typical features.

However, if soil conditions are such that fibrous layers are being encouraged then attacking them by scarification may be a losing battle as scarification does nothing to attack the actual cause of thatch formation. If fibre or thatch can be seen to be building up or if an established layer is present then measures are required to remove its cause and these are likely to be more effective in the long-term than a direct attack on the layer itself by scarification or hollow tining. In practice both approaches are usually useful.

Control of thatch and fibre
In the specific case of fibre, as defined above, effective control can often result from frequent aeration work. All forms of aeration allow air into the layer and encourage natural organisms which break down the dead material. Aeration also encourages water penetration into very dry fibre and underlying soil and hence increased bacterial activity. Fibre is often very common on high spots in an undulating bowling surface and levelling and re-laying can sometimes be advisable. The deep hand forking of dry mounds can also be beneficial as irrigation water and rain otherwise tend to run down into adjacent hollows. Dry, fibrous mounds often become associated with a fungal condition known as 'dry patch' which exaggerates the contrast between dry, fibrous-looking mounds and the lusher, greener and wetter low areas. Aeration is, therefore, the primary method of controlling the fibre, with scarification to remove the existing material. If soil analysis shows extreme over-acidity then lime treatment may be advisable, but only with extreme care as undesirable side effects can occur. Lime can easily increase weed, worm and weed grass populations and encourage the very damaging take-all patch disease.

In contrast, thatch, again as defined above, is a result of poor surface drainage and any measures aimed at improving water penetration will help dry the layer and promote natural breakdown. Aeration is again of importance but it is essential to penetrate down below the thatch layer into underlying soil layers. The new generation of aeration equipment capable of penetrating up to 6 in. (150 mm) or more is particularly useful in this respect. Usually the causes of thatch are to be found in barriers to water penetration below the layer itself - peat layers, sand layers marking former compacted wet surfaces, or simply compaction are the commonest causes. If slow drainage is being caused by a heavy clay subsoil or by poor initial construction with the whole of the soil profile compacted, then even deep surface spiking is unlikely to prove effective. Complete re-construction is then the only answer. Occasionally special aeration work using sub-aerators like the Charterhouse Verti-Drain can be a helpful supplement to more conventional spiking. If carried out when the soil is dry, these operations can produce a cracking effect at a greater depth than the machine actually penetrates.

Thatch is undesirable as it holds water on the surface and makes the turf wetter than it should be. Fertiliser as well as water is held in the surface and root is confined to the thatch layer, dead root adding to the layer and making the situation worse. Such a wet surface is prone to fusarium and damage from play. Over-watering, of course, makes the problem infinitely worse. Turf with a thick thatch layer is often very soft and mattress-like and hence easily footmarked giving an uneven surface at the end of a busy playing period. Soft thatch also gives a following player an unfair advantage, as he can see the indented track left along the surface by the bowl previously played by his opponent. Wet thatch layers tend to discourage the finer turfgrasses and annual meadow-grass increases as it is one of the few grasses which can reasonably grow under such conditions. On thick thatch layers, however, even annual meadow-grass tends to weaken, particularly in wet winters. Removing the thatch can, therefore, have many beneficial effects in producing firmer and truer surfaces which are better able to withstand play even under adverse conditions.

Top dressing can be beneficial in firming up and helping the break up of thatch. Compost in the thatch, well worked into spike holes, makes the layers less spongy. It also maintains air penetration and natural breakdown. Regular applications of sandy compost are, therefore, an essential part of the fight against thatch. Scarification, aeration and top dressing are all essential weapons but victory hinges on identifying and eliminating the prime cause of thatch formation.

[c] Compaction
Compaction in the soil profile may be responsible for slow surface drainage, for encouraging thatch layers and their attendant ills, and for poor root growth. Look for zones in the soil which resist the penetration of the coring tool and which appear rather structureless with no visible soil air spaces. Many greens have been subjected to heavy rolling in the past, sometimes with vibrating rollers and other machines more suitable for consolidating the

foundations of a motorway than for use on a bowling green. Such implements can produce severe over-compaction. Sea-marsh silt layers, representing the original turf surface buried by subsequent top dressings, are often very compacted by rolling and form an almost impenetrable barrier to water percolation and root growth. Silt layers, usually about 1 in. (25 mm) thick are of a uniform grey colour, are composed of very fine silty particles of even size, and are usually a very obvious feature of the soil profiles underlying old sea-marsh turf greens. Over-compaction can also be produced by continuous treading by the players themselves as well as by heavy rollers. The compacting effect of the players feet may be unevenly distributed over a green, being particularly common on the rink ends of a flat rink green.

[d] Layering

An old green, as already mentioned, may show a soil profile showing as many varied layers as an expensive chocolate gateau. Apart from the thatch and sea-marsh silt layers described above layering is usually the result of top dressing with various materials over a long period of time. Sand or peat rootbreaks are most commonly the result of a heavy top dressing of such materials, subsequently buried by further annual top dressing. Ideally a bowling green soil profile should remain uniform and homogeneous by consistent top dressing, after preliminary scarification and aeration, with the same type of material from year to year. Aeration work can help break up and mix together the different layers in a profile where they have formed. To avoid the danger of layering, top dressing should be thoroughly worked into a well-spiked green and not simply left lying on the immediate surface. New greens built with a carefully chosen sand/soil rooting medium should be top dressed with a similar sandy mix to preserve uniformity. Once one has decided upon a suitable top dressing mixture therefore, one should be consistent in using it from year to year. The practice of using sand one year, peat the next, etc. etc. should be avoided. Layered profiles themselves can add to water percolation problems and encourage shallow rooting and are therefore to be prevented if at all possible.

[e] Total soil depth

It is useful to obtain a clear idea of the total topsoil depth which exists over underlying free-draining clinker or broken stone drainage layers.

[5] CHEMICAL ANALYSIS OF THE SOIL

After carrying out a visual examination of the soil profile, one should complete one's knowledge of basic soil conditions by having an appropriate chemical analysis of the soil carried out. It is not something which the amateur can undertake for himself - it really requires the facilities of a well-equipped chemical laboratory and the analysis results need to be interpreted by someone experienced in such matters. Some commercial firms involved in the turf maintenance industry offer a service of this kind and some public analysts might be able to help. The Sports Turf Research Institute also offers a comprehensive soil testing service. (It should be remembered that soil analysis by trade firms is sometimes followed by commercially biased advice.)

The sample taken for analysis should be truly representative of the whole green. Most laboratories would require about 1 lb. (0.5 kg) of soil, this quantity being made up of sub-samples taken here and there in a random fashion over the surface. A hollow tine fork is an ideal sampling tool or one of the soil-coring tools referred to in the previous section. 50 or 60 cores should be collected and the core depth should be 5 in. (125 mm).

A basic soil chemical analysis should produce information on soil acidity or alkalinity (i.e. the pH level), and on two of the three major plant nutrients, phosphate (P_2O_5) and potash (K_2O). The third major nutrient, nitrogen, cannot be meaningfully included in such an analysis as levels in a particular green can change from day to day and any figure obtained tends to have very little significance. Phosphate and potash levels are determined by extraction into weak chemical solutions under standardised conditions. pH is best determined electrometrically using a pH electrode in the laboratory under standardised conditions. Various kits for do-it-yourself pH determination are commercially available but these do not really give reliable results. Chemical testing kits where a coloured soil solution is compared with a standard colour chart tend to be rather inaccurate, while various battery-operated stick pH meters which give a reading when inserted into the surface of a green are woefully unreliable - the reading for one thing may vary according to how damp the green is at the time.

The pH scale indicates soil acidity or alkalinity as mentioned above, on a 0 to 14 scale. Soils usually fall within the range 4.0 to 8.0. Figures between 6.0 to 6.5 may be regarded as neutral for practical purposes, 6.0 to 5.5 mildly acid and below 5.5 acid. Similarly a bowling green soil with a pH of between 6.5 and 7.0 would be mildly alkaline and above 7.0 definitely alkaline. Theoretically, inland bowling green soils should be slightly acid within the range 5.0 to 5.5 but it is to be stressed that figures must be looked at with caution and always in the light of the general condition of a particular green. For example, if a green is found to have a very low pH and is therefore theoretically over-acidic, this does not automatically mean that lime treatment is required. A green showing a pH level of 4.5 for example is strictly speaking over-acidic but if the sward was healthy and the bowling surface very satisfactory, lime treatment would probably be most unwise. Liming is best regarded as a rather drastic treatment which, if overdone, encourages weeds, worms, undesirable grasses and the very damaging take-all patch disease. It should therefore only be undertaken in situations where the sward is perhaps thin, mossy and fibrous and showing obvious symptoms of over-acidity, and then only with extreme caution and preferably with expert advice. Many seaside greens constructed using local sandy soils are naturally alkaline - in this situation high pH levels should not be a cause of concern.

Soil nutrient figures giving phosphate and potash levels are an invaluable and essential guide to future fertiliser requirements. The question of how much fertiliser is needed will be discussed more fully later so at this point suffice it to say that fertiliser should not be overdone. Applying too much encourages fusarium patch disease and annual meadow-grass, promotes thatch development and produces heavy lush growth and consequently a slow bowling surface.

Making arrangements for a competent analysis of the soil completes our assessment of the present condition of the green. Such a survey should provide a firm basis for planning future maintenance and should highlight aspects of the green where improvement would not come amiss. Bowling greens are as individual and idiosyncratic as the bowlers who play upon them, so the details of the maintenance programme must be tailored to the specific needs of a particular green. It is, however, possible to lay down general guidelines as to maintenance requirements which are applicable to all greens, whether crown or flat rink.

Setting out such maintenance requirements on a seasonal basis allows one to compile a greenkeeping calendar. For the sake of clarity, maintenance operations are here divided into two categories, Primary and Secondary.

PRIMARY MAINTENANCE consists of those operations which should be performed on **every** bowling green **every** year as a matter of routine. Neglect of any one of them can be expected to result in an at least gradual deterioration in the quality of the playing surface. **Primary operations are set out here in bold type.**

SECONDARY MAINTENANCE covers work required on certain greens at certain times to correct specific faults or to meet an unforeseen problem such as an outbreak of disease or weed invasion.

The timing of maintenance work is often vital for success and it is impossible to be dogmatic on this point as weather and climatic factors vary from year to year. The following calendar must therefore be understood to be a very general guide only.

THE GREENKEEPING CALENDAR
JANUARY, FEBRUARY, VERY EARLY MARCH
(In frost ,snow or very wet weather leave well alone!)

MOWING: Cut if any growth is taking place. Set mower high initially and gradually lower level as growth strengthens.

SWITCHING: Switch or brush green each morning to disperse dew, as required by weather conditions.

MOSS CONTROL: If necessary, when weather is reasonable.

DISEASE CONTROL: Fusarium can strike if weather favours it. Treat at once.

TOP DRESSING: Supplementary to autumn top dressing - sometimes advisable. Only if weather is suitable, with some growth taking place. Material used at this time must be thoroughly and finely screened.

MARCH - APRIL
MOWING: Gradually lower cutting height.

SWITCHING: Continue as necessary.

WORM CONTROL: If required in mild moist weather, or leave until autumn.

DISEASE CONTROL: Fusarium still common. Treat at once.

SCARIFICATION: When growth is taking place and ground conditions good.

ROLLING: On one or two occasions to prepare surface for play.

FERTILISER: Apply spring dressing if growth is established. May have to postpone until after play starts.

PLAYING SEASON COMMENCES (usually Easter)

APRIL - MAY
MOWING: Three times weekly usually necessary.

FERTILISER: Spring dressing when growth is established, if not given before play starts.

RAKING: Fit comb to mower. Use throughout growing season.

RINK MARKERS (flat greens): Move frequently.

WEED CONTROL: Selective weedkiller when growth is strong. Late spring or early summer.

DISEASE CONTROL: Fusarium can still strike.

ROLLING: Light roll for important matches. Keep to a minimum.

SWITCHING: Continue each morning.

SCARIFICATION: Regular light rotary scarifying may be useful, perhaps monthly?

JUNE, JULY, AUGUST, EARLY SEPTEMBER
SWITCHING: Continue each morning.

MOWING: Continue frequently.

RAKING: Comb on mower. Use continuously.

FERTILISER: One or two summer dressings, say at end of June and in late August.

WATERING: In drought periods.
DISEASE CONTROL: Red thread disease - treat by fertilising or with fungicide.

WEED CONTROL: If weather unsuitable earlier, or a repeat treatment if required.

DRY PATCHES: Fork, use wetting agent.

RINK MARKERS (flat greens): Move frequently.

AERATION: Spiking or pricking may be useful on some greens.

SCARIFICATION: Continue programme. Not in drought.

SEPTEMBER, OCTOBER
(Play finishes at some point - the earlier the better from the greenkeeping point of view! Autumn work under reasonable weather conditions is vital.)

MOWING: Continue as growth demands, gradually raising height of cut to winter level.

SCARIFICATION: Thorough rotary scarification before growth ceases.

RENOVATION: Seeding, turfing, general repairs. Overall overseeding?

AERATION: Overall aeration of some appropriate type.

DISEASE CONTROL: Fusarium common in damp weather. Treat promptly.

WORM CONTROL: Mild moist weather.

TOP DRESSING: Overall sandy compost dressing (4 tons at least) absolutely essential. More if necessary. Extra on low spots. Spread and work in while weather still reasonable with some growth occurring, and when the surface is dry.

NOVEMBER, DECEMBER, JANUARY
AERATION AND TOP DRESSING: May have to be completed if not done earlier. Now getting too late. This vital work now urgent.

MOWING: Do not neglect if growth occurs. Winter cutting level.

SWITCHING: Continue if necessary. Keep surface as dry as possible.

RENOVATION: Turfing can still be carried out (up to Christmas).

AERATION: Winter slit tining can be useful when weather permits.

MOSS CONTROL: Under reasonable weather conditions as required.
NOTE: On completion of the above, go back to the start and begin the whole cycle all over again. Like that of the proverbial (and possibly fictional) housewife, a greenkeeper's work is never done.

❄ ❄ ❄ ❄ ❄ ❄ ❄ ❄ ❄ ❄ ❄ ❄ ❄ ❄ ❄

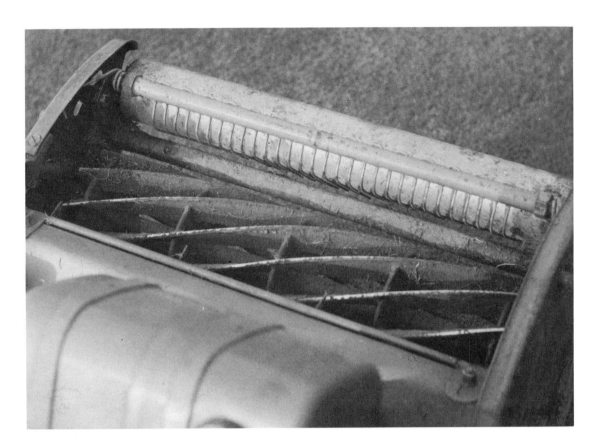

PLATE 32. A grass comb or wire rake in place behind the front roller of a Ransomes Auto-Certes mower.

CHAPTER 7
MODERN BOWLING GREEN MAINTENANCE:
mechanical work

In this section, the intention is to cover all bowling green maintenance operations which involve the use of mechanical equipment rather than chemical treatments. The term mechanical equipment covers everything from sophisticated powered implements to simple hand tools.

Experience confirms that the majority of bowling clubs are under-equipped. Obviously, financial considerations are usually the underlying cause of this unsatisfactory state of affairs, but it is also often a question of club officials being ignorant of what equipment is required or what is commercially available. Rapid improvements have taken place in turf maintenance equipment in recent years and many of the smaller bowling clubs have therefore been left rather behind the times in this respect, the greenkeeper's shed being crowded with obsolete, often almost antique, maintenance machinery. This can be a major handicap as up to date equipment can make maintenance work far more efficient and less time-consuming. Investment in good equipment makes sound financial sense in the long-term, even if meeting the often high initial cost of machines is difficult for many clubs. Unfortunately, it is invariably true that one cannot achieve and maintain a first class bowling surface without considerable monetary investment and the acquisition, servicing and replacement of equipment has to be quite a major item for the club's budget.

The annual exhibitions of greenkeeping equipment which are held nowadays at Peterborough, Edinburgh and elsewhere are a most useful show-case of new developments and all greenkeepers and green chairmen would benefit from occasional attendance at such shows.

When acquiring a particular item of equipment is simply beyond club resources, then machinery hire can be a very useful solution. Most parts of the country now have contractors who will hire out equipment on a daily basis, sometimes complete with operator. Many clubs find such arangements most useful although the system does have its weaknesses. Many maintenance operations must be carried out at the right time of year and under the right ground and weather conditions for completely successful results, and when equipment has to be booked from the supplier well in advance for a certain day, there is, of course, no guarantee that weather conditions will be suitable on the day the machine arrives. One also has the problem of uneven seasonal demand - often many clubs in a given area want a particular machine at the same time (for example, a spiker at the end of the bowling season) and this means that some clubs have to take the machine too early or, more often, too late in the year. In most situations, however, hiring a suitable machine is infinitely preferable to omitting a vital primary maintenance operation altogether.

Once equipment has been purchased it should be well looked after if it is to continue to perform the task for which it was designed. In the case of powered equipment like mowers, scarifiers, etc. this means an annual overhaul and service (usually in the winter months) plus regular care before and after use. Tools should be washed or cleaned after use, particularly fertiliser distributors as many fertiliser materials are corrosive and play havoc with neglected spreaders. Tines on spikers and scarifiers should be replaced as required - a rotary scarifier with worn and rounded blades for example is almost useless.

When one carries out consultancy and advisory work around the clubs, one soon reaches the conclusion that a brief look into the greenkeeper's shed is a completely reliable method of assessing his general competence. An equipment shed full of rusting machines, mowers caked with old grass clippings and decaying sacks of old fertiliser, is a clear indication of an incompetent greenkeeper - this being usually confirmed by the condition of the green as well!

As a general guide, every club should try to acquire the following range of equipment:

MOWER: All important, and the most expensive item. Grass comb attachment is vital.Verti-grooming attachments should also be considered if finances permit.

AERATION EQUIPMENT: Powered aerator if possible. Hand-pushed spiker is a reasonable substitute for some greens. Hand forks with round, flat and hollow tines. Shallow pricker (e.g. Sarel Roller) can be very useful.

SCARIFIER: Powered rotary scarifiers are by far the most efficient. Spring tined wire rake useful for small areas but no substitute for the powered machine.

SPRAYER: For weed control, fungicides, etc. Wide range of types available. The new CDA types likely to become more popular in future.

DISTRIBUTOR: For even application of solid materials - fertilisers, etc. Belt or spinner types. Hand spreading is possible but is a skilled and time-consuming job - the machine makes the job much easier.

ROLLER: 5 cwt. is heavy enough. Trulevel type particularly useful.

WATERING EQUIPMENT: Automatic pop-up system or water square or sprayline are to be preferred.

ASSORTED HAND TOOLS: Drag mat or drag brush. Switch. Hole cutter or turf repairer. Hand shears, etc.

Large and costly machines which are only infrequently used, such as top dressing spreaders, cam-action punch-type deep hollow tining equipment and sub-aerators are invariably hired unless the green is part of a local authority recreation department or very large sportsground.

Most of the equipment mentioned above will be covered in detail in this present Chapter. Sprayers are, however, more appropriately dealt with in the Weed & Pest Control section, and distributors in the chapter which deals with fertiliser and top dressing. Watering equipment is covered in Chapter 10. For the present, mowing equipment is an obvious first topic.

Mowers & mowing

Hand mowers have now gone almost completely out of use for bowling green mowing, petrol-engined motor mowers being the preferred alternative. A high quality professional machine is essential if a first-class bowling surface is to be obtained so it is foolish and ultimately uneconomic for a club to invest in a cheaper machine more suitable for domestic lawns. Nothing but the best is good enough for bowling green mowing and in practice this means a mower with a cutting mechanism between 18 in. and 24 in. in width and a revolving cutting cylinder with 10 or 12 helical cutting blades. A machine of this type allows an average 42 x 42 yd. flat green to be cut in 1 hour 30 min. to 1 hour 40 min. on average, although cutting time obviously varies with length of the grass before cutting, weather conditions, etc. Larger crown greens take proportionally longer to mow. Narrower 16 or 18 in. wide machines are probably preferable where there are surface undulations but of course increase the cutting time. The wider machines speed up the task but are slightly more prone to scalp high spots and leave long grass in hollows where the surface is uneven. Wider mowers therefore perform best on truer greens, but it must be remembered that an uneven green is best improved by levelling its surface rather than by using a smaller mower.

The evenness of the finish produced by a mower depends on the number of cuts made by the mechanism per yard or metre of forward travel. A machine giving 110 cuts per metre is very suitable. Machines giving much fewer cuts per metre tend to produce a ribbed or corrugated finish to the cut sward, obviously undesirable for bowls purposes. (A similar problem can arise with even the best machines if they are poorly set or are trying to cope with grass which has been allowed to grow excessively long.)

Although the topic should, strictly speaking, come under the heading of raking or light scarifying, it is worth mentioning at this point that the mower chosen should be capable of being fitted with a grass comb, a device invented by Mr A.J. Whitfield of Uttoxeter in 1956. The design of conventional cylinder mowers has one inherent and unavoidable fault - the small front roller flattens down the grass before the actual cutting mechanism passes over it. This means that there is a tendancy for procumbent and long, wiry growth to escape cutting as it is lying horizontally close to the surface as the cutting mechanism passes above. Attempts have been made to minimise this by fitting a ribbed front roller, which means that at least some of the grass escapes this flattening action. Alternatively, the front roller may be replaced with a castor-like wheel at each side - this unfortunately increases the chances of scalping over even a slightly undulating surface, because the castor-type machine fails to ride over a small surface hump which happens to pass between the two side castors. By far the best solution to this problem is to fit a small wire rake or stiff brush on the mower immediately behind the small front roller but ahead of the actual cutting reel (a rake towed behind the machine, i.e. behind the large driving roller, has a different action and is not effective for the purpose being discussed). Such grass combs are now available as standard attachments for many professional-quality mowers and are of considerable value in helping produce faster and more uniform bowling surfaces. They are particularly useful in the case of greens which exhibit procumbent, coarse or matted growth. Pace can be very significantly improved for such greens simply by fitting a comb to the mower and using it continuously for a season. Combs can also reduce the rate of accumulation of fibre or thatch - they do not penetrate far enough to attack existing thatch layers but they certainly slow down the build up of fresh thatch or fibre. Correct setting of the comb depth is essential - too deep and the mower yaws from side to side as it travels, too shallow and the comb misses procumbent growth. The comb should be set to just drag through the sward and its setting regularly checked. The comb should be placed on the mower when growth is established in the spring and used continuously until the autumn as a general rule. It can occasionally be removed, e.g. for cutting in very wet, dirty conditions or during drought when very little growth is occurring, but generally the more often the comb is employed the better. It is unfortunate that the advantages of this simple mower attachment are not more widely appreciated - the standard of British bowling surfaces would be significantly improved if combs were more widely and consistently used.

A recent development is the availability of pedestrian-controlled motor mowers fitted with a rotary scarifying unit ahead of the actual cutting mechanism. Now usually termed verti-grooming or thatching units, such attachments allow light, superficial scarifying and mowing in a single operation. They were originally developed for the large ride-on triple mowers used for golf green cutting, but a number of pedestrian bowling green mowers can now be purchased with this feature, namely Toro, Ransomes, Jacobsen, Bunton and John Deere machines. Taking the form of rotating steel blades or stiff-bristled brushes, verti-groomers add significantly to the purchase price of a mower, but on the other hand can result in a considerable long-term saving in labour costs as their use means much less scarifying as a separate operation. Indeed, except where there is a thick established thatch or fibre layer, which requires severer scarification than mower reels are capable of, they might obviate the necessity of purchasing a separate scarifier as such, and a club might hence achieve an overall saving by meeting the high initial cost of a mower so equipped.

Returning to the main subject of mowing itself, it may seem an instance of stating the obvious but clippings should invariably be boxed off. Allowing them to fly, besides being of course undesirable from the bowlers' point of view, also spreads weed grass and broad-leaved weed seed (annual meadow-grass seed is particularly pernicious) and increases problems with earthworm activity and thatch formation. It has been argued that allowing clippings to fly can be an advantage under particular conditions - long drought periods are the instance usually cited - when clippings can act as a mulch and preserve otherwise sparse growth by conserving moisture. On balance however, effective irrigation is a better solution to drought problems than removing the box from the mower.

The cutting height is a most important subject - the mowing level must be correct for the season and should be checked at regular intervals. Mowing height is defined as the vertical distance between the cutting edge of the fixed bottom blade (sole plate) of the mower (not the revolving cylinder) and a straight edge placed across from the front to the rear roller. The machine should be turned on its side to check cutting level - take care with possible spillage of petrol from the tank! With the straight edge in place across the rollers, height of cut can be checked with a ruler or with 5p coins - the latter are 1/16 in. in thickness. Height of cut adjustment is simplified if one has a mower gauge as shown in the illustration. This is simply a straight bar with a threaded hole bored at a convenient point along its length. Screwed into the hole is a bolt with a fairly large head, fitted with a wing-nut to allow it to be locked into position. The bolt is

PLATE 33. Using a mower gauge. Note the head of the bolt hooked over the fixed bottom blade of the mower.

PLATE 34. The Lloyds Palladin is a high quality motor mower suitable for bowling green use. It gives 126 cuts per yard. (Courtesy Lloyds & Co Letchworth Ltd.)

adjusted until the distance from the underside of its head to the bar is the desired cutting level. The bolt head can then be hooked over the mower sole plate and the machine's height adjustment altered until the bar is held tight over front and rear rollers. Height of cut should be checked at each end of the sole plate, otherwise an uneven cut is a possibility with the machine cutting higher at one side of its run than at the other.

The standard cutting level during the bowling season can be taken as being 5 mm ($^3/_{16}$ in.). In the case of very true flat greens where a fast finish is required, cutting to 3 mm ($^1/_8$ in.) is permissible providing there are no high spots to scalp. Care is necessary when cutting levels are set much below 5 mm ($^3/_{16}$ in.) as even the fine grasses can be weakened by very close mowing - if growth is checked by drought or otherwise poor growing conditions, then it is wise to raise the level back to the 5 mm ($^3/_{16}$ in.) standard. Persistent over-close mowing will tend to produce a thin sward with the gradual appearance of bare patches, moss and low-growing weeds. In the case of crown greens, surface levels are seldom if ever uniform enough to permit close cutting with any safety and for crown greens the cutting level should never be set lower than 5 mm ($^3/_{16}$ in.). To mow below 5 mm ($^3/_{16}$ in.) the mower must be fitted with a thinner-than-standard sole-plate.

Bowlers often place too much stress on the importance of cutting height as a method of producing a faster bowling surface. If a slow green is being produced by excessively lush growth or by an underlying thatch layer then very close mowing is not really the answer to the problem. If thatch is the cause of surface slowness then the only sensible method of improving matters is to eliminate the thatch (by scarification, aeration, etc.) as close mowing will do nothing to eliminate the cause of the problem. Where spongy thatch is present then the mower tends to sink slightly into the surface under its own weight, so it is probably cutting at a lower level than that at which it is theoretically set. In such circumstances, setting at significantly less than 5 mm ($^3/_{16}$ in.) is almost guaranteed to seriously weaken the sward in the long-term.

In the autumn at the end of the playing period when growth is gradually tailing off, the cutting level for all greens should be gradually raised until a level of 8 mm ($^5/_{16}$ in.) is reached. Cutting should continue at this setting whenever growth is taking place throughout the late autumn, winter and early spring. In frost when no growth is taking place cutting can obviously be suspended but if any growth occurs then the green should be cut, irrespective of the time of year. The grass should never be allowed to grow more than about 13 mm ($^1/_2$ in.) in height before mowing is repeated otherwise sward density will be lost, and rank grasses such as ryegrass or Yorkshire fog encouraged.

When growth rate starts picking up once again in the spring, the mowing height should be gradually lowered once again until the 5 mm ($^3/_{16}$ in.) height of cut is again reached for the start of the bowling season.

In addition to checking cutting height at frequent intervals, a good greenkeeper will also periodically check that the rotating cutting cylinder is tight against the cutting edge of the fixed sole plate (but not too tight). A well set machine should cut a piece of thin paper cleanly across its full cutting width. Sole plates should also be checked for flaws and notches which can be caused for example by hitting small stones during cutting. Damaged plates should if necessary be replaced. Poorly set machines can produce a ribbed surface or chew the grass blades rather than cutting them cleanly. Patches of the coarse weedgrass perennial ryegrass are particularly prone to this chewing effect as ryegrass leaves are very tough - it takes a sharp and well-adjusted machine to cut them cleanly.

The frequency of mowing which is required depends entirely on season, weather conditions and on how much growth is taking place, so it is difficult to lay down hard and fast rules. On average in the bowling season most greens, flat and crown, need thrice-weekly cutting but this may have to be increased if growth is heavy. Mowing should be timed to immediately precede popular playing days or important competitions.

The mowing pattern which is followed is also an important feature of good greenkeeping - the main requirement is to vary it as much as possible. Cutting a given area of a green's surface continuously in one direction tends to produce a nap or pile in the growth habit of the sward with the result that all grass blades tend to slope in one direction away from the direction of mowing. This affects the run of the wood, with the bowl rolling faster along the line of cut than in the opposite direction. This effect occurs to some extent even after a single cut, so flat rink greens should never be cut up and down the rinks in the line of play but always diagonally during the playing season. This diagonal cutting should be varied as much as possible - in practice this means commencing the diagonal cut at each of the four corners in turn as far as flat greens are concerned. For crown greens where play takes place in all directions, the mowing pattern can be even more varied with diagonal cutting supplemented by mowing parallel to the sides of the green in what is usually termed a "Union Jack" pattern. Cutting parallel with the sides can also be useful on flat greens, but only in the off-season when play is not taking place.

Careful perimeter cutting is also important. It is sometimes the practice to take a single perimeter cut around the edge of both flat and crown greens before commencing the main diagonal cutting pattern. Following such a practice rigidly does, however, mean that the mower is invariably turned at the end of each run on the same narrow strip of turf around the edge of the green, so increasing the chances of excessive wear developing around the edge. It is therefore wise to vary the procedure by sometimes taking one or two extra perimeter cuts to provide a wider turning area and so spread wear away from the edges into the body of the green. Perimeter cutting before tackling the body of the green is useful where the grass is rather long and would be flattened by turning at the ends of diagonals. Perimeter cutting before and after diagonal cutting does, however, increase edge wear.

The standard procedure is to take the perimeter cut after the mowing of the body of the green has been completed. This picks up any clippings dropped at the ends of each diagonal run and rolls out any slight marks which may have been left after turning the machine.

Some greenkeepers take this process of minimising perimeter wear one step further by setting the machine rather higher for the perimeter cut, giving a so-called "picture frame" effect. To avoid having to keep altering the setting of the mower, many greenkeepers have a second machine for perimeter cutting, this being a hand mower or small petrol-driven machine permanently set at a slightly higher level than the larger mower used over the body of the green. Picture frame cutting is of particular value in the not uncommon situation where the edges of the green curve sharply down to the ditches. Such curved edge profiles tend to develop over the years as the body of the green rises due to repeated top dressing and particularly where the inner edge of the green is inadequately supported by kerbing or ditch boards. Crown greens are particularly prone to develop this kind of edge profile. In extreme cases, the degree of slope round the extreme edge of the green makes perimeter cutting very difficult and the game itself is also adversely affected - it becomes impossible for a wood to come to rest near the edge of the green. In this situation levelling and re-building the four edges of the green is the only complete solution. Even in less extreme cases, however, it is common to see a line of mossy and thin patches around the edge of a green where the mower continuously scalps the sward as it moves along the convexly curved surface profile during perimeter cutting. Mowing at a higher level around the edge helps minimise scalping and turf weakness in such circumstances. It may, however, not be acceptable where championship bowls are to be played.

Finally, there is the question of ensuring that the mowing lines are perfectly straight across the playing surface. Greenkeepers take a pride in the straightness of the cutting pattern and it can be difficult to achieve, particularly over crown greens or rather uneven flat greens. Straight mowing is a skill only learned with practice but the trick lies basically on keeping one's eye on the end-point of a particular run rather than on the mower itself.

Rolling

Time after time one encounters bowling greens where long-term problems and a poor bowling surface are a direct consequence of the use of an excessively heavy roller in the past. The circumstances leading up to this regrettable state of affairs usually start with complaints about the unevenness or slowness of a particular green. Without pausing to consider what the cause of the slowness or unevenness might be, a well-meaning club official then advocates the use of a heavy roller and the operation is duly carried out using a machine borrowed from the nearest cricket or tennis club, or even using a vibrating road or pavement roller. Unfortunately a temporary improvement in pace or uniformity can often result from such treatment, allowing the

PLATE 35. The Ransomes 51 and 61 Super bowl mowers have been specially developed as bowling green machines. (Courtesy Ransomes Sims & Jefferies PLC, Ipswich.)

PLATE 36. A Ransomes Greenspro mower showing the Vertigrooming reel which allows light scarification. A brush is also fitted. (Courtesy Ransomes Sims & Jefferies PLC, Ipswich.)

PLATE 37. The Sisis Trulevel roller has some advantage over single rollers in that it tends to ride over low areas. (Sisis Equipment [Macclesfield] Ltd.)

PLATE 38. Grass comb and brush attachments for the Ransomes 61 Super Certes. Note the mounting brackets just behind the front roller. (Photo courtesy Ransomes Sims & Jefferies PLC, Ipswich.)

112

individual concerned to congratulate himself on curing a worrying deficiency in the quality of the surface. It is doubly unfortunate that the dire and sometimes disastrous consequences of such rolling can take quite a long time to become manifest, by which time our steam-roller enthusiast may have moved on to repeat the damage at another club.

The deleterious consequences of heavy rolling are largely a result of the increased soil compaction which it produces. This in turn can lead to poor surface drainage and a green which is even heavier in wet weather than it was before the rolling was carried out. Compaction also weakens root growth, encourages thatch development and the spread of undesirable annual meadow-grass at the expense of the required bent and fescue grasses. Moss patches and bare areas are encouraged as a result of poor grass growth and the essential uniformity of the bowling surface is lost. In a case where heavy rolling is advocated as a method of improving surface levels, it is essential to realise that a roller rides up and down major surface undulations producing an even compacting effect and doing nothing to promote a more level surface. In the case of more minor humps and hollows, a large roller could well squash down the high spots but this results in uneven soil compaction over the area of the green and again ultimately in the loss of all-important surface uniformity.

As has been previously pointed out, the commonest cause of excessively slow bowling surfaces is thatch or fibre formation in the immediate sub-surface layers. It is essential to realise that even the heaviest roller has very little consolidating effect on a thatch layer. It can be likened to rolling a layer of sponge-rubber or a deep pile carpet - the thatch simply springs back into its original thickness after the roller has passed over, leaving the surface as slow as it was before. For a thatchy green, thatch removal is the only way to improve pace and rolling is likely to make thatch development even worse. In the case of undulating surfaces the only way of improving matters is to raise hollows by top dressing, or in extreme cases to re-turf uneven areas.

It is hoped that the above is sufficient to deter even the most determined advocate of heavy rolling. The criticism is often levelled at turf experts and agronomists that they are more concerned with growing perfect and healthy swards than with providing good bowling surfaces. Their condemnation of rolling is often cited as a case in point, with critics saying that although heavy rolling may adversely affect the grass cover to some extent, it is essential for the needs of the game. This is certainly true in the case of cricket, and to some extent tennis, where compacted soils are absolutely essential if the required surface for the game is to be produced. The information given above should prove that the same is not true for bowls - a heavy roller in the medium or long-term produces a deterioration in the quality of the bowling surface as well as a deterioration of the grass sward. Good greenkeeping practices are in everyone's interest and they do not include the use of road rollers.

The use of light rollers on bowling greens is another matter entirely and there is certainly a place for a roller weighing about 5 cwt. (250 kg) in every bowling club's equipment shed. Every green, whether crown or flat, should be rolled perhaps two or three times in different directions just before play starts at Easter. This serves primarily to settle the turf after the effects of winter frost-heaving and irons out any small marks or scars. A single cylinder roller of the usual "garden roller" type may be used, or alternatively a tandem roller which features more than one roll linked on a rigid frame (the Sisis Trulevel roller is the only implement of this type commonly encountered). For start-of-season rolling, the Sisis machine should be used with extra weights in position on its frame.

Additional rolling during the playing season may be considered necessary, say to polish the surface for an important match. There is certainly no harm in this providing the work is not carried out when the green is too wet and soft. The Trulevel machine mentioned above is ideal for this purpose and should be used without its extra weights. There is, however, no need for the frequent and regular rolling which was standard practice in the days when bowling greens were invariably cut with hand-pushed mowers. It should be borne in mind that the average motor mower is a weighty machine driven by a powered roller and hence has a significant rolling action built in. In other words the green is actually rolled every time it is cut and this reduces the amount of rolling which is required as a separate operation.

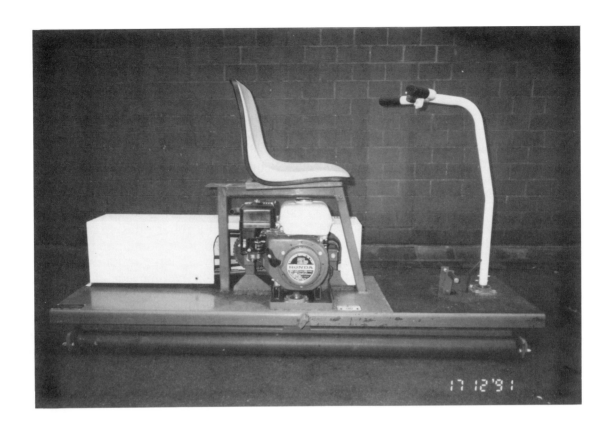

PLATES 39 & 40.   The Smooth Roll Turf Iron, developed in Australia, is a motorised roller on which the operator travels sideways.   (Courtesy Better Methods Europe of Poole, Dorset.)

An interesting and fairly recent development in bowling green rolling is the importation of the Smooth Roll Turf Iron from Australia. This motorised roll-on machine has a distinctly odd appearance - the operator sits sideways to the line of travel. Weighing 220 kg (plus of course the driver's weight) and having three 5 ft. 3 in. long rolls of only $4^1/_2$ and $2^1/_2$ in. diameter, the machine has a greater smoothing effect than older and more conventional rollers. Sisis of Macclesfield are currently developing a comparable British machine which may ultimately form the power-unit for a range of bowling green maintenance equipment. This may parallel the adoption of miniature tractors as versatile golf green maintenance power units in recent decades.

When rolling a green care should be taken to cover it uniformly and to avoid scarring when turning at the ends. Rolling should be carried out when the surface is dry and the soil not too wet and waterlogged. It should be at right angles to the line of play to be followed during the days immediately following the rolling operation.

Scarification
Originally, the terms "raking" and "scarification" were synonymous as far as turf culture was concerned, but nowadays it is usual to refer to the use of the traditional spring-tined wire rake (and similar implements like the comb mounted on the mower) as raking, while scarification (or vertical mowing or verticutting) describes work carried out using a powered rotary machine. Verti-grooming describes the lighter scarification performed by small rotary scarifiers mounted as motor mower accessories. The rotary scarifier essentially peforms the same job as the old spring-tined rake, but performs it with such enhanced efficiency that it can achieve results that could not be secured with a wire rake, even if the latter were to be used for a month of Sundays.

Before considering the rotary scarifier, it is worth noting that there is still a place for the old Springbok-type wire-tined lawn rake in bowling green maintenance. The rake would still be used, along with the hand fork, for preparing the surface of a bare patch prior to overseeding, or perhaps for repeatedly attacking a patch of coarse Yorkshire fog or perennial ryegrass to promote a gradual loss of vigour and take over by the finer grasses. It can also be usefully employed for raking out the odd patch of moss or creeping weed.

For covering the bowling surface in its entirety, however, the rotary machine is generally a far superior alternative. Large-scale wheeled or even power-drawn wire rakes are sometimes still used for overall green treatment but they tend now to be used only where powered scarifiers are unavailable.

Scarifiers are used for a number of purposes. Firstly they are used to lift and tear out the procumbent, horizontal, matted and fibrous growth which tends to accumulate in all swards. If allowed to develop, such growth in time produces a softer, slower and less uniform bowling surface. The rotary scarifier will also reduce the vigour of coarse weed grasses and creeping weeds like clover and mouse-ear chickweed and will tear out spongy moss. Regular scarification also has a beneficial effect as far as underlying thatch or fibre layers are concerned. It should, however, be appreciated that scarifiers have their limitations as far as thatch or fibre removal is concerned. They can reduce the thickness of thin superficial thatch layers and certainly slow down the accumulation of fresh thatch or fibre. They do very little, however, to attack the causes of a serious thatch problem and where such a problem exists, scarification should be only one aspect of a management programme formulated to correct the situation. Deep aeration work and the use of sandy top dressings are probably more important in the process of eliminating established thatch layers although scarification is a useful supplementary operation for tearing out the upper surface of a heavy accumulation of thatch.

Scarifiers cannot be set deeply enough to attack a thick thatch or fibre layer in its entirity - such severe scarifying would in any event destroy the grass cover. A little-and-often approach is usually best as far as scarification is concerned, with the object of producing a gradual improvement over perhaps a three year period, rather than attempting to achieve the desired result in a single pass at a very severe machine setting. Repeated light scarifying avoids excessive damage to the grass cover and playing surface. Excessively vigorous scarification can produce bare ground where annual meadow-grass and other weed seed may develop, and which reduces surface uniformity.

PLATES 41, 42 & 43. Wire rake scarifiers fitted to either hand frames or motorised machines are still used but have to a large extent been superceded by rotary machines. (Photographs courtesy of Sisis Equipment [Macclesfield] Ltd.)

PLATE 44. Rotary scarifiers work on the principal of a series of rapidly-rotating vertical blades, here shown on an American Ryan machine.

Rotary scarifiers feature a power-driven horizontal shaft on which a number of vertical blades or tines are mounted. Revolving rapidly, these should be set to cut through the sward, so tearing out matted growth in a manner which is sometimes described as vertical mowing. Some commercially-available machines have boxes which collect the considerable quantities of material which can be torn out; some are hand pushed while others feature land wheels which are powered as well as the cutting mechanism. Professional machines are petrol-engine driven but some smaller scarifiers (primarily intended for domestic lawns) are mains-electric machines. The latter are rather small for bowling green use but are certainly better than nothing.

All bowling greens should be scarified in the spring when growth has strengthened. Ideally, the work should be completed before play starts but in late springs scarifying may have to be postponed until after the green opens for play. Scarifying should only be performed during good growth so that the lines and marks left by the machine heal rapidly and cause minimal disturbance to the quality of the bowling surface. Spring scarifying is aimed at removing the soft and matted growth which tends to accumulate over all bowling greens during the winter when the mower is set high and no play is taking place.

Light scarifying during the playing season is also beneficial for most greens, supplemented by the continuous use of a comb on the mower. The rotary scarifier can be used every two or three weeks, varying the direction each time. As with mowing, scarification should be diagonal in the case of the flat rink green and should not be performed in the direction of play. Avoid scarifying during poor growth in drought periods when the recovery rate would be slow. In the playing season light scarification only should be the rule to avoid unacceptable damage to the playing surface. Mower-mounted verti-groomers scarify only very lightly and can be used very frequently in the growing season, cutting down the need for a separate scarifying operation as we have already seen.

117

PLATE 45. The Sisis Fibamo is a small budget-priced scarifier. (Photograph courtesy Sisis Equipment [Macclesfield] Ltd.)

PLATE 46. Light summer scarifying, in this instance with an old Ransomes Hahn Machine.

Autumn scarification should also be regarded as an absolutely essential annual operation for all greens. Since good growth to aid recovery on completion of the work is essential, play should finish in reasonable time to allow this end-of-season work to be carried out while growth is still fairly vigorous. As play is not taking place, autumn scarifying can be carried out rather more vigorously at this time, particularly if the green shows a thatch or fibre problem. Repeating autumn scarification two or three times may be a possibility when weather conditions are favourable and can speed up the process of thatch removal and surface improvement where these are required. When repeating scarification at close intervals, vary the angle of scarification across the green only slightly - if a second scarification is performed at right angles to a previous recently-completed pass then there can be a danger of tearing out small cubes of turf and therefore encouraging surface unevenness.

To sum up therefore, scarification should be peformed fairly frequently when growth is taking place. Autumn work can be rather more severe than spring or summer scarifying but care should be taken to avoid excessive damage to the bowling surface. Where there is a thatch or fibre problem, the frequency or severity of scarification could usefully be increased but again players should not be unacceptably inconvenienced in the short-term. As with all other machines, scarifiers should be maintained in good working order. Blades can wear down quite quickly and it is essential to fit a new set before the old ones become really short with rounded points. Experienced greenkeepers know that a scarifier with worn tines has only a fraction of the effect of a better maintained implement.

Aeration

To put it simply, aeration work consists of making holes in the surface of a bowling green down into the underlying soil profile. A wide range of tools are currently available for aeration work, ranging from the lowly hand fork to sophisticated powered machines. The range of equipment obtainable includes hand-pushed drum-type aerators but since the tines of the machine must penetrate at least 75 mm (3 in.) below the surface (and preferably much more), the lighter non-powered machines are of limited value, particularly where soils are compacted, as they tend not to penetrate deeply enough. For really effective aeration one is therefore left with a choice between the simple hand fork and the petrol-engined machine. Two types of mechanism are utilised for the powered machines. Some (the drum-type) have a series of tines mounted on a roller-like rotating device, the tines being driven into the surface by the forward motion and weight of the machine. The second group of aerators (the punch-type) have tines which are power-driven into the soil by cam action. A number of patterns of tine are available for use with aerating equipment, these being basically classifiable as flat knife or chisel, round solid or hollow coring varieties.

Aeration work is aimed at improving surface drainage, increasing the soil air supply, encouraging root growth and relieving the compacting effect of the players' feet. Indirectly, it also improves soil structure and hence sward health, increases drought resistance (by deepening the root zone) and assists the natural breakdown of fibre or thatch layers. It assists the latter both by speeding up the penetration of water down into the green foundation and by promoting the activity of naturally occurring soil fungi and bacteria which feed on and break down such accumulated organic matter.

Aeration work of one form or another is an essential primary maintenance operation which must be completed on every green every year on at least one occasion if a deterioration of the bowling surface is to be prevented. The standard practice is to carry out aeration as part of the routine autumn end-of-season work - usually after scarifying but before top dressing. For greens where there are no outstanding soil problems (like thatch layers or very poor surface drainage), autumn aeration using the flat knife or chisel tine is adequate - this type of spiking is relatively simple and speedy and usually causes minimal surface disturbance. A green would normally be covered at least twice in different directions in the autumn to increase the effectiveness of the operation. As mentioned above the machine should penetrate at least 75 mm (3 in.) although generally the deeper the better. Some machines will now give up to 175 mm (7 in.) spiking depth. The conventional drum-type machines are perfectly adequate for work of this kind. Overall machine spiking can often be usefully supplemented by additional hand forking of obviously weak or compacted areas - the rink ends of a flat green for example. The hand fork should be inserted at close intervals (every 75 mm - 3 in.) and as deeply as possible. The fork should be used straight up and down to avoid prising and raising the turf, holding the turf down with the feet if necessary when withdrawing the fork.

PLATE 47. Slit tining is not recommended during the bowling season as slits can open out in dry weather to give an uneven playing surface, as has occurred here.

Such slit tining with flat knife tines is certainly useful where there are deficiencies in soil conditions, but where obvious sub-surface problems exist it is often preferable to carry out a more severe form of aeration using hollow coring tines. These, it will be remembered, were developed by William Paul in Paisley, Scotland in the early 1920s. Hollow tining actually removes a finger-like plug of turf and is particularly effective for removing thatch or fibre, encouraging root growth and breaking up any compaction or root limiting layers which lie within reach of the tine. Possible hollow tine penetration is up to about 125 mm (5 in.). Although shallow hollow tining is possible with the drum-type of spiker, the punch-action machines are to be preferred as they penetrate more deeply and have a cleaner action with less surface disturbance.

Hollow tining was traditionally carried out using hand forks and this still produces perfectly satisfactory results. To hand hollow tine fork an entire green is, however, a laborious, time-consuming and tedious job - it takes 2-3 weeks of effort to cover an average sized green. Mechanical hollow tining is therefore infinitely preferable from the point of view of the greenkeeper's welfare! There is, however, no reason why hand hollow tining should not be performed over restricted areas of the green - where players concentrate and create particular compaction problems or where there are obvious signs of particular weakness.

Although autumn is the main season for aeration work, there is no reason why the work should not be repeated at other times. For greens with compaction, thatch or drainage problems this of course speeds up the process of improvement. Overall hollow tining is very seldom recommended more than once each year but slit or solid tining can be repeatedly performed with beneficial results. Most greens for example can be improved by slit tining in late autumn, winter and early spring providing one is careful to choose periods of suitable weather. The work should obviously be postponed during frost, snow or very heavy rain. There is also a case for some aeration work during the playing period, although care is necessary to avoid undue interference with play. A poorly drained green in a wet summer could well be spiked at intervals and spiking can also be a useful precursor of fertiliser treatment as it helps the application to penetrate the surface, particularly in the case of a thatchy or fibrous green.

Caution must, however, be exercised if spiking in summer, particularly if the green's water supply is less than adequate. The danger lies in the spike holes opening out as the surface dries to leave an uneven bowling surface. This problem can be minimised by using round solid tines in the summer rather than the flat slitting type but damage can still occur in drought. On the other hand spiking prior to artificial watering can increase penetration and effectiveness, minimising water run-off into ditches paticularly in the case of crown greens. Summer spiking is therefore a matter of judgement at the time, bearing in mind prevailing weather conditions and the particular requirements of an individual green. It is difficult to be dogmatic on this aspect of aeration work.

The hand hollow tine fork can also be used as a method of surface improvement. Many greens show undulations and hollow tining the tops of humps with the hand fork can result in slight sinkage over a period as soil cores are actually removed so allowing scope for settlement. Hollow tining with this aim in view should not be followed by top dressing. In dry periods in the summer high spots often shed water and hence become brown, sparse and mossy as compared to the lusher appearance of hollows or more level areas. Judicious hand forking of high spots can help correct this too.

One other type of machine definitely deserves mention, this being the surface pricker or Sarel roller. Such machines should be distinguished from the true aerators and spikers as they are designed for a rather different task and are by no means a substitute for the aerating equipment described above. The traditional Sarel roller is a roller fitted with about 60 short (about 40-50 mm : 1 1/2-2 in.) nail-like tines. Elm rollers were originally employed but modern versions have steel drums. An alternative design features small star-shaped steel discs which can usually be fitted, along with a selection of alternative implements like wire rakes and brushes, to a hand-pushed or motorised frame. Such machines are best termed Surface Prickers to distinguish them from the aerators proper. Such implements can usefully be used prior to summer watering to help the penetration of irrigation water. The small holes created by the machine can also increase the success of overseeding work by providing sites in which seed can germinate. They do not, however, penetrate deeply enough to relieve soil compaction, help thatch breakdown or significantly improve surface drainage.

Aeration work is therefore a routine operation which must never be neglected. One word of caution, however. One occasionally encounters bowling greens where root development is so shallow and poor that the turf has virtually no hold on the underlying soil and is in fact capable of being rolled up like a heavy carpet. Spiking is the obvious method of improving this situation by strengthening and deepening root development but one may find, particularly when attempting to use the drum-type of machine, that the turf rips and rolls up round the spiking drum so causing considerable surface damage. The answer lies in preliminary hand forking or to use the punch type of machine. When rooting has improved as a result of the use of such alternative methods, it is usually possible to revert to the drum-type spiker without undue damage.

Sub-aeration
Work of this kind may be defined as a particularly deep form of aeration work using specialised equipment designed to penetrate far more deeply below the surface than the conventional spikers covered previously. Machines of this type are expensive and would only be used at rare intervals to deal with a particular problem: they are certainly not machines which the average bowling club would need to purchase and sub-aerators are therefore always obtained on a hire basis, except possibly where a green is part of a much larger organisation with a comprehensive range of specialised equipment.

PLATE 49. A Sisis Hydromain tractor with fine turf aerator. Local authorities are increasingly turning to tractor mounted equipment for speedy maintenance of bolwing greens.

PLATE 48. There is still a place for the traditional hand fork, in this case fitted with round, solid tines (photograph courtesy Sisis equipment (Macclesfield) Ltd).

PLATES 50 & 51. Hollow tining using a punch-type aerating machine, the Ryan Greensaire, and a close-up of the extracted cores.

PLATE 52. **Increased root growth in the hole left by hollow tining. Note the layered profile of this old-established green.**

Available subaeration equipment falls into four categories:

[a] Sub-soilers depending on their action on a vibrating share which is dragged through the soil. Such equipment, although successful on football pitches etc., cannot really be employed for a bowling green due to the danger of disrupting surface levels and because manoeuverability of the equipment is so restricted by surrounding ditches and banks.

[b] Heavy spikers which drive long tines down into the surface, performing a prising action before withdrawal. The Charterhouse Verti-Drain machine (in its smaller versions known as the Popular and Captain) has been widely used on bowling greens, particularly in the Local Authority situation and can produce impressive results in the case of poorly drained or very compacted greens. A careful operator is, however, required - the entire green surface must be evenly penetrated and such tractor-mounted equipment must therefore be carefully reversed into corners etc. to ensure uniformity of effect and to minimise wheel-marking. Some surface heaving may result and this may be unacceptable on flat-rink greens, even if the operation is carried out circumspectly and under ideal ground conditions. Nevertheless, Verti-Draining has produced excellent results on a number of greens - the tines can penetrate 10 in., although under fairly dry conditions radiating soil cracks are produced to a much greater depth. This effect is lessened if the soil is too wet. On the other hand, if the green is too dry then the machine will either not penetrate adequately or tear turf off the surface. The Verti-Drain and its tractor is a fairly large unit which may not be able to pass through the narrow entrance-ways, which are a feature of some bowling clubs. The operation is best performed in late August or early September, although obviously this creates difficulties as far as bowling fixtures are concerned. Heavy top dressing with sand or sandy compost is advisable immediately after Verti-Draining - if this is well worked down the holes left by the tines then semi-permanent sand-filled drainage channels are created, which have a lasting effect.

Verti-Draining is therefore a rather difficult operation as far as bowling greens are concerned and can produce significant surface level changes. It should therefore be contemplated only where there are very serious deep compaction and drainage problems so that the improvement gained far outweighs the sometimes problematical side effects.

[c] Machines which force a long probe or probes into the soil profile and then inject high-pressure air through the tine point. The Robin Dagger and Terralift machines are currently available. Much of the effect of the air-blast in dissipated if the probe penetrates into an underlying ash or gravel drainage carpet so careful depth setting is required. This problem does not of course arise in the case of greens which do not have underlying features of this kind. Careful usage can produce excellent results but here also some heaving and alteration of surface levels can be a consequence.

[d] Recently developed equipment (the Toro HydroJect) directs high-pressure water jets at the surface. Penetration is 3 in. down to 20 in., the latter using repeated water pulses over the same spot. Good results have been claimed for golf greens, but at the time of writing experience of such equipment is very limited as far as bowling greens are concerned and one must reserve judgement as to effectiveness until more data are available.

There is one alternative to machine sub-aeration which should not be forgotten - the hand fork. Some models of hand fork frame are available to which extra-long (180 mm : 7 in.) deep drainage tines may be fitted, these being of the round-sectioned solid type. It is appreciated that hand forking the entire surface of a green is a laborious operation but it is certainly a viable alternative to the use of sub-aeration machines to relieve deep compaction and improve water penetration down to the gravel foundation layer. Surface disruption need not be an inevitable consequence of hand forking, providing the fork is used in a straight up and down manner without an obvious prising action. There is also of course the possibility of hand forking only selected areas of a green, concentrating perhaps on weak, wet or obviously compacted areas. Subsequent sanding can again be a useful operation.

Surface care
Under this heading are included operations aimed primarily at preparing the green's surface for play. Other benefits are also obtained however, such as minimising the chances of a damaging attack of fusarium patch disease.

One of two types of hand implement are normally used for this purpose, the switch or the brush. The switch, traditionally of bamboo but now usually of metal tubing with a fibre-glass extension piece, is simply a long flexible rod which is used with a vigorous side to side motion, progressively covering the entire playing surface. The drag brush, a 4-6 ft. wide brush with whalebone (or now more commonly synthetic) bristles, is simply dragged behind the greenkeeper until the whole surface has been covered.

Switching or brushing disperses any worm casts or deposits of grass clippings which may have been left by the mower. The main aim of the work is however to remove morning dew from the grass blades. A cleaner, drier and faster bowling surface results. A third variety of implement is sometimes used for the same purpose, this being a specialised type of roller with very light narrow rolls perhaps 7 ft. long and of only 3 in. in diameter. When dragged over the green, the rapidly spinning rolls disperse water back into the soil and facilitate rapid surface drying. Dew rollers work best on flat greens with good surface levels.

During the playing season, the ideal is to carry out one of the above operations each and every morning before play commences, primarily from the point of view of maintaining a clean playing surface. It is, however, an advantage to carry out the work during the off-season as well, particularly during the early spring and late autumn - the seasons when fusarium patch disease is most likely. In fact greens would benefit from the work being completed each morning throughout the year if this is practicable, although obviously not during winter frost or snow, or during continuous heavy rain. The fusarium fungus is most active during damp misty weather and keeping a green as dry as possible is a significant method of control, much more economical that repeated fungicidal treatment, particularly if an unpaid volunteer can be found to carry out the task each morning.

Switching or brushing may also be used as a preliminary to mowing, to prevent worm casts being smeared by the mower for example. Brushing also has the added advantage of acting like a very mild form of scarification, helping to raise creeping growth up into the blades of the mower. In this respect, however, it is not nearly as efficient as rotary scarification or the constant use of a comb on the mower. Grooming prior to mowing is of course always worthwhile as a better cut is obtained on a clean and dry surface. This simple operation therefore has many advantages and should never be neglected if a first-class playing surface is to be achieved.

As a footnote to the above, one groundsman (Chris Parsons of Aylesbury Vale DC) has refined morning dew brushing into what is virtually an art-form. By brushing different sections of a green in different directions, extra-ordinary patterns of stripes and squares can be produced - even a dart-board design - giving a new dimension to the Art of Bowling Green Maintenance.

PLATE 53. The long tines of the Charterhouse Verti-Drain sub-aerator.

PLATE 54. The surface pricker typified by this Sarel roller is an essential summer maintenance tool. (Photo couresty H. Pattisson & Co. Ltd.)

Times 4889 *Removal* 4926 *P+w.*

PLATE 55. Dispersing dew with a drag brush.

127

PLATE 56. Dew dispersal using a dew roller - the 7 ft. Pattison Twindew roller.

CHAPTER 8
MODERN BOWLING GREEN MAINTENANCE:
fertiliser, lime and top dressing

When dealing with the subjects covered by the above heading, it is first necessary to define our terms as fertiliser treatment and top dressing tend to be confused on occasions. Let us therefore make it clear from the outset that fertiliser treatment involves the use of chemicals in relatively small quantities, aimed at meeting the nutritional requirements of the growing sward. Healthy growth is hence maintained and the effects or wear and continual mowing counteracted. On the other hand, the term top dressing describes the application of relatively bulky materials (such as soil, sand or compost) at much heavier application rates than would be appropriate for fertilisers. Top dressing may well have some useful nutritional properties but it is primarily used to improve the physical properties of the soil and to maintain a suitable playing surface by its levelling effects, etc. Here, the question of plant nutrition and fertiliser will be considered first, and top dressing later in the chapter. Lime is a separate question, the material being used to correct excessive soil acidity, and will also be covered later in this section.

FERTILISER
To produce healthy grass growth of the desired turf a number of requirements need to be satisfied. These include:-

[1] A minimum light level.
[2] A minimum temperature.
[3] A carbon dioxide supply to leaves.
[4] Oxygen supply to leaves and roots.
[5] An adequate but not excessive supply of water.
[6] Good root hold.
[7] The absence of excessive acidity and of toxins.
[8] A minimum of competition from other plant species.
[9] A supply of a balanced range of mineral nutrients.

Some of these factors can be controlled to a degree, others cannot. For example, good construction and careful aeration work can influence oxygen supply to roots, (and, conversely, escape of toxic gases), water retention in the soil and root hold: use of selective herbicides can reduce competition: choice of topsoil along with lime and high pH top dressings and the type of fertiliser used can influence the effects of some toxins and the rate of acification of soil: and, of course, we can apply fertilisers to improve the supply of individual plant nutrients. Light can be only improved by eliminating shading, while water can easily be applied artificially if rainfall is deficient. We cannot influence day length or overall supply of essential gases.

So, although the total plant environment cannot be fully controlled, it can still be seen that to have best effect fertiliser treatment must be part of an integrated maintenance programme which is fully aligned to the needs of each particular green. Hence, fertiliser treatment is in no way the be all and end all of good turf culture.

Turf nutrition
In bowling green culture the greenkeeper manipulates grass growth in such a way as to produce a playing surface for this particular game. As surface requirements for different sports vary widely it is necessary to have to select particular grasses or groups of grasses which will, under treatment, provide the characteristics sought. The growth of each type of turf grass plant is a crucial factor in this selective process, both the way in which individual species grow and their rate of growth. The ultimate aim of fertiliser treatment should be as a tool to persuade the right kind of turf to grow at such a rate as to produce the right playing surface, without creating a requirement for unnecessary treatments (e.g. excess mowing or thatch removal) and to encourage it to be sufficiently hardy to recover from periods of wear or climatic stress. This might be termed optimum growth.

The nutrient which stimulates plant growth is nitrogen. So if there are no other limitations to healthy grass growth (as listed above) then applying extra nitrogen will make the grass grow faster. Careful use of nitrogen aids a good turf density, good resistance to wear, helps the grass plant to overcome climatic stress, and stimulates an attractive colour. Under-use of nitrogen on turf grasses can lead to a thin, bumpy, disease-prone sward, while over-use of nitrogen causes a lush, drought-susceptible, thatchy and, again, disease-prone turf. Over-use may also change the botanical composition of the sward, encouraging unwanted annual meadow-grass and tending towards producing an excessively slow bowling surface. What is the right amount of nitrogen to apply per year varies from one site to another, as well as between turf types, and is best assessed visually.

Nitrogen is, in many situations, the only fertiliser element required to promote the necessary amount of grass growth on a bowling green. However, if there is an imbalance in the soil of any other nutrient needed for healthy growth of a particular grass species, then the grass plant may not be able to make best use of nitrogen supplied. So, in certain situations there may be a requirement to supply additional elements at some period in the year as part of a fertiliser programme. Such a need is determined by soil analysis in a chemistry laboratory because this cannot be assessed visually, as was noted in Chapter 6.

Soil analysis

To be able to grow satisfactorily, any plant needs to extract suitable quantities of each of the following elements from its environment, i.e. the soil solution and air:-

Macronutrients			**Micronutrients**	
Carbon	)	Chlorine	)	
Hydrogen	) from air and water	Boron	)	
Oxygen	)	Iron	)	
		Manganese	) from soil solution	
Nitrogen	)	Zinc	)	
Potassium	)	Copper	)	
Calcium	) from soil solution	Molybdenum	)	
Magnesium	)			
Phosphorus	)			
Sulphur	)			

The overall quantities of elements required by a plant are very small, but those of micronutrients are extremely tiny (measured in parts per million). Indeed, too much of some, e.g. zinc or copper, in a soil can be toxic. For sports turf grown on soil in Britain micronutrient deficiencies are very rare, and indeed severe deficiency of any nutrient (other than N) is not very common. However, low levels of potassium and phosphorus in particular do occur. What would be considered a deficient level of any one nutrient varies between the different sward types (e.g. between bent grass and annual meadow-grass turf), soil types and whether or not an established sward is being treated. The levels present are determined by soil analysis and should be regularly monitored - with a soil which has some clay content this might be carried out every 3 years - as trends are more important than set values.

For bowling greens constructed of soil/sand mixes with a high sand content, soil analysis is of even greater importance because changes can take place far more quickly, e.g. leaching of potassium and magnesium is very rapid in comparison with a soil which contains some clay, and a wider range of nutrients may be leached too. This rapid leaching is due to a reduced or eliminated clay content, a low organic fraction and fewer or no soil aggregates. Use of the correct sand type in very sandy constructions will help to offset this to some extent. But, basically, in very sandy constructions additional nutrients (potassium in particular) may be needed per annum for the turf grasses to make best use of the nitrogen supplied. Hence, in such situations soil analysis might be carried out annually. Indeed, the nitrogen supply should be increased too because of this rapid leaching.

Nitrogen level is not usually measured during soil analysis because the soluble forms supplied during fertiliser treatment are very mobile and readily washed down from the zone which can be tapped by roots. So there is negligible carry-over of added nitrogen from one year to the next. Therefore, it can be assumed that a fairly constant amount of nitrogen will need to be supplied each year, and this can be visually assessed fairly easily.

A further measurement made during soil analysis procedures is that of pH. This pH figure reveals the reaction of the soil, i.e. whether or not it is acid and the degree of acidity. For the purposes of turf culture a figure of less than pH 6.5 is considered acid. The degree of acidity is important to fertiliser studies because this affects the availability of certain nutrients to grass roots. So in a very acid situation, even if a particular element is present in sufficient quantity in the soil its chemical form may prevent it entering the soil solution. Increasing acidity also increases the level of organic matter in the soil as breakdown is slowed while, at the same time, it reduces the capacity of the organic matter to reduce leaching. A pH of 5.0 to 5.5 is probably theoretically ideal for an inland bowling green but the quality of the playing surface is a more important consideration than the pH level. A green which is theoretically over-acid but which plays extremely well should not, for example, be limed. The low pH should, however, be borne in mind if difficulties in maintaining an adequate sward do start developing. It is easy to over-estimate the significance of pH in practice and the pH figure should only be looked at in the context of the characteristics of a particular green as a whole.

Sources of nitrogen (N)
In a natural situation nitrogen is supplied to grass plants mainly through the breakdown of the soil organic fraction. This process takes place very slowly and in a heavily used sports turf situation is usually insufficient for promoting the grass growth required for the plants to tolerate intensive wear and maintenance. So nitrogen fertiliser should be supplied in sufficient quantities per annum to compensate for this deficit, and this quantity can vary according to soil type, turf type and intensity of wear.

Grass plants can take up nitrogen in the form of ammonium (NH_4) and nitrate (NO_3) but of the two the ammonium supply is somewhat more difficult for the plant to tap as ammonium becomes attached to the clay and organic fractions in soil but it is then converted to nitrate in a short time. For a very quick reaction in growth, nitrogen is supplied in nitrate form, e.g. ammonium nitrate. To reduce the initial flush to a small extent just the ammonium salt is supplied as in, e.g. ammonium sulphate: this would be normal in bowling green treatment.

The fertilisers noted above tend in some degree to make topsoil more acid with time and this is an important feature fertilisers for use on turf. Experimental and practical evidence has shown this to be helpful in maintaining the playability of a turf surface. Acidic fertilisers achieve this by discouraging: [a] invasion of the turf by weeds and moss and; [b] profuse development of worm casting, as can occur through long-term use of a fertiliser such as calcium nitrate which tends to foster alkalinity.

On high quality fine turf like bowling greens extra sources of nitrogen are often added to those materials mentioned above. These are organic sources such as dried blood and finely gristed hoof and horn meal. Such organic sources release their nitrogen rather more slowly than ammonium sulphate (the most commonly used inorganic nitrogen source), so they prolong the overall period of response by the grasses to one dressing of fertiliser. They also help to slow down the effect of reduced drought tolerance which can arise as a result of repeated, long-term use of ammonium sulphate.

The nitrate form of nitrogen is very readily leached because it is so soluble. Where leaching can be a significant problem, e.g. on sandy constructions, more control over the rate at which soluble forms of nitrogen are released into the soil solution may be required (similarly, where the expense of labour to apply fertiliser regularly is a criterion). In such situations the use of slow release fertilisers is becoming increasingly popular. There are now a number of slow release products commercially available for use on turf. The oldest type is ureaform which contains a range of different chemical compounds. These compounds vary in their solubility in the soil and therefore also in the rate at which break down takes place increases with soil moisture and temperature. Isobutylidene diurea (IBDU) is used as a slow release nitrogen source in a range of fertilisers, often combined with a quick release nitrogen source. The solubility of IBDU is low and as soil moisture content increases, its breakdown to soluble urea increases. It is also affected by temperature - at less than $10^{\circ}C$ ($50^{\circ}F$) very little nitrogen release occurs.

Sulphur-coated urea is comprised of soluble urea surrounded by a coating of sulphur. The urea enters into the soil by diffusion through the coating or by degradation of the sulphur. Again, the rate of nitrogen release increases with soil temperature. However, its slow release properties are impaired by any mechanical damage of the coating, which may occur when mowing a green when the fertiliser is still visible on the surface. This material is at present used only on coarse turf areas like football pitches.

A different approach to producing a slow release nitrogen fertiliser is to add a nitrification inhibitor to the product. This works through restricting the conversion of ammonium to nitrate by soil bacteria which means that fertiliser nitrogen remains as the ammonium form for a longer time in the soil. As mentioned above, the ammonium becomes attached to the clay and organic fraction in soil. The nitrification inhibitor used most commonly for turf fertilisers is dicyandiamide (DIDIN). This chemical itself contains nitrogen which is only slowly released to the turf.

Sources of other elements

[a] Potassium (usually measured as potash, K_2O)

A variety of compounds can be used to provide a source of potassium but the two most common are potassium chloride and potassium sulphate. Of these the potassium sulphate is the easier to handle and store and is less prone to scorching. Potassium chloride is widely used in commercial formulae. They are similar in effect on turf and the potassium is quickly made available.

Leaching of potassium is controlled by the clay fraction of the soil, hence in very sandy soils extra potassium is likely to be needed in the annual maintenance programme than is the case with turf grown on a loam soil. The amount of potassium supplied annually in fertiliser should be determined by soil analyses carried out where appropriate.

The availability of potassium has influences upon drought tolerance, susceptibility to fungal attack and nitrogen up-take by turf grasses.

[b] Phosphorus (usually measured as phosphate, P_2O_5)

Like nitrogen, phosphate fertiliser is available as organic and inorganic fertiliser forms. Bone meal is an organic source from which the phosphate is a slowly soluble form and so is only made slowly available to the grass plant. In addition, bone meal contains a small amount of slow release nitrogen. This material was frequently used as an autumn/winter fertiliser in times past but this procedure has now fallen into disuse. A further, and perhaps more important, use of bone meal is as a conditioner to prevent setting when superphosphate is included in a compound mix of powder fertilisers.

Superphosphate is the commonly used inorganic source of phosphate. The phosphate supplied is largely soluble in the form in which it is applied but it is quickly converted into fairly insoluble forms in soil (and in sand).

Relatively insoluble forms of phosphate held within any rootzone material maintain a balanced quantity of phosphate in the soil solution. Repeated applications of phosphate fertiliser add to this insoluble reserve and can lead to accumulations of this material in rootzones, which in turf can maintain a fairly constant high concentation of phosphate in the soil solution. However, in increasingly acid situations this release of available phosphate is progressively slowed down.

High concentrations of available phosphates are considered to have detrimental effects on the quality of established fine turf. Unfortunately, until a few years ago, there was a tendency to use far too much phosphate in bowling green fertiliser programmes. This is clearly indicated by the results tabulated in the survey reprinted here as Appendix A. High phosphate levels have a tendency to favour the growth of the undesirable weed grass, annual meadow-grass, at the expense of the desirable bent and fescue grasses. It is not the only factor which encourages annual meadow-grass, but it is an important one and not over-fertilising with phosphate is a relatively easy way of discouraging the spread of this undesirable species. Phosphate should therefore only be included in bowling green fertilisers when soil analysis shows it to be necessary to prevent actual deficiencies developing. It should be understood that the behaviour of phosphate in soils is extremely complex and judging requirements is very difficult.

Phosphate is required for a vast range of chemical compounds which are involved in plant structure and metabolism, but still in terms of quantity the weight is fairly small and what the grass plant takes from the soil solution is in most circumstances replaced from the rootzone material's large store.

[c] Magnesium
Magnesium is usually applied to turf in the form of magnesium sulphate, often in solution as a spray. Deficiencies of this element are not very common and treatment is usually a one-off application. Such deficiencies may occur where very rapid drainage rates have been achieved (e.g. in sandy constructions) or in situations where the rootzone is very acid. In this latter case, if an application of lime is appropriate too, then both calcium and magnesium could be supplied by using ground dolomite (magnesium limestone).

[d] Other elements
Recorded deficiencies of other elements are extremely rare and are confined to particular soil types. These other deficiencies being so rare indicate that the quantities used by turf grasses are so small they do not deplete reserves (even when clippings are removed) and/or the quantities used are replaced, i.e. through clippings returned or as impurities in fertilisers applied or when top dressing.

PLATE 57. Using a spinner-type fertiliser distributor - note the pattern of spread.

133

Approximate rates at which individual material might be applied

	per 100 sq.metre	or	per 100 sq. yd.
ammonium sulphate	1.5 kg		3 lb.
dried blood	0.5 kg		1 lb.
hoof and horn meal	0.5 kg		1 lb.
superphosphate	1.0 kg		2 lb.
bone meal	0.5 kg		1 lb.
potassium chloride	0.5 kg		1 lb.
potassium sulphate	0.5 kg		1 lb.
ferrous sulphate (calcined)	0.5 kg		1 lb.

[e] Iron

While iron is an essential nutrient to plant growth the primary reason for its inclusion in fertiliser mixtures is not for this purpose. Calcined ferrous sulphate is added because it helps to control mosses and weeds (through scorching), and worm casting (by acidifying the turf surface). It also has some effect in discouraging fusarium patch disease. It has a further advantage (especially to commercial manufacturers) in that application induces an attractive dark green colour. However, regular repeated use of ferrous sulphate is not something to do with abandon as there can be drawbacks due to the extra acidification of the topsoil and inducing drought susceptibility in turf.

Fertilisers for fine turf

For fine turf areas such as bowling greens where bent and fescue turf is sought, fertilisers can be produced by on-site mixing of sources of nutrients, to suit the requirements of the turf at each Club. Such a procedure has a further advantage in that the cost can be as little as one third of the price of a similar programme using proprietary fertilisers. Of course, dry shed space is essential for storage as is a clear concrete floor for mixing. The fertiliser programme applied to such fine turf areas should be, as with all turf fertiliser programmes, based on sources of nitrogen. If soil sample analysis has shown that other elements need to be added for the grasses to make best use of the nitrogen supply, then these are usually most effectively included as part of the spring dressing. (On sandy constructions it may be wise to include potassium with every dressing of nitrogen.)

A single dressing of fertiliser should contain no more than say the equivalent of 40 kg/ha of nitrogen to minimise losses through leaching. As an example, such a dressing could contain:- *4gm/m*

	per 100 sq.metre	or	per 100 sq. yd.
ammonium sulphate	1.5 kg		3 lb.
dried blood	0.5 kg		1 lb.
fine hoof and horn meal	0.5 kg		1 lb.

For ease of spreading such powder mixes it is usual to bulk with a carrier as sandy compost top dressing or suitable sand at up to 14 kg/100 m^2 (28 lb/sq. yd). The carrier must be dry.

A fertiliser programme for fine turf might simply consist of at most 3 dressings of the inorganic plus organic nitrogen-only mix as above (or with variations) plus carrier, spread at intervals throughout the growing season to maintain an even turf density under close mowing. Nitrogenous fertilisers must not be applied any later than the end of August - lush autumn growth is very prone to fusarium disease attacks. For this reason it may be wise to use ammonium sulphate and iron alone for the last August dressing, leaving out the organic nitrogen.

Nowadays, most clubs purchase commercial fertiliser for convenience, e.g. to save mixing or to apply fertiliser in a mini-granular form. Sometimes, however, it is difficult to locate a proprietary fertiliser with the right balance of nutrients to suit the particular turf at any one club or which is readily available at reasonable cost. Also while the balance of a commercial fertiliser may be right, the form in which nutrients are supplied is not usually stated, e.g. whether or not the inorganic content is acidifying or what organic source has been used.

PLATE 58. A linear or box-type fertiliser distributor (left) compared to the spinner type of machine.

PLATE 59. Using a belt-feed linear fertiliser distributor (photograph courtesy Sisis Equipment [Macclesfield] Ltd.)

135

Past experience suggests that many greenkeepers tend to use too much nitrogen during each growing season giving perhaps three applications of nitrogen following after the spring treatment whereas in fact they should only be giving one or two. In this the object is to produce an attractive-looking green - many bowling greenkeepers take a pride in maintaining their square of perfectly even coloured dark green turf. Such pride is commendable, but it should always be borne in mind that a bowling green is primarily a playing surface and not an ornamental lawn. Heavy fertilising may produce excellent turf appearance but lush growth can slow down a bowling surface to an excessive degree and necessitate almost daily mowing. One should therefore always remember that a good bowling surface more often results from minimal but adequate fertiliser treatment. Over-fertilising is directly detrimental to playing quality as well as encouraging problems like annual meadow-grass and fusarium patch disease.

For the average green, the spring dressing should be given when growth is established in the spring. This is usually mid-April, but later in slow springs and as one moves north up through England into Scotland. A summer nitrogen booster dressing might be given in late June and another at the end of August but one cannot be too dogmatic - timing and frequency depend on the amount of growth taking place and on the weather, etc. Giving the spring dressing early is always a temptation as it is convenient to complete the application before the playing season starts, and satisfying to promote good growth and colour for the opening of the green. This is not always possible, however - applying fertiliser too early increases the risk of the material simply washing through the green at a time when temperatures are still too low to permit grass growth to occur.

At the other end of the playing season, autumn/winter fertilisers are normally not recommended due to the dangers of encouraging fusarium. There is in any event no point in promoting strong growth when no play is taking place. There is also no point in supplying P and K at this time as in the vast majority of cases they are simply not needed.

Mini-granular, slow release nitrogen fertilisers may be useful for sandy constructions or where labour costs to spread the material are high. Generally 2 dressings per year of such fertiliser are sufficient to maintain adequate growth.

Correcting over-acidity
There is no correct pH value of soil for bowling greens and in any situation if good turf is thriving without long-term problems developing then there is no need to worry.

However, there are certain basic principles to be followed to avoid the problems which arise due to an over-acid topsoil, e.g. slow/weak growth, poor response to fertiliser, susceptibility to drought, and excess fibre development.

On very fine turf rapid changes of pH values can alter sward composition away from the desirable fescue and bent species to a *Poa annua* (annual meadow-grass) dominated turf. So if the soil becomes over-acid beneath such turf it must be corrected very slowly. Using top dressing of relatively high pH over a period can prevent topsoil becoming over-acid. Use of lime in such cases is generally to be avoided but if it has to be used then again a little at a time approach should be adopted - but take advice first. Lime applications must be based on correctly-interpreted soil analysis. Excess lime encourages worms and weeds like daisies as well as annual meadow-grass. Liming can also directly lead to attacks by the very damaging and virtually incurable take all patch disease, so liming is not something to be undertaken without a great deal of thought. If it is to be carried out, the form of lime used should be inert, i.e. either ground limestone or ground chalk, to prevent scorching.

Storage of fertilisers
fertilisers should always be stored in dry conditions but especially so if they are kept in containers other than polythene bags. Care should be taken to protect bags from sharp points or jagged edges and bags should be dropped flat rather than on their corners. To maintain dry conditions it is wise to have a platform of duckboard or similar between the floor and the bags and to ensure ventilation around the bags and in the building, though doors and windows should be closed in damp weather. The most convenient arrangement is usually to have the bags stacked in a criss-cross arrangement, keeping the height down to about six bags and certainly not more than ten bags. Always close a part-used bag to conserve the remainder of the fertiliser in good condition.

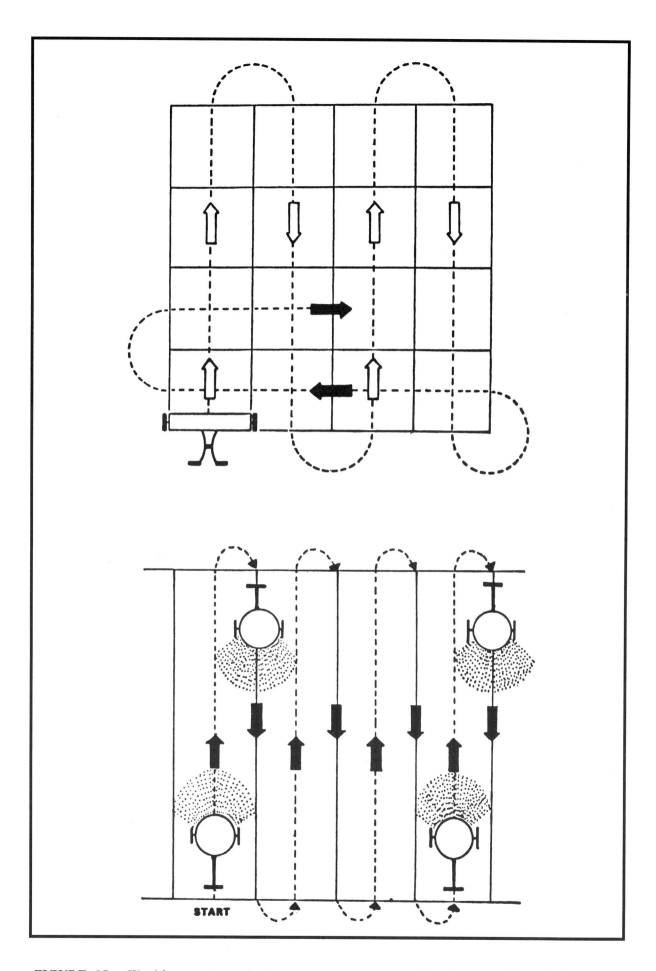

FIGURE 35. Working patterns for linear (top) or spinner (bottom) fertiliser distributors.

Application of fertilisers & fertiliser distributors

Uniformity is an important characteristic of good turf and it is very important that fertilisers be applied as evenly as possible. Uneven application results in uneven growth and excess applications (such as caused by overlapping) may damage the turf severely. Preferably, treatment should be carried out during a dry spell in broken weather when rain can be expected to fall shortly afterwards to wash in the fertiliser. If no rain falls immediately after application, where practicable, generous watering should be undertaken to achieve the same end.

Fertiliser mixtures in powder form may cause considerable scorch damage to turf, this being particularly true of site-made mixes. Bulking up such mixes with suitable dry carrier (of screened topsoil, compost or sand as appropriate) dilutes the mixture so reducing scorch risk and at the same time gives more bulk to facilitate uniform application. In practice fertilisers to be applied at 17-70 g/m^2 ($^1/_2$-2 oz. per sq. yd) have carrier added at the rate of 140 g/m^2 (4 oz. per sq. yd). Proprietary fertilisers are formulated to minimise scorch risk but even with these many people use carrier. Mixing of fertiliser with carrier must be carried out thoroughly to ensure an even and uniform mix.

For relatively small turf areas like bowling greens it is possible to spread fertiliser by hand from a bucket but the area must be strung out into square yard (or square metre) sections and each covered individually to ensure uniformity. Best results will be obtained by halving the total quantity of fertiliser and putting half on in one direction and then covering the green again at right angles to apply the other half. This is, of course, very time-consuming.

top dressing distributors are hence now very widely used, but it is a mistake to assume that these will automatically do a good job. Linear type distributors spread fairly evenly within their width (subject to uniform fertiliser in good condition, evenness of the ground, etc.) but great care is needed to achieve correct marrying of successive widths and to avoid difficulties at the ends of runs. For first-class work it is wise even with good distributors of this type to divide the fertiliser into halves and apply these in two directions at right angles (see Fig. 35).

The small distributors of the spinner type used on fine turf can give more fertiliser in the middle of their spread than they do at the outside and so to improve the evenness of spread it is wise, once again, to divide the fertiliser into two but to work so that all the turf is treated twice in opposite 180° directions. This is achieved by marking successive runs *half* a breadth away instead of the full breadth of the spread. (See Fig. 35.)

Since fertilisers differ in their density and spreadability (even the same fertiliser may perform differently on different occasions) it is wise to regard calibration marks on a machine merely as guides to a first approximation and to check the setting of the fertiliser distributor before use.

This can be done by passing the loaded distributor at working speed over an area on which suitable collectors (e.g. tin trays) have been placed strategically. The amount falling on each collector can be weighed so as to allow calculation of the rate of application.

Liquid fertilisers

Interest is frequently expressed in the possibility of the application of plant nutrients in solution, this interest no doubt being fostered by the availability of watering systems and of sprayers obtained for putting on weedkillers and fungicides. In practice the idea has severe limitations and solid applications are preferred. Restrictions on the value of liquid application include:-

[1] The requirements for solubility and compatibility limit the choice of fertilisers which can be applied in solution.

[2] Watering systems never achieve the degree of uniformity required for fertiliser.

[3] With high volume applications the liquid may infiltrate unevenly, particularly if applied to dry swards, or to uneven surfaces.

[4] With low volume applications (as in sprays) only small amounts of suitable fertiliser can be applied and even then there can be scorch risk.

[5] Soluble fertilisers may easily be leached away so frequent applications may be necessary.

Some optimistic claims have been made regarding the supposed benefits (e.g. in efficient nutrient utilisation) to be obtained by foliar nutrition, i.e. feeding plants through the foliage by means of sprays, but these are difficult to justify on valid experimental results. There is, however, a case for using them in special circumstances, e.g. to improve colour and growth in drought when there might be a ban on the use of water, so making the watering-in of powdered fertilisers difficult.

Top dressing

As mentioned previously, top dressing involves the application of bulky material, aimed at improving the quality of the underlying soil and the playing surface itself, rather than at feeding the grass plants. The top dressing materials used may have some nutritional value but this is not the primary object of the exercise.

Top dressing is the most effective method of building up a true surface, thus directly improving playing quality and also improving the uniformity and general quality of routine mowing operations. It is a far more efficient method of improving surface levels than heavy rolling which produces soil compaction and a variety of associated problems as we have already seen. Top dressing may also be used to improve surface drainage - sand is particularly useful in this respect to help ameliorate excessively heavy clay soils and to increase porosity and hence water percolation. Conversely top dressing may sometimes be used to increase drought resistance by including organic materials such as finely-ground peat. This is relatively rare in the bowling green situation however as far more British greens are too wet than too dry! Top dressing may also be used to change the characteristics of the bowling surface, for example to increase its resiliency and hence produce a faster and firmer (as well as a truer) surface.

Because top dressings often contain organic matter which acts as a slow-release nitrogen source, top dressing may have some fertilising action and regular top dressing can cut down the amount of artificial fertiliser which has to be used. In the case of new greens, top dressing may also act as a protective mulch for new-sown grass in the earlier stages of its development.

Top dressing is a vital primary maintenance operation and it is essential to top dress each green at least once per year if a good playing surface is to be formed and preserved indefinitely. In normal circumstances, top dressing is an autumn operation best timed to follow scarification and aeration work. Top dressing is best timed to immediately follow aeration as this facilitates working the material into the surface - much material drops into the tine holes, particularly after hollow tining. Top dressing must be dry for ease of application and must be applied to a dry surface otherwise the operation tends to become messy and indeed almost impossible to carry out efficiently. Scarification, aeration and the final top dressing must therefore be completed early in the autumn before the weather deteriorates too far. Top dressing should also be undertaken while some grass growth is still taking place.

Unfortunately therefore the playing season must not be permitted to drag on too long or vital autumn work will suffer and there is a danger of the bowling surface deteriorating for the subsequent bowling season. Timing of the close of play is often a bone of contention between bowlers and greenkeeper so it is to be stressed that ceasing play in reasonable time is in everyone's long-term interest.

Quantities and timing

For a standard 42 x 42 yd. flat green, 4 tons (or 4 metric tonnes) of material should be regarded as a minimum standard top dressing requirement each and every autumn. This can be quite expensive but is absolutely essential. After hollow tining and where surface levels are uneven, the requirement may often increase to 5 or 6 tons or more, and the standard required quantity also of course increases in the case of somewhat larger crown greens.

Where there are particular problems with uneven levels, poor soils, thatch, etc., the process of green improvement can be speeded up by increasing top dressing frequency to more than the standard once per year. In some circumstances it could be possible to top dress twice (at the

PLATE 60. Top dressing spreaders are not often used on bowling greens but simplify the operation considerably.

PLATE 61. Tractor-mounted top dressers have their place where several greens have to be covered, for example, by local authorities. A Sisis Hydromain Seventeen unit. (Courtesy Sisis Equipment (Macclesfield) Ltd.)

above rate) in a given autumn, giving the second application as soon as the first has been absorbed. Work would have to start particularly early for this to be practicable. Alternatively supplementary spring top dressing is a possibility. The spring dressing should be given as soon as reasonable weather occurs, with some growth taking place, i.e. before play starts. A spring application might be at half the autumn rate or possibly even at the full end-of-season rate depending on individual requirements.

Bowling greens (except new greens not yet opened for play) are virtually never top dressed during the summer playing season. Material dampened by rain or dew after application would adhere to woods during the playing period and vociferous complaints would not be unlikely. Small pieces of grit might also damage mowers if dressing were to be applied when mowing at the low 5 mm (3/16 in.) summer level.

In addition to overall autumn top dressing, it can often be useful to give extra quantities to particular parts of a green - low areas, scarred or scuffed patches, or areas of the green which have been re-turfed or re-seeded. The technique would be to give the overall top dressing first and when this has disappeared into the surface, to give extra quantities where required. This process can be repeated as long as the weather remains co-operative with some growth still taking place.

Application and working in
Top dressing materials should be screened to 5 mm or preferably a little less (particularly for spring use) to facilitate even application and easy penetration into the surface. Large particles of grit, peat granules, and so on are nothing but a nuisance if left lying on the surface and may damage the mower. They often have to be swept off which is laborious and wasteful of purchased material. Coarse material applied in autumn can still be lying around on the surface when the green is opened in the spring and scratch the surface of bowls and otherwise interfere with play. Adequate screening is therefore essential.

It is usual to spread the overall application by hand using shovels from a barrow, or from bagged material placed at convenient points over the green surface. Spreading machinery is sometimes also employed - some larger fertiliser distributors can be opened up to a sufficient aperture to allow them to be used for spreading the larger amounts required for top dressing work. Purpose-designed top dressing spreaders are also available (they are commonly used for larger areas, e.g. the golf course situation) and could possibly be hired or borrowed for top dressing a single bowling green.

After initial spreading over the surface, the top dressing should be worked in. The material should not be left lying on the surface in quantity as it can smother the grass, with the ultimate development of bare patches. Grass covered with an excess of top dressing is also prone to severe fusarium patch disease attacks. Such problems are intensified if the work is left too late in the autumn.

Several varieties of tool are available for working in top dressing materials. The chain link drag mat is particularly useful on crown greens as it tends to follow uneven surface contours and hence deposit a uniform layer of material. Drag brushes as described earlier for dispersal work, old-fashioned birch besoms, fibre glass switches or small lutes may also be employed. For flat rink bowling greens, however, where there is a need to produce truer levels (unfortunately this is usually the case), there is really only one type of implement which should be considered for the working-in of an overall top dressing. The essential, flat green, top dressing tool is a large rigid-frame lute, although a long, straight edge is a possible alternative. Lutes have the advantage of scraping material off high spots and depositing relatively more on low areas of a green, so producing a gradual level improvement. Lutes can be obtained in various widths, but for flat greens with wider the implement the better. In the case of flat rink greens where there are distinct humps and hollows the larger lutes cannot be used at first as they will scalp the turf off surface prominences. Here, it would be wise to top dress for two to three years with one of the smaller lutes (perhaps 4-6 ft. wide), before moving up to one of the larger models. Ultimately, a flat green should be true enough to allow use of a lute 9-12 ft. wide. These larger lutes have the disadvantage of being expensive and heavy (2 or 3 men may be required to drag the really large ones) but are really an absolutely essential maintenance tool if a truly level, flat

PLATE 62. Working in top dressing on a flat green with a 7 ft. Pattison Levelawn Lute. (Photo courtesy H. Pattisson & Co. Ltd.)

PLATE 63. The 30 in., 36 in., 40 in. and 48 in. Level-lawn lutes marketed by Better Methods Europe of Poole, Dorset. Suitable for more uneven flat-rink greens.

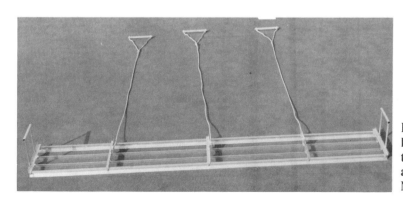

PLATES 64-67. Use of a large lute is recommended if a really true flat-green is to be developed and maintained. (Courtesy Better Methods Europe, Poole, Dorset.)

PLATES 68 & 69. Working in top dressing with a drag mat and alternatively a small lute. Such tools are most suitable for crown greens or for localised top dressing of small areas.

144

green is to be created and maintained. Any flat-rink greenkeeper who does not use a large lute is not doing his job properly. For surface level improvement, top dressing should be worked-in in more than one direction.

Hollows needing extra top dressing are best located by means of a green survey as described in Chapter 6. The location of puddles after heavy rain, long straight edges or strings laid taut across the surface can also be used to indicate low spots.

It is essential when top dressing to try to avoid forming the layered soil profiles described earlier as being a problem as far as root development and surface water penetration are concerned. This can be achieved primarily by applying top dressing to a well spiked surface with the object of incorporating the top dressing into the surface soil rather than forming a distinct deposit on the immediate surface only. (Surface deposits are, however, to some extent unavoidable where top dressing is being used to build up hollows.) Top dressing should always be carried out in association with adequate spiking. It is also important to maintain consistency of top dressing material from year to year, once the appropriate mix for a particular green has been decided upon. In the case of newly-constructed sand/soil bowling greens, the chosen top dressing should match the mix used in original construction.

Where annual meadow-grass is a problem and it would be an advantage to improve botanical composition, it is often useful to mix bent and fescue seed in with the top dressing. The sowing rate should be 35 g/m^2 (1 oz. per sq. yd). New seed can germinate in spike holes in the compost mulch provided by the top dressing. Overseeding must, however, be a part of a general management programme designed to favour the better grasses if overseeding is to stand a chance of achieving significant results.

Top dressing materials

In the past, many bowling clubs mixed their own top dressing using varying proportions of sand and topsoil, sometimes with peat added. In some cases the soil constituent was replaced by compost manufactured from grass clippings and other available sources of organic matter. Today, most bowling clubs have decided that they do not have either the space, time or labour resources for the home manufacture or mixing of top dressings, and most clubs now tend to purchase ready-made top dressings from commercial suppliers. As well as being time-consuming and laborious, home manufacture also has the disadvantage of producing an unsterilised product. Annual meadow-grass and other weed seed can therefore be spread by using such material.

Using commercial bowling green top dressings is certainly much more convenient although also relatively expensive in purely financial terms. (Labour, however, is also an expensive resource and this must be balanced against the retail price of commercial dressings.) A club is also more limited as to the exact composition of the commercially available material - one has to take what is available in many cases, although on the other hand there are some suppliers who will make up special mixes to the requirements of an individual club. Some commercial materials are sterilised and this point should be carefully checked before purchase.

Commercial dressings are most often based on varying proportions of sand, soil and peat with sand usually predominating. It is difficult to be dogmatic about exactly what make up of top dressing is required as the appropriate specification varies according to the condition of the green concerned. However, a mix containing:

6 parts (by bulk) suitable sand	or	3-4 parts (by bulk) suitable sand
3 parts screened sandy loam topsoil		1 part screened sandy loam topsoil
1 part fine peat		

might be regarded as appropriate in many situations. For a wet, heavy green the proportion of sand could well be increased and the peat content eliminated. There has been a tendency for too much peat to have been used in the past, often simply because peat is relatively cheap. An excess of peat can build up into a soft, spongy water-retentive layer, in turn leading to a heavy, wet and easily footmarked playing surface. The peat content of dressings should therefore be limited to a small percentage of the whole except in the case of very free-draining sandy greens where drought damage is a problem and where there is a clear need to increase water holding capacity (this situation is rarely encountered in practice). Peat should certainly never be used straight, without admixture with sand or soil.

In most circumstances it is a requirement that the top dressing mix should be lime-free, except in situations where gradual and gentle liming is a definite requirement, as was discussed earlier in this chapter. The sand component can contain significant quantities of lime, for example sea-side and dune sands contain broken shells, made up of calcium carbonate and therefore a very significant source of lime. This should be avoided on inland greens as a general rule. Sea sand may on the other hand be acceptable in cases where greens have been initially established in coastal situations using the local sandy soil.

Sand for top dressing purposes is an important subject and fortunately scientific knowledge of the effects of various sands on turf has increased considerably in recent years. The result is that quite rigid requirements can with confidence be laid down for the type of sand which should be employed. Sand is used to dry and firm bowling surfaces. River and quarry sands are normally to be preferred as in many parts of the country it is possible to obtain sands of this type which have a little or no lime content. Many sands are quarried on a large scale for the building or construction industry. Sands are sieved to specified grades and are hence generally consistent, or at least more consistent than many natural ungraded sands. Washed sand is particularly desirable.

When ordering sand for bowling green top dressing (or initial green construction for that matter) it is vital to specify the particle size. In the vast majority of cases a medium-coarse particle size is required, i.e. a sand with the majority of its particles (80% or more) within the range 0.25 to 0.75 mm. The sand should be free of fines because these pack down and tend to clog soil pore spaces leading to drainage difficulties. Coarse grit is difficult to work in as we have seen. It should be appreciated that sands with as narrow a particle size range as possible are required for top dressing purposes as such sands produce better drainage properties and are superior for soil amelioration purposes. Most reputable firms now supplying bowling green top dressing mixtures use sands which conform to the specification given above, but it is always wise for a purchaser to check on this point.

The sand content of the top dressing mix given earlier by way of paradigm could well be usefully increased to 80% or more for thatchy or water-retentive greens. Straight sand dressing is not often advisable due to the danger of layering in the soil profile, but could be useful after very thorough spiking for a particularly problematical green.

Top dressing is therefore an essential operation which must be completed at least once each year. Not only does it directly encourage healthy grass growth, but it also heals the scars left by play, improves soil conditions and helps form and maintain the true and uniform surface required, to a greater or lesser extent, for all varieties of bowls. Top dressing must never be neglected, otherwise sward deterioration is inevitable in the long-term.

CHAPTER 9
MODERN BOWLING GREEN MAINTENANCE
the control of weeds, moss, pests and diseases

The maintenance work covered in this Chapter consists of secondary operations which are not automatically necessary on every green every year, but only as necessary to combat a particular threat to the general condition of the green or the quality of its bowling surface.

Having said this, some degree of weed invasion is such a common occurrence that the majority of greens usually need some form of weed control work every year, even if it only consists of hand lifting the odd daisy or plantain. Weed control therefore attains almost the status of an annually required primary maintenance task and forms an obvious starting point for our consideration of the various invaders which can affect even the most well-managed of greens.

WEEDS AND WEED CONTROL
A weed can only be defined as a plant growing in the wrong place: thus a petunia or a potato would definitely be a weed if growing in a bowling green. Turf for bowls surfaces should consist of only two grass species. In such swards all other plants are weeds, which may spoil the appearance and playing surface of the sward, compete with the desired turfgrasses, and harbour diseases or insect pests.

The potential turfgrasses have been described elsewhere. Weed control in swards of these species means the elimination of broad-leaved species, rushes and mosses, and also of undesirable grasses. These may include perennial ryegrass (*Lolium perenne*) or Yorkshire fog (*Holcus lanatus*), which are seldom considered acceptable in fine turf and annual meadow-grass (*Poa annua*), which is best considered a pernicious weed in turf and not an essential turfgrass.

Chemical weed control
The term "weedkiller" is best restricted to proprietary products, sold under trade names. The active ingredients in these products are described as "herbicides". For example, three different proprietary products or weedkillers "x", "y" and "z", might have in common the same active ingredient (a.i.) or herbicide, for example mecoprop. Some weedkillers contain two or more active ingredients.

The proportion of active ingredient varies between products. Thus if two firms sell weedkillers with the same active ingredient, firm A may formulate its product with 20% a.i. while firm B formulates its product with 30% a.i. In a situation where, for example, the greenkeeper is recommended to use 2 kg/ha of the active ingredient, he could apply the 2 kg a.i. by using 10 litres of A's product per hectare but would only need to use 6.7 litre/ha of the more concentrated product of B. (For some herbicides, the active ingredient is expressed as "acid equivalent" or "a.e.". Although the two terms are not the same, they have a similar meaning for the layman, both being used to distinguish the active herbicide from the "carrier" in a proprietary product.)

All recommendations in this book, as in other independent advisory publications, are in terms of a.i. and a.e. Manufacturers, however, give rates in terms of product. Some firms specify the % a.i. or a.e. of their product on the label or in leaflets, so that rates can be compared with independent recommendations: some do not, and the user then has to rely entirely on the manufacturer's statement of the rate appropriate for a particular job.

Remember that under legislation currently coming into force, it is only permissible to use approved products and that, except for any authorised "minor uses", the conditions and restrictions on the label must be strictly observed. Approved products are listed in the blue book "Pesticides 1992" or succeeding editions. The current BAA "Directory of amenity chemicals" is also a useful source of information on appropriate products.

Always follow instructions carefully. All herbicides are potentially dangerous to the user: some are very dangerous indeed. Always be careful in measuring out and mixing concentrated herbicides: avoid inhaling the spray: and store and dispose of containers carefully. If appropriate, use gloves, protective clothing and face mask. Above all, read everything on the label before opening the container. This is now a legal requirement and all pesticide users

147

should therefore be familiar with the Food and Environment Protection Act (1985), Part 3: and the Control of Pesticides Regulations (1986).

Discouraging weed invasion

With the range of herbicides now available, most broad-leaved weeds of turf are fairly easily controlled. The same applies to rushes and mosses. The use of chemicals, however, is only one method of weed control in turf, and all weed control measures are only one part of good general management aimed at maintaining a first-class turf.

Playing under wet conditions may result in a scarred weak surface, providing conditions under which annual meadow-grass for example may thrive. Although such treatment generally cannot be avoided if turf is to fulfil its purpose, it may sometimes be possible to minimise damage and, at least, preparations can be made to deal with a foreseeable weed problem. Height of cut affects weed population. Allowing grass to grow very long and then shaving it right down will encourage weeds by weakening the grass. In fact any treatment which weakens the grass will encourage weeds; for example, careless fertiliser application can kill grass and leave bare patches which then fill up with weeds. A plentiful earthworm population results in a large number of casts; each of these smothers grass and provides a seed bed for weeds. For this and other reasons it pays to limit earthworm number. Earthworms thrive where there is lime: therefore do not use it unnecessarily. The wise use of lime and sensible fertiliser treatment have a considerable effect on the number of weeds in turf. "Alkaline-type" fertilisers and organic fertilisers encourage both earthworms and weeds. Sulphate of ammonia and sulphate of iron tend to eliminate weeds and keep them out.

Weeds may indeed serve a useful purpose by indicating turf faults or mis-management, focussing attention for example on excessive acidity, bad drainage or lack of nutrients. When this happens, it is essential to pay attention to the underlying fault. Unless this is corrected, no amount of chemical weed treatment will be effective; but if the fault is corrected, the weed will probably disappear without chemical treatment, simply because conditions are no longer favouring it.

Hand-weeding at an early stage is often the cheapest and simplest method of weed control and the only really reliable one at present for grass weeds, though it must be done efficiently, cutting weeds out at root level rather than just pulling up leaves.

Weeds are distributed in the various ways listed below, as seed or as plant fragments (especially pieces of rhizome of underground stem).

[i]   Wind.

[ii]   Flooding.

[iii]   Birds and animals.

[iv]   From weed infested banks or surrounding lawns.

[v]   Contaminants in grass seed.

[vi]   Weed-infested, unsterilised compost or other top dressing.

[vii]   Equipment (particularly mowers) and shoes.

[viii] Use of poor quality turf.

These sources of contamination should be constantly borne in mind by the greenkeeper, especially those which are under his control and particularly the last three.

The use of weedkillers

Once turf is well established, herbicides for controlling broad-leaved weeds can be used at the normal rates as shown in the table which follows. Most manufacturers also provide detailed information on the weeds controlled by their products, and a list of weeds and their reactions, closely similar to that in the table here, is given in the Weed Control Handbook Vol. 2.

A herbicide mixture widely used on turf is a 1 : 2 mixture of 2,4-D and mecoprop at rates equal to about 1 kg/ha 2,4-D and 2 kg/ha mecoprop (14 + 28 oz./acre). The three columns below show how the two elements of this broad-spectrum mixture complement each other, each controlling some important weeds but not others:

2,4-D	**2,4-D or mecoprop**	**mecoprop**
bulbous buttercup	cat's ear	mouse-ear chickweed
creeping buttercup	heath bedstraw	pearlwort
daisy	plantains	self-heal
dandelion		white clover
hawkbits		

MCPA is used instead of 2,4-D in some herbicide mixtures. It has broadly the same effectiveness as 2,4-D to which it is similar chemically: MCPA is better against mouse-ear chickweed and white clover, but possibly worse against daisy.

Mecoprop is replaced in some broad-spectrum mixtures by the related herbicides dichlorprop or fenoprop, at a similar rate, i.e. about 2 kg/ha. These are more effective against some weeds but do not give such good general weed control.

All the herbicides mentioned above are growth-regulator herbicides. After being taken into plants, chiefly through the leaves and also to a small extent through the roots, they act to destroy susceptible species, upsetting normal processes and distorting growth. Effects can be seen in twisting of leaves and freak growth within a day or two of application, but weeds may not die for four to eight weeks. Resistant species either take in less (e.g. because of angle and type of leaf, which partly accounts for selectivity between grasses and broad-leaved species) or avoid the poisoning effect in various ways.

Other herbicides act primarily by contact. Ioxynil is one such. It is valuable against broad-leaved weeds in turf, either by itself or, more importantly, in combination with mecoprop at 0.63 + 1.9 kg/ha (9 + 27 oz/acre) to make a useful broad-spectrum mixture. This has special value for some problem weeds, e.g. speedwells if applied in early spring before the speedwell flower heads form.

Calcined sulphate of iron is a slightly different contact "herbicide". It is often included in fertiliser mixtures for turf. It helps to keep weeds out of clean turf and to reduce their numbers in weedy turf. A lawn sand consisting of 1 part calcined sulphate of iron, 3 parts sulphate of ammonia and 20 parts (by weight) sand or compost at 140 g/m² (4 oz/sq. yd) will help to eliminate or at least control, many weeds, including some like parsley piert and speedwells which are difficult to control with other herbicides. Sulphate of iron is also used against moss (see later section on moss).

Common weeds and their susceptibility to herbicides

The first requirement for successful weed control is the correct identification of the weed or weeds occurring on a particular green. It is outside the scope of this present volume to provide instruction which would allow the identification of all the weeds likely to be found in bowls turf. An inspection of the green in company with an experienced greenkeeper or other expert is probably the best way in which the amateur can learn weed identification, but a Flora of the British Isles (with colour illustrations) can be helpful. As with the grasses, however, the appearance of a weed can be rather different when it is growing naturally than it is in close-mown turf. However, broad-leaved weeds are at least easier to tell one from the other than the grasses.

In the following weed list, only those weeds which are commonly encountered in bowling greens are included - it is by no means a comprehensive list of British turf weeds. The five columns to the right of the weed name show the susceptiblity or resistance of the mature weed species to the main herbicides. Abbreviations are as follows:

S	= susceptible, i.e. consistently killed by one application.
MS	= moderately susceptible: one application usually kills but second sometimes needed.
MR	= moderately resistant: two or three applications usually needed for adequate control.
R	= resistant: no useful effect.
–	= information lacking.

PLATE 70. Rosette weeds like this broad-leaved plantain are relatively easy to remove by hand and are susceptible to selective weedkillers.

PLATE 71. The moss-like weed pearlwort is one of the commonest and most troublesome of bowling green weeds.

Common Name	Botanical Name	Susceptibility				
		MCPA	2,4-D	Meco-prop	"Mix-ture"	Ioxynil/mecoprop
Creeping buttercup	*Ranunculus repens*	S	S	MR	S	MS
Bulbous buttercup	*Ranunculus bulbosus*	MS	MS	MR	MS	MR
Mouse-ear chickweed	*Cerastium holosteoides*	MS	MR	S	S	S
Pearlwort	*Sagina procumbens*	MR	MR	S	S	S
Blinks	*Montia fontana*	-	-	-	MR	-
Suckling clover	*Trifolium dubium*	R	R	MR	MR-MS	MS
White clover	*Trifolium repens*	MR	R	MS	MS	S
Birdsfoot trefoil	*Lotus corniculatus*	R	R	MR	MR	MS
Parsley piert	*Aphanes arvensis*	R	R	MR-MS	MR-MS	MS
Sheep's sorrel	*Rumex acetosella*	MS	MS	R	MS	MS
Thrift (in sea-marsh turf)	*Armeria maritima*	S	S	S	S	-
Sea milkwort (in sea-marsh turf)	*Glaux maritima*	MS	MS	S	S	-
Slender speedwell	*Veronica filiformis*	R	R	MR	MR	MS
Self-heal	*Prunella vulgaris*	MR	MR	MS	MS	MS
Broad-leaved plantain	*Plantago major*	S	S	S	S	S
Hoary plantain	*Plantago media*	S	S	S	S	S
Ribwort plantain	*Plantago lanceolata*	S	S	S	S	S
Sea plantain	*Plantago maritima*	S	S	MS	S	MS
Buck's-horn plantain (starweed)	*Plantago coronopus*	S	S	S	S	S
Lady's bedstraw	*Galium verum*	MR?	MR?	-	MR?	-
Heath bedstraw	*Galium saxatile*	MS	MS	MS	MS	MS
Daisy	*Bellis perennis*	MR	MS	MR	MS	MR
Yarrow	*Achillea millefolium*	MR	MR	MR-MS	MR-MS	MS
Dwarf thistle	*Cirsium acaule*	MS	MS	MR	MS	MS
Cat's ear	*Hypochaeris radicata*	MS	MS	MS	MS	MS
Dandelion	*Taraxacum officinale*	MS	MS	MR	MS	MR
Toadrush	*Juncus bufonius*	R	R	MR	MS	MS
Field woodrush	*Luzula campestris*	R	R	MR	MR	MR

151

PLATE 72. Mouse-ear chickweed can be troublesome, particularly early in the bowling season.

PLATE 73. White clover is a common creeping weed which can be weakened by scarifying and combing. It is moderately susceptible to mecoprop weedkillers.

The application of selective weedkillers to turf

Selective weedkillers are generally formulated as liquids for application by sprayer or by watering can.

There is a wide range of spraying equipment available. For comparatively small areas like bowling greens, a knapsack sprayer may be adequate but even better are "knapsacks on wheels" or other pedestrian equipment. A horizontal boom with several nozzles is essential if even coverage is to be achieved.

The volume of liquid applied by a sprayer depends partly on the machine itself (e.g. pump output), partly on nozzle size, and partly on speed of movement over the ground (see "Calibration of equipment" below). The generally accepted definitions of the various volumes of application are as follows:-

low volume	- 55 - 225 litre/ha	(5 - 20 gal/acre)
medium volume	- 225 - 675 "	(20 - 60 ")
high volume	- 675 - 1125 "	(60 - 100 ")

Low volume applications require greater accuracy, have greater drift risks because of finer spray, and are often less effectively taken up by weeds. High volume spraying entails more water-carrying. Medium volume, about 450 litre/ha (40 gal/acre), is normally best, but sometimes manufacturers specify a particular volume of application for a certain job.

For small confined areas near flower beds, or other places where drift must be avoided, a dribble bar or an ordinary watering-can rose should be used, or a no-drift application machine with a fluted roller. (See Plate 76.)

It is important to ensure uniform coverage and to avoid overlapping. To ensure success one should use strings or pegs as guide lines. Grass is resistant to recommended rates but not to over-application. A very skilled and knowledgeable operator may be able to make successful spot treatments with a hand sprayer or watering-can but scorch is the most common result. Aerosol cans or weed-sticks are a safter method of spot treatment but the risk of grass scorch is by no means eliminated.

Selective weedkillers based on growth-regulator herbicides may be applied at any time from spring to early autumn, but late spring applications usually give most satisfactory results. The best conditions are fine, warm weather when the soil is moist and growth is vigorous. Late autumn treatment or treatment during drought may damage turf. Heavy rain shortly after application may reduce effectiveness. Wind gives risk of drift. Catching the right weather and growth conditions is the key to success. Make sure equipment is calibrated and in good condition in advance. Don't leave this until the last minute.

It is beneficial to give nitrogenous fertiliser, e.g. sulphate of ammonia at 17 g/m^2 ($\frac{1}{2}$ oz/sq. yd) suitably bulked with carrier, 10-14 days before applying growth-regulator herbicides which act best when both weeds and grass are growing vigorously. Weed control work can thus be linked in with the normal spring fertiliser treatment.

Leave turf unmown for a period after spraying to allow intake of herbicide from foliage before it is mown off. An interval of 2-3 days is preferable, but at the very least leave one clear day before mowing.

Growth-regulator herbicides are very powerful and can affect plants even in minute doses. Risks are very real where plants other than grass and cereals are grown nearby. Do not treat areas of turf near valued plants in flower beds, etc. except on a calm day. If contamination of such plants is suspected, wash them down copiously with clean water. Clean out equipment thoroughly after use.

Combined "weed and feed" weedkillers and fertilisers are convenient for use on domestic lawns but are not very effective against the weeds normally troublesome on bowling greens. Weedkilling should therefore always be carried out as a separate operation.

153

PLATE 74. All speedwells are very difficult to eradicate with selective weedkillers but are fortunately not all that common in bowling surfaces.

PLATE 75. Sheep's sorrel (like heath bedstraw and Luzula) is one of those weeds which are useful indicators of acidic soil conditions.

154

Calibration of equipment
The following procedure will allow accurate calibration of small spraying equipment.

Steps
[1] Select type and size of nozzle to be used
eg: D/2.5/1.0

D   = deflector type nozzle
2.5   = flow rate (litres per minute)
1.0   = pressure (1 bar)

This describes the red polijet nozzle which will be used for this exercise.

[2] Set pressure
Some sprayers are fitted with a pressure control valve. The settings will vary between different manufacturers and types. For example, the Cooper Peglar knapsack may have the following:

H   = high approx 40 psi
L   = low   approx 20 psi

or   15, 30, 45 = psi
or   1, 2, 3 = bar

Remember these values are not very accurate so it may be useful to fit a pressure gauge to check the pressure being delivered.

Record your settings here

[3] Speed of walking
The next step is to record the amount of time it takes the operator to walk over 100 metres at his normal walking speed, wearing the correct protective clothing and spraying out water. You may need to get an average of 3 or 4 separate runs. Ensure you maintain a consistent rate of pumping.

Record this information here; seconds per 100 m

eg: 95 seconds

[4] Calculate speed of walking
eg: 95 seconds per 100 metres

To discover kilometres per hour (kph) divide 360 by the number of seconds it took to cover the 100 metres

eg: $\dfrac{360}{95}$ = 3.8 kph

Record your speed here   kph

[5] Spacing of nozzles or swath width if using a single nozzle
Discover this by getting the operator to hold the lance in a comfortable position and measure the swath width

eg: 1.7 metres

Record your information here

[6] Flow rate
Record the amount of water which comes out of the nozzle for the 1 minute. Do this by getting the operator to spray water into a bucket for 1 minute

eg: 2.2 litres

Record your quantity here ☐

So now we know the following, eg:

[a] width of spray (swath width) = 1.7 m
[b] walking speed = 3.8 km/h
[c] amount of water = 2.2 ltr

Record your information here

Swath width ☐ metres

Walking speed ☐ metres

Amount of water ☐ litres

[7] Volume per hectare

The next step is to discover the amount of water which will be sprayed out over one hectare.

Do this by calculating the following:

600 x flow rate per minute ÷ spraying width ÷ speed of walking = litres per hectare, eg:

600 x 2.2 ÷ 1.7 ÷ 3.8 = 204.33

rounded up to 205 litres per hectare or 18.2 gallons per acre.

Record your information here

600 x ☐ ÷ ☐ ÷ ☐ = ☐

rounded up to ☐ litres per hectare

[8] Dose rate

Now obtain the dose rate per hectare (chemical label)
For this exercise assume the rate of chemical to be applied is 5.5 litres per hectare which needs to be added to the amount of water shown in Section 7.

eg: 205 ltrs

Next, find out the number of tanks full per hectare

eg: 205 ÷ 20 ltrs (size of tank) = 10.25

Now find out amount of concentrate per tank full

eg: 5.5 ÷ 10.25 = 0.54 litres per tank full

If not you may have to use a nozzle with a different flow rate.

Record your rates here:

Litres per hectare ☐

Capacity of sprayer ☐

No. of full tanks per hectare	

Concentrate per hectare	

Amount of concentrate per tank	

Weed grasses

This subject has already been covered in Chapter 6, but it is appropriate to reiterate here that there are as yet no recommended selective herbicide treatments for annual meadow-grass or coarse weed grass in turfgrass swards, although there have been promising results with some trial materials. Various herbicide treatments developed for agricultural grassland or grass seed crops are either unsafe or still untested for the conditions of intensive turf management and use.

The best prescription for avoiding annual meadow-grass in turf is to prepare a clean seed bed, sow good cultivars of the required species and then manage the turf to favour them rather than the annual meadow-grass. Fuller details of such management are given in the earlier section on annual meadow-grass.

In the absence of herbicide treatments that can be recommended for turf, scattered plants of weed grasses are best dealt with by hand weeding (pulling or cutting out) young plants as soon as they are noticed. Always take care to remove the whole plant. "Mowing out" is a slow and often unreliable process, much improved by the use of the grass comb or Verti-Groomer on the mower.

Yorkshire fog is often a special problem. In newly-sown areas, remove young plants by hand. Once plants become well-established, they may be weakened by slashing by hand with a knife across the patch, coupled with raking during mowing, or by scarification or Verti-Grooming. The only certain treatment, however, is to cut plants out at the roots and, if necessary, replace the turf with new sod.

MOSS AND MOSS CONTROL

Basically, mosses are weeds like any other, but are distinguished from the broad-leaved weeds covered previously in that they are members of a group of relatively primitive non-flowering plants, the Bryophyta. Selective weedkillers are not effective against mosses, and other chemicals must therefore be used for their control. It should be appreciated that a persistent moss problem is often an indication that the grass cover is weak in some way and cannot therefore compete vigorously enough to keep moss patches out of the sward. In such a situation strengthening the grass cover is the long-term answer - using mosskillers is merely disguising the problem and has a purely temporary effect doing nothing to counter the underlying causes of moss invasion. A number of management factors can encourge moss - low fertility, over-acidity, excessively close mowing and so on and such malpractices must be corrected if moss trouble is to be eliminated. The golden rule is therefore to cure the cause of the moss and not to simply apply a mosskiller unthinkingly. On the other hand even the most skilfully maintained greens can develop moss patches at times, often as a result of poor growing weather weakening grass competition. In such circumstances prompt use of a mosskilling chemical is all that is required and the moss disappears once the weather moderates and grass growth picks up.

Mosses found in British bowling greens fall into three groups.

Type 1

Fern-like, usually trailing: *Hypnum* and *Eurhynchium* ssp.
Present in many types of turf but often overlooked. Characteristic of moist, rather spongy swards where there is a soft surface mat. Such mosses are often a problem on neglected greens.

Type 2

Tuft, mat forming: *Ceratodon purpureus, Bryum* spp.

PLATE 76. The Driftmaster fluted-roller type of machine (left) is useful where there is a danger of drift onto surrounding flowerbeds. The Drake & Fletcher Mystifier constant pressure pedestrian sprayer (right) has been popular at bowling clubs for some years.

PLATE 77. CDA Spraying equipment like this Nomix Grasshopper which use pre-packed herbicides requiring no dilution are not yet in widescale use but could well become more popular in future as they simplify calibration problems.

A very troublesome type of moss especially on acid soils. *Ceratodon purpureus* is common and is the so-called "winter" moss since it appears to die out in spring when active growth starts, only to reappear in the autumn. It tends to become progressively worse each winter unless checked.

Type 3
Upright: *Polytrichum* spp.

Most commonly found on the dry mounds of an undulating green. Not normally very troublesome, except occasionally under acid conditions.

Moss soon establishes on thin swards where there is a lack of competition from vigorous turf. Most mosskillers are palliative - the moss soon returns unless the factors responsible for a thin sward are removed. A strong, healthy turf is the best answer to moss, as stated above. The following factors can favour the growth of moss:-

[1] A moist turf - poor drainage encourages the fern-like and tufted mosses.

[2] A very dry soil, e.g. over drains, on mounds and ridges - inadequate watering or over-drainage -encourages the upright type.

[3] Cutting too closely.

[4] Poor surface levels - scalping.

[5] A soft, spongy sward with a thick fibre layer.

[6] Low fertility, e.g. deficiencies of plant foods, lime, etc. or insufficient soil depth.

[7] Over-consolidation of the soil - compaction.

[8] Shade.

The cultural control of moss therefore depends on finding the underlying cause and then correcting the factor responsible.

Chemical control works well in the long-term only if it is combined with cultural control.

The traditional chemical for moss in turf is sulphate of iron, applied in the calcined form, with or without sulphate of ammonia.

Sulphate of iron gives a fast kill and is cheap but is not long-lasting. It can be used alone bulked with a carrier such as sand, especially in winter, but is more often used for spring/summer application in lawn sand, e.g. a mixture of 1 part sulphate of iron : 3 parts sulphate of ammonia : 20 parts (by weight) carrier (sand or compost). This mixture is used at 140 g/m^2 (4 oz. per sq. yd).

Other mosskillers include:

[a] *Dichlorophen*
This is the material now normally recommended. It is fairly quick acting and moderately persistent.

[b] *Phenol*
This can be useful and may also have some action against speedwells. Some discoloration of grass may occur, particularly of annual meadow-grass in poor growing conditions.

Moss on paved areas or non-grass paths around bowling greens can be controlled using proprietary total weedkillers containing borax, atrazine, monuron, diuron or simazine applied at makers' recommended rates.

ALGAE AND LICHENS
Bare ground in turf areas is often quickly covered by a green scum which may be a mixture of algae and moss protonema (filaments from which the adult moss develops). Once grass is established on the bare ground, the algae growth usually disappears. Occasionally algae form black or very dark green jelly-like masses in turf during autumn or spring. Cultural control

should always be attempted by improving grass growth and taking steps to dry the surface - spiking and sanding are often useful. Chemical control involves the use of sulphate of iron at approximately 50 g in 8 litres of water/4 m^2 (1½ oz. in 1½ gal. water per 4 sq. yd. Dichlorophen (see above) may also be used, at normal mosskilling rates. Cresylic acid products (e.g. Bray's Emulsion) are also effective.

Lichens, which are a combination of alga and fungus, can occur on walls, tree trunks, soil, rocks, etc. They also occur on damp turf areas or in dry, acid situations where grass growth is weak. They are rarely as troublesome as moss in the bowling green situation. Cultural control is best, by improving grass growth. More adequate fertiliser treatment and liming may be required. Lawn sand used at the rate recommended for moss is effective if chemical control proves necessary. Lichens are seldom found on actual bowling surfaces except possibly where greens have been very seriously neglected or mis-managed. They are, however, sometimes seen on grass banks around greens where maintaining an adequate grass cover can be difficult.

EARTHWORMS AND WORM CONTROL

About 25 species of earthworms occur in this country but only a few produce surface casts on turf areas. Worms feed on dead and decaying plant or animal material found in the soil and are therefore more common on humus-rich soils. They cannot tolerate very acid conditions or very dry soils.

Each worm is both male and female but cross fertilisation is necessary. Mating takes place on the surface at night at any season of the year, providing the weather is damp and mild: 8-16 eggs are produced in a cocoon and take from 4-20 weeks to hatch. The young worms resemble their parents except in size, and mature in 40-70 weeks.

Worms are most active in moist warm weather which usually occurs in the spring and autumn. In cold frosty weather and in dry weather they burrow deeper into the soil. Control measures should therefore be taken in spring or autumn when they are near the surface and more likely to come into contact with the wormkiller used.

Worm control can be achieved by managerial methods and/or chemical control.

[1] Inhibition - management of turf areas to discourage worm activity. Avoid creating limy conditions, using excessive amounts of organic materials, or allowing clippings to fly.

[2] Chemical control - wormkilling by means of specific chemical treatment. The wormkillers available today fall into two groups.

[a]   Non-selective wormkillers
Products which actually kill worms below the surface have generally replaced traditional expellents. No clearing-up operations are necessary as modern materials kill worms below the surface, whilst the older expellants brought them up to the surface..

[i] Chlordane
Until very recently, chlordance was the most effective wormkiller available and was widely used, giving excellent and quite long-term control. It is, however, a dangerous, toxic and environmentally unacceptable chemical and recent legislation has banned its sale, storage and use. If a stock remains in the greenkeeper's shed it should therefore be disposed of in an approved manner and under no circumstances be used for the treatment of a bowling green.

[ii] Carbaryl
Carbaryl is an insecticide and wormkiller available in proprietary form as a wettable powder or flowable suspension. It should be applied during mild, damp weather in autumn or spring (autumn is preferable) when the worms are active near the surface. In the case of a severe infestation two applications, one in autumn and one in spring, give better control. Watering after application increases the efficiency of the material. Carbaryl kills worms below the surface and, therefore, no sweeping-up is required. The makers claim that 93% control of casting worms is achieved in 4 days. The duration of control is short; even the makers claim only one season's control. Proprietary preparations of differing carbaryl content are available through normal channels. Though the material is less unpleasant and persistent than chlordane, prolonged or repeated contact with the skin should be avoided, as should breathing the dust or

spray. Wash exposed skin after using the material and wear protective clothing as advised by the supplier on the product label.

[b] *Selective wormkillers*
These recently introduced materials are claimed to kill only surface-feeding, casting species, leaving unharmed earthworms which live deeper in the soil and which cause no damage to turf.

[i] *Thiophanate-methyl*
Applied to the surface, it kills worms which feed and cast on or near the surface. It should be applied when active casting can be seen, usually spring or autumn. The effect is not reduced by rain after treatment. Duration of control is about three months or so only. It is safe to use on all turf areas but take normal precautions in handling and storage.

[ii] *Carbendazim*
Available as a liquid, carbendazim is better known as a fungicide, effective against fusarium, dollar spot and red thread disease. It is said to kill harmful casting species only and should be applied to moist soil when worms are active. Do not mow immediately after treatment. Duration of control is short when compared to chlordane. Normal precautions applicable when handling chemicals should be observed.

INSECT PESTS OF TURF AND THEIR CONTROL
The most common insect pest of British turf is the leatherjacket, which is the larva of the crane fly or 'daddy long-legs' (*Tipula* species). The adults are active and fly in the autumn when they may be attracted to lights in houses. Eggs are laid in grassy places and the larvae hatch within ten days to feed either on plant tissues or decaying vegetable matter in the soil. Their feeding increases in the spring as they develop and grow. When they are fully grown the leatherjackets are about 5 cm long, grey-brown, legless and without obvious heads. Pupation occurs below ground but just before emergence the pupa pushes itself out of the soil.

PLATE 78. Regulations given on the label of the pesticide product being used must by law be obeyed. Where appropriate, approved protective clothing must be worn.

Leatherjackets feed throughout the autumn and winter during mild weather, causing damage to If established turf and to re-seeded grass, especially later-sown turf. They feed particularly voraciously in the spring. Leatherjackets can attack young plants, biting off the stems at or just below ground level. The cut ends of the plants have frayed edges. Leaf tips may be eaten or even pulled below the soil surface. Leatherjackets are usually found near to the damaged plants or if conditions are mild, close to the soil surface. Autumn-sown grass will usually show signs of damage by early April, although occasionally this will be seen in the autumn (November-December).

On heavily infested established turf areas bare patches appear where the plants have been destroyed. These may quickly be covered with weeds or weed grasses. However, in other cases the first signs are either straw-coloured areas of grass debris or the turf being pecked by birds. Often attacks remain undetected until the flush of spring growth reveals patches of greatly reduced vigour in the turf.

If poor, weak areas are seen in the early spring, with accompanying bird activity, leatherjacket damage should be suspected.

Where visible signs of damage are evident and where leatherjackets can be easily found then chemical control measures are justified. Any of the chemicals mentioned below can be used. In established turf it is usually more reliable to use a high volume spray.

Similar in their habits are the grubs of the fever fly (*Dilophus* and *Bibio* sp.). These look like small leatherjackets with shiny brown heads and occasionally appear in definite nests in bowling green turf.

The grubs of five species of chafer beetle are also pests of local importance in Britain, although rare on bowling greens. The species which is most widespread and the most troublesome in grassland is the garden chafer (*Phyllopertha horticola*). The adult is about 9 mm long with a metallic-green head and thorax and reddish-brown wing-cases. The grubs are white and about 18 mm long when fully grown.

The life-cycle occupies one year. Adult beetles swarm during June and July, feeding on a variety of plants. Eggs are laid in the soil, usually in the same area where the beetles emerged. Thus, infested turf is regularly re-infested each summer, although the areas with obvious damage are often different each year. Grubs feed from the summer until late autumn.

Damage appears in September and October and the severity depends on the numbers of chafer larvae in the soil. Generally more than $50/m^2$ must be present before damage becomes obvious.

Usually poorly growing patches become obvious and these turn brown in dry weather. The grubs can be found immediately below the surface. Soil in these areas is often fine in texture and 'fluffy'. This is due to the grubs actually ingesting soil as they feed on roots.

Severely damaged areas are usually sharply defined, and because the roots are severed, the turf can be rolled up like a carpet. Frequently birds cause further damage to the turf as they rip up the grass whilst searching for the grubs.

Insecticides for control of insect turf pests

PEST	INSECTICIDE		
	Chlorpyrifos	gamma-HCH	gamma-HCH/thiophanate-methyl
Chafer grubs	–	✓	–
Frit fly	✓	–	–
Leatherjackets	✓	✓	–
Wireworms	–	✓	✓

PLATES 79 & 80. The leatherjacket is the commonest and most troublesome insect pest of bowling greens.

163

THE MOLE AND ITS CONTROL

Irish and Manx greenkeepers can of course skip this topic as their native islands are free of the little gentlemen in the velvet waistcoat. In fact the mole is not all that serious a pest of bowling greens in mainland Britain as the presence of paths, banks and ditches around greens tends to act as a barrier to their burrowing activities - certainly moles are a more serious pest of other types of turf area. Occasional trouble with moles is, however, sometimes reported by bowling clubs and where it does occur it can be extremely damaging.

There are five methods of control. The first two are the methods recommended by the Ministry of Agriculture, Fisheries and Food (MAFF).

[1] Trapping
Probably best dealt with by a professional mole trapper.

[2] Poisoning by baits
Very effective poison baits consist of worms treated with strychnine placed in the deeper main runs. This is a very dangerous poison: permits are available from MAFF issued strictly according to requirements and to professional users only. (Poisons based on warfarin are sometimes advertised, but are unlikely to be effective.)

[3] Gassing
A sodium cyanide product is available to professional pest control operatives only. This gives off hydrogen cyanide in contact with soil moisture. For non-professional use, there are mole smokes based on sulphur, on on thiourea, lindane and tecnazine. Engine exhaust gas is also quite effective. All these methods are more effective in repelling or moving moles than killing them.

[4] Electronic
A device generating sonic vibration is claimed to clear an area up to about 1000 m^2.

[5] Removal of worms
Moles feed almost entirely on earthworms so wormkilling can indirectly control moles.

TURFGRASS DISEASES

It is not the intention in this section to provide a full and comprehensive guide to the full range of British turfgrass diseases. It will be sufficient to cover only those diseases which cause frequent and damaging attacks to bowling green swards. For a fuller coverage of the problem one should consult *Turfgrass Pests and Diseases* by Neil A. Baldwin, 1990 published by and available from the STRI, price £2.50, from which the information given here has been abstracted.

Good general bowling green management is, through its aim to produce a uniform, true visually attractive surface suitable for bowls, undoubtedly the best approach to disease problems. Fungicides are only part of an integrated disease control programme and their ready availability must not reduce the attention paid to those practices which reduce the risk of disease.

As a general rule, application of fungicides should be made when the first signs of disease are seen. This will, of course, require that the turf receives regular inspection as diseases may cause substantial damage in short periods of time. There are three principal reasons why preventative spraying is to be discouraged in most situations. Firstly, the repeated, often unnecessary application of fungicides can be expensive, both in the cost of material and the labour required. Secondly, several fungicides currently available for use on turf have been shown to kill not only the fungus responsible for the disease but also other, possibly beneficial organisms, some of which may help to prevent disease. This may be the reason for the observation that disease attack may be more severe after a course of fungicidal treatment has ended than if no applications had been made at all. Thirdly, repeated exposure to a fungicide increases the risk of selection of strains of the fungus which are resistant to its toxic effects.

There are circumstances, however, when the prevention of a disease by fungicidal treatment is a sensible course of action. A preventative fungicide application strategy should only be deployed when disease is very likely to occur and when without the fungicide severe damage is anticipated. The greenkeeper must make his decision on the basis of experience of a paticular green and its history, and take into account any environmental factors which might favour disease attack.

When disease appears on a green the first problem is to identify the cause. An incorrect diagnosis can lead to wasted (and costly) fungicide applications. Disease identification is not easy in practice, especially if more than one disease is present but reference to the descriptions given in the following pages should help.

Available fungicides fall into two groups. Systemic products are actually absorbed into the grass plant during growth and tend to last for some weeks - growth must be occurring for this process to take place. In the winter months when no grass growth is occurring it is therefore preferable to use one of the alternative group of products, the contact fungicides.

The systemic fungicides available, i.e. benomyl, carbendazim, thiabendazole and thiophanate-methyl all belong to the same group known as the benzimidazoles. Consequently, these products have a similar mode of action.

The contact fungicides iprodione and vinclozolin also belong to a common group of fungicides known as the dicarboximides. Again, these chemicals work in similar ways. A third contact fungicide, chlorothalonil, is available which is independent of the above two groups. Another contact fungicide is quintozene which again works in a different way to the dicarboximides and chlorothalonil.

Benodanil and oxycarboxin are grouped together as they are selective in their toxic effects and may be only used effectively against fairy rings.

Dichlorophen is primarily used for moss control but some effect against fusarium patch disease has been demonstrated.

The following diseases are those most commonly occurring on bowling green swards.

FUSARIUM PATCH

Other names	None.
Causal fungus	*Microdochium nivale* (formerly *Fusarium nivale*).
Importance	Probably the most common and damaging disease of fine turf in the UK.
Season	It can occur at any time of the year if conditions are favourable. Most often seen in spring and autumn.
Symptoms	First appears as small, dark brown or orange circular spots. These may increase in size and number very rapidly to produce patches of dead grass. The diseased grass may be wet and slimy. Diseased patches have a dark brown ring around a paler centre. Sometimes fungal mycelium (appearing white or pink) can be seen around the edges of patches, often matting dead leaves together.
Grasses and turf types affected	Most troublesome in fine turf, particularly if types affected are managed intensively. Annual meadow-grass (*Poa annua*) is the species most frequently affected. Other grasses are also sometimes attacked.
Conditions under which the disease is likely to occur	The disease is favoured by humid atmospheric conditions and a moist turf surface. Excessive nitrogen applications, particularly the organic type, applied in the autumn lead often to rapid disease development. Top dressings applied at too high a rate or not worked in properly will smother the grass and render it liable to attack. An alkaline turf surface will also favour the disease.

Integrated disease control	Moisture control to avoid humid surface conditions will do much to prevent disease attach. This can be achieved by attention to drainage, ensuring free movement of air over the turf surface by not siting fences or walls too close and by switching to remove dew. Aeration and careful top dressing with a sandy compost make the surface less moisture retentive. Reduction of moisture-holdingthatch is also beneficial, as also is limiting artificial watering which can cause excessive moisture. Nitrogen fertilisers and lime should not be applied during periods favour-able for disease development. Cuttings should be boxed off as returning them can favour the disease. Good turf management practices, to minimise the annual meadow-grass content, should be deployed

Under very favourable environmental conditions for disease development these preventive measures may not give satisfactory disease control. If the need arises, outbreaks can be fairly easily controlled with fungicides provided they are used correctly. Most fungicides sold for turfgrass use will control the disease. Systemic fungicides (benomyl, carbendazim, thiabendazole and thiophanate-methyl) are most effective in the growing season as they need to be absorbed into the plant. Contact fungicides (chlorothalonil, iprodione, vinclozolin and quintozene) will control attacks in late autumn and winter when grass growth is slow.

Preventative spraying on a routine basis is rarely justified as a well timed fungicide spray applied at the first signs of the disease will give usually satisfactory disease control. A repeat fungicide application may be necessary under prolonged conditions favourable for disease development.

RED THREAD

Other name	Corticium disease.
Causal fungus	*Laetisaria fuciformis* (formerly *Corticium fuciforme*).
Importance	Very common disease. Severe outbreaks may kill the grass but generally infected areas will recover from attack. Often occurs together as a disease complex with pink patch disease.
Season	During summer and autumn. May persist into winter if conditions remain mild.
Symptoms	Patches of damaged grass which often have a pink or red appearance. This is due partly to the presence of red "needles" which stick out from diseased leaves. These needles are the survival phase of the fungus. They may be straight or branched, brittle and up to 25 mm long. The size and shape of infected patches vary from 20-50 mm up to 350 mm in diameter. Commonly, unless the grass growth is poor and the attack serious the appearance is of a fairly superficial damage to the leaves, which die back from their tips. Such patches do not have a very distinct margin and live green leaves exist within them.
Grasses and turf types affected	May be found on any type of turf. Red fescue (*Festuca rubra*) and perennial ryegrass are the species most often affected but other species are attacked occasionally.
Conditions under which the disease is likely to occur	Low fertility, particularly insufficient nitrogen.
Integrated disease control	The disease can be prevented by the selection of cultivars that are less susceptible to the disease, especially if they are to be grown in low fertility situations. During summer, applications of nitrogenous fertiliser should be made if sufficient moisture is available. This will assist grass growth and reduce the severity of the disease. However, care is needed as excessive

nitrogen applications can encourage fusarium patch disease, especially where there is a large percentage of annual meadow-grass present. In situations known to be susceptible to fusarium patch disease, it may be better to rely on timely fungicide applications together with judicious application of nitrogenous fertilisers. Systemic fungicides (benomyl, carbendazim, thiabendazole and thiophanate-methyl) are generally effective in controlling red thread. Contact fungicides chlorothalonil, iprodione, quintozene and vinclozolin) are also effective.

DOLLAR SPOT

Other name	Sclerotinia dollar spot.
Causal fungus	*Sclerotinia homoeocarpa*.
Importance	Common disease of slender creeping red fescue turf from certain locations. Otherwise the disease is not often seen.
Season	Summer and autumn.
Symptoms	The patches of dead grass formed are usually small, typically about 50 mm in diameter, are very distinct and often circular. They give an infected area a spotty appearance, hence the name. In severe attacks, individual spots may coalesce to form larger patches. Within the patches, the dead grass is usually dry, bleached white or straw coloured.
Grasses and turf types affected	In the UK certain types of red fescue only are susceptible. Slender creeping red fescues, particularly those of sea-marsh origin, are very susceptible. The disease is seen usually only in fine turf. In other countries, the host range of dollar spot may be much wider and may not necessarily correspond with the UK situation.
Conditions under which the disease is likely to occur	Dollar spot is favoured by the present of susceptible grasses and low fertility, particularly low nitrogen.
Integrated disease control	The disease can be prevented completely by choice of resistant fescue Sea-marsh turf should be avoided if freedom from dollar spot is the aim. Good control can be achieved with benomyl, carbendazim, thiabendazole or thiophanate-methyl, particularly if nitrogen is also applied.

Note: On red fescue, dollar spot may occur at the same time as red thread/pink patch. In such case the red stromata of red thread disease are seen easily and diagnosis is assumed to be complete. If the fescue is susceptible to dollar spot, careful examination is essential. If in doubt, get expert advice.

TAKE-ALL PATCH

Other name	Ophiobolus patch.
Causal fungus	*Gaeumannomyces graminis*.
Importance	Not a common disease. Under suitable conditions for disease development, it may cause severe damage.
Season	Most active in summer and autumn but infected patches may remain all year round.
Symptoms	Rings of yellow or orange grass, ranging in size from 0.1-1 m in diameter. A ring of dying bent, up to 0.1 m across, may be seen which is the result of a fungal attack on the roots which become discoloured. The centres of the patches tend to be occupied by grass species not susceptible to the disease, e.g. fescue and also by weeds.
Grasses and turf types affected	May be seen in any type of turf. Bent (*Agrostis* spp.) is usually the grass affected.

Conditions under which the disease is likely to occur	Wetness and surface alkalinity increase the likelihood of attack and the disease occurs often when wet acid greens are limed. Take all may occur on new turf areas which have been sterilised prior to seeding and also on greens made using very sandy topsoil mixes. The susceptibility of these areas to take all may be due to the absence of antagonistic fungi and bacteria in the soil.
Integrated disease control	Once the disease has become established it is very difficult to control. It is better to prevent a disease outbreak by good management. Wet conditions can be alleviated by ensuring good drainage. Ideally, turf should be maintained so that lime applications are not required but if liming is essential this should be done in autumn and followed in the spring by an acidic fertiliser, e.g. ammonium sulphate, to counteract the effect of the lime in the surface layer. Surface alkalinity may also be increased by alkaline sands used for top dressing and irrigation water from boreholes has often a naturally high lime content. Take these factors into account when considering the management of surface alkalinity. Few fungicides may give effective control. Carbendazim and chlorothalonil will suppress the disease for a time if they are well watered in but could also harm beneficial antagonistic fungi as well. More than one application is usually required.

ANTHRACNOSE

Other name	Colletotrichum basal rot.
Causal fungus	*Colletotrichum graminicola.*
Importance	A fairly common disease if conditions are suitable. Severe attacks will cause significant damage.
Season	Usually in late summer and autumn.
Symptoms	The leaves of infected plants turn yellow. Often the youngest leaf on the plant is red. On the base of the shoot, black reproductive structures (acervuli) can be seen if old sheaths are removed. Often occurs in patches but individual plants in a sward may sometimes be affected.

Note: Leaf yellowing in annual meadow-grass may also be due to a physio-logical stress reaction.

Grasses and turf types affected	Annual meadow-grass is particularly susceptible to this disease, but other grasses have also been reported to be affected.
Conditions under which the disease is likely to occur	Usually occurs when growing conditions are poor, particularly when soil compaction restricts air supply to the grass roots and where soil fertility is inadequate.
Integrated disease control	Long lasting control can be achieved only by rectifying the predisposing condition, i.e. attention to fertility and relief of compaction. Fungicides are not normally used. However, chlorothalonil may be effective. It is sufficient usually to improve the growing conditions.

TYPE 1 FAIRY RINGS

Other names	Fairy walks, fairy dances, fairy courts.
Causal fungus	Usually *Marasmius oreades.*
Importance	Fairly frequently seen on golf fairways and other areas where they are quite destructive. Not often seen on bowling greens.
Season	Rings may persist for many years but symptoms are most obvious during dry weather in the summer.

Fusarium patch disease (general view)

Fusarium patch disease (close up view)

Red thread (general view)

Red thread (close up view)

Dollar spot (general view)

Dollar spot (close up view)

Earthworm casting and take-all patch disease after liming

Take-all patch bent/fescue sward (close up view)

PLATES 81-88.   Fungal diseases.

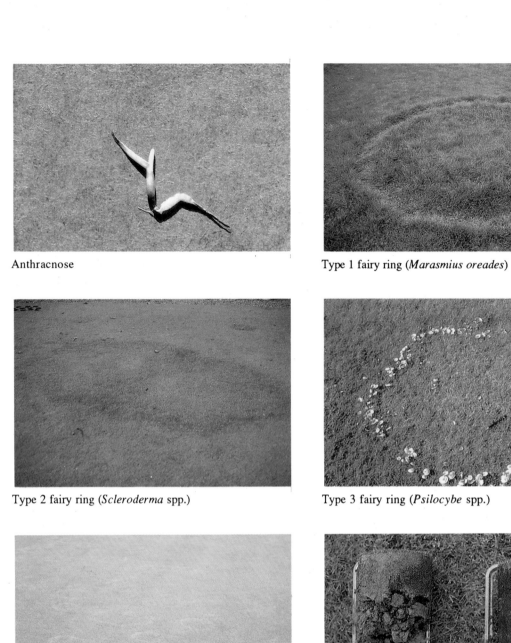

Anthracnose

Type 1 fairy ring (*Marasmius oreades*)

Type 2 fairy ring (*Scleroderma* spp.)

Type 3 fairy ring (*Psilocybe* spp.)

Superficial fairy ring

Plugs from normal turf (right) and affected by dry patch (left)

Algal slime or "squidge"

Damage due to insect larvae feeding

PLATES 89-96. Fungal diseases. Algal squidge and leatherjacket damage are shown for comparative purposes.

Symptoms	Type 1 rings are those that kill the grass or badly damage it. Two rings, arcs or ribbons of stimulated and darker green grass growth are seen. Between them there is a ring of bare ground. There are several ways in which *M. oreades* is able to kill the grass in this bare zone. The most important way is that the fungus creates extremely hydrophobic soil conditions, thus droughting plants out. Beneath the ring are large masses of white mycelium which has a characteristic musty smells. Small tan-coloured mushrooms may be seen in the outer ring any time between early summer and autumn.
Grasses and turf types affected	May occur in any type of turf.
Conditions that favour development	The conditions that favour the original establishment of rings are not understood fully but surface moisture may be important. Rings may be found on all soil types but are most noticeable on light sandy soils.
Integrated control	Several possible methods are available for the sup-pression of rings but complete eradication is difficult to achieve. An effective method of control is the laborious one of digging out most of the soil from an infected area and sterilising with formaldehyde any contaminated soil that remains. Digging out alone may be sufficient, if done thoroughly but the addition of a sterilisation agent increases the likelihood of success.

The mycelium of *M. oreades* is very difficult to wet effectively. Consequently, fungicide solutions in water are easily repelled. To enable maximum concentration of fungicide to come into contact with the fungal mycelium wetting agents are needed.

Three systemic fungicides, benodanil, oxycarboxin and triforine are effective against type 1 rings providing the following procedure is adhered to strictly.

[1] Measure area to be treated and mark off with string. This must include turf within the ring and 0.5 m around the edge.

[2] Thoroughly spike the area with a hollow tine fork. This will assist the penetration of fungicide into the turf.

[3] Apply a solution of wetting agent to the area and leave to soak in for 1 hour.

[4] Apply either benodanil, oxycarboxin or triforine at the recommended rate and dilution using a watering can.

[5] Again water with wetting agent to assist penetration by fungicide. The most suitable time for this treatment is thought to be in the spring when the mycelium of the fungus is starting to grow actively. Often, to suppress the most aggressive rings, a second treatment is necessary during the autumn.

TYPE 2 FAIRY RINGS

Other names	None.
Causal fungi	*Agaricus, Lycoperdon* and *Scleroderma* spp.
Importance	Seen commonly on many fine turf areas. Cause little actual damage to the grass.
Season	Symptoms are usually most noticeable during the summer and autumn but the fungi are present all the year round.
Symptoms	Rings, arcs or ribbons of stimulated grass which is darker green and faster growing than that nearby. No actual damage is done to the grass. Occasionally fruiting bodies (toadstools, mushrooms or puff balls) are associated with the stimulated grass.

Grasses and turf types affected	Many types of turf may be affected. Most noticeable on bowling and golf greens.
Conditions that favour development	Not known. Symptoms are most marked when nitrogen is deficient.
Integrated control	No method of preventing type 2 rings is known. As the grass is not damaged rings are often tolerated but they can spoil the appearance of fine turf. As described for type 1 rings, it is possible to dig out type 2 rings but this is rarely thought worthwhile. During the growing season the symptoms can be disguised by giving extra nitrogen to the whole area. Applications of sulphate of iron will also mask the rings by generally darkening the area. Fungicides benodanil, triforine and oxycarboxin can be effective.

TYPE 3 FAIRY RINGS

Causal fungi	Many basidiomycetes, e.g. *Hygrophorus* spp., *Psilocybe* spp.
Importance	Very common. Usually no effect on the grass.
Season	The fungus is present all year round but the ring is seen only for a short period, often in autumn but depending on species sometimes in spring or early winter.
Symptoms	Fungal activity is indicated by a ring or sometimes a less distinct pattern of fruiting bodies (toadstools or puff-balls).
Grass and turf	Found in most types of turf but not seen usually on types affected heavily worn areas.
Conditions that favour development	Not known.
Integrated control	Control is attempted rarely as there is no change to the grass. To prevent rings from spreading to other areas, fruiting bodies are sometimes picked by hand to stop the liberation of spores. If thought necessary, fruiting bodies may be suppressed by applying a fungicide. Benodanil, oxycarboxin and triforine are thought to be effective.

Note: As well as forming rings, fruiting bodies of Basidiomycete fungi may occur also on turf areas and be seen as solitary specimens arranged apparently in a ring or circular fashion. Some of these fungi may be true lawn fungi whilst others may be colonising buried debris such as twigs or tree roots. The "magic mushroom" (*Psilocybe*) is known to occur in this manner on a wide range of amenity turf surfaces. This can present problems due to members of the public trespassing to pick the mushrooms for their hallucenogenic effects. No chemical control method is available as yet but the fruiting bodies may be destroyed using a mower or a hand brush.

SUPERFICIAL FAIRY RINGS

Other names	Superficial basidiomycetes, thatch fungi.
Causal fungi	*Trechispora alnicola*. Possibly many non-sporing basidiomycetes involved. Very difficult to identify.
Importance	Common problem which seems to be increasing. Most severe forms may kill the turf. Some implicated in the dry patch condition.
Season	May be seen at any time of the year.
Symptoms	Intense fungal activity in the thatch layer of the turf, often invading grass sheath bases. Dense white mycelium is visible frequently and the thickness of the thatch layer may be reduced. Grass in infected areas is often greener than that on adjacent areas but may sometimes turn yellow or bleached.

172

Various patterns are formed, including circular patches, complete rings, parts of rings and irregular narrow lines.

Grasses and turf types affected	Any type of turf may be affected. Particularly troublesome on fine turf areas where a deep thatch layer is present.
Conditions that favour development	The presence of a marked thatch layer. There is some evidence that the use of benzimidazole systemic fungicides may favour the fungi responsible also soil sterilisation, which may inhibit antagonistic fungi, has been implicated in this condition.
Integrated control	Reduce the thatch layer by turf management practices such as aeration and mechanical thatch removal. The fungicides benodanil, oxycarboxin and triforine have some effect.

DRY PATCH

Causal fungi	Strictly speaking, dry patch is not a disease. However, certain types of dry patch may be of fungal origin. Certain superficial fairy ring fungi have been implicated.
Importance	Becoming increasingly common in fine turf. In severe cases large areas of damage may be caused.
Causes	Mounds, slopes or undulations in turf are more prone to drying out in drought conditions. These areas may be levelled or aerated and watered by hand using a wetting agent. Compacted soils due to foot traffic or the extra mowing around the perimeter of the green can also cause water-repellent areas of turf. Additional aeration and watering with a wetting agent should relieve the problem.

Barren patches in fescue/bent turf can also be hydrophobic. Dead shoots accumulate and if not removed choke out live green growth. This leaves a fibrous surface that may become compacted and consequently very difficult to re-wet. The drier the thatch the more water repellent it becomes. Once this process has started, it is very difficult for new growth to disrupt the barren surface.

Dry patch can also be caused by type 1 fairy rings. *M. oreades* produces waxy mycelium which is water repellent. This creates localised drought which will account partly for death of grass.

Water-repellent conditions due to fungal deposits on soil particles. Due to intense fungal activity in the thatch and rootzone, waxy materials may be deposited on sand or soil particles immediately below the thatch layer. The condition is worse in coarse sands and often sand particles may be bound together in a completely impermeable layer.

The water-repellent effect is intensified if an area is allowed to dry out completely so this should be avoided if possible. Prevention of the problem may be achieved by localised spiking and hollow tining and watering supplemented with a wetting agent.

CHAPTER 10
MODERN BOWLING GREEN MAINTENANCE:
miscellaneous work

To complete our survey of modern bowling green maintenance techniques, it now only remains to consider a varied hotch-potch of greenkeeping tasks not covered by the previous three chapters. It should not be assumed that the topics covered in this section are of only minor importance because they have been left until last - many are vital if the required standard of bowls surface is to be achieved.

WATERING AND IRRIGATION SYSTEMS
The average rainfall for Britain is about 1090 mm (43 in.) but there is tremendous variation, e.g. East Anglia is less than 640 mm (25 in.), whilst wet, mountainous areas of Wales is over 2030 mm (80 in.).

The potential loss of moisture by evapo-transpiration during the summer is between 60 and 75 mm (2½ and 3 in.) per month on average, according to district. Thus, in dry areas in dry months, when the rainfall may be down to 13 mm (½ in.) or less, the soil is very likely to dry out to the point where grass roots are unable to obtain sufficient moisture to make up for evapo-transpiration losses, and there is a case for artificial watering if colour, appearance, texture, growth and suitability for use are not to suffer. This is particularly true on closely mown turf which usually has shallower rooting than less intensively maintained turf and therefore is dependent on a smaller volume of soil for its moisture supply.

Apart from the direct benefits to the turf of ensuring sufficient supplies of moisture to prevent deterioration, an efficient irrigation system facilitates other aspects of management, making it much simpler to arrange fertiliser application, weedkilling, scarification, etc.

To maintain satisfactory top growth and colour in turf there must be sufficient soil water in the rootzone. A deficiency of water results in stress and if this is allowed to persist for more than a few days, wilting may occur and the turf can develop brown patches. In time, some of the grass could die, but such extreme circumstances are rare in the British Isles.

Stress occurs whenever the rate of water loss by transpiration from the leaves exceeds the rate of water intake through the roots. Thus, stress may occur when there is a reasonable supply of water in the soil if, for any reason, the root system is inadequate. For example, there could be insufficient root available to absorb water quickly enough at high temperatures. Shallow rooting can be related to management practices, including over-watering. Root growth depends on the soil conditions, including drainage, grass species, mowing practice, irrigation management, aeration, etc. Irrigation management which keeps the soil near saturation constantly will restrict soil air supply and rooting depth. The grass roots tend to develop mainly in the mat or thatch above the soil surface because of the better aeration there. When a large proportion of the grass roots is in the mat, the turfgrass may require watering every day in drought conditions. This means, in turn, constant wetness and more surface rooting - the problems feeds upon itself. As these conditions encourage root growth in the mat or thatch, the depth of fibre increases and becomes a distinct problem in overall turf management.

When soil physical conditions are favourable, roots will penetrate deeper if irrigation management provides water only as needed, without excessive applications, and where there is time in between waterings to allow partial drying.

Some bowling clubs may have been persuaded to part with considerable sums of money to improve and update irrigation facilities because of a marked lack of drought resistance of their greens in situations where this was not primarily due to a lack of water *per se*, but due to an excess of fibre (or thatch) and shallow rooting. In view of these remarks, it is clear that if we have a fibrous mat problem to begin with, watering may make it worse, especially since the mat itself is water-holding and tends to impede percolation of water down into the soil. With or without a watering system, it is still necessary to eliminate the excess of fibre and obtain better rooting.

Some grasses are known to be more drought resistant than others; thus fine fescue is relatively resistant to drought, whereas annual meadow-grass is drought susceptible. Constant heavy watering is likely to reduce the proportion of fine fescue in a turf and to increase the annual meadow-grass content.

Irrigation management

Whilst grass roots need moisture at all times, a slight deficiency and some degree of stress is not always a bad thing - it allows air into the soil and encourages the roots to grow deeper, which is highly desirable. Moreover, a deficiency reduces risk of a subsequent excess from possibly unexpected natural rainfall.

Just when to water is essentially a matter of knowing a particular green. The greenkeeper uses his experience - he may find help from probing the ground or from taking core samples to a depth of 150 mm (6 in.) to examine the soil but often he will base his judgement on keen observation of known sensitive spots, which show up shortage of water before the rest of his turf and before anybody else has spotted that anything is wrong.

The amount of water given at any one application should aim at moistening the top 150 mm (6 in.) or so and in drought conditions this may need to be applied at, say, two to three day intervals (longer intervals in less droughty conditions), allowing a period between for the surface 50-75 mm (2-3 in.) to dry out slightly and let in air. The frequency may have to be greater on light, freely drained soils than on heavy, poorer drained soils. Soil type, as on would expect, has a great influence on the need for irrigation. Frequent light watering may also be necessary to bring on areas seeded during renovation and "syringing" is sometimes useful during very hot weather to keep the grass cool, if a pop-up system is available to allow this to be carried out.

The rate of application of the water should not exceed the infiltration rate of the turf, water will penetrate quicker into sandy soils than into clay soils and quicker into uncompacted soils than into compacted soils. There is also the question of the mat or thatch, which can at different times be very water-repellent or water-holding. Where there is difficulty in ensuring adequate penetration of added water, spiking before watering can be of assistance. On some areas of turf there may be patches which, after drying out, take water with great difficulty and on these areas spiking is particularly important. In some cases a suitable wetting agent may be used to assist moisture penetration.

Watering during the heat of the day is likely to lead to greater evaporation losses during application. In addition, a dry surface during the day also usually means more suitable playing conditions and a reduction in the compaction effects of traffic.

There is a fairly common belief that turf which is irrigated needs more fertiliser, particularly nitrogen. This may be true where over-watering and heavy leaching take place, but with good watering practice, irrigation losses should be very low and it should only be necessary to increase fertiliser rates very slightly to make good losses from increased growth.

When watering bowling greens, it must always be borne in mind that the needs of the grass cover are not the only consideration - the amount of watering carried out also has a direct effect on the characteristics of the playing surface. Wet greens as a general rule play heavier and lack pace when compared to dry greens (although sometimes one finds that a very light slick of surface moisture has in fact the very opposite effect on the speed of the surface). The needs of the grass sward are therefore not the only consideration as far as water management is concerned - the needs of the bowlers must be catered for as well. The two aspects of the situation are of course inter-related and the interests of the grass plant and those of the bowler often coincide - no player would be happy where areas of the grass cover had actually died from water loss, for example. On the other hand there is a tendency for some greenkeepers to water with the primary object of maintaining the appearance of the green, sward colour and lushness taking precedence. It should always be remembered that the green is primarily a bowling surface - some loss of sward colour and growth rate in summer drought is neither here nor there providing the process is not allowed to go too far with the grass actually dying back. Some degree of drought stress can actually temporarily improve the quality of the surface and if the appearance of the green suffers in such a situation it should not be regarded as too important. Ultimately a balance must be struck between the players' point of view and the requirements of the grass sward. One thing is clear enough - over-watering is to be condemned from both points of view. A permanently wet green is not only unacceptable from the bowlers viewpoint, but will also suffer from annual meadow-grass invasion, soil compaction, shallow rooting and thatch development - all undesirable as far as sward health is concerned.

Wetting agents

Wetting agents are detergents (materials which reduce the surface tension of water), the use of which assists the penetration of water into soil. There are proprietary turf wetting agents on the market, but some **non-ionic** commercial detergents can be used too. When using ordinary detergent over a protracted period, care must be taken to select a material which does not contain bleach and/or a high concentration of sodium.

Wetting agents can be used on a routine basis on turf areas subject to dry patches, at intervals throughout the summer months. They can be of particular value as spot treatments on high areas where water tends to run off. The point of using them is simply to make the watering that much more effective in sustaining uniformity of the turf area.

For further comments on this point see the discussion of 'dry patch' in the Turf Diseases section of the previous Chapter.

Watering equipment

Most bowling green watering systems work off mains supplies. This is often the most convenient water source but liable to be restricted or cut off entirely when most needed. Bore holes, rivers and streams are sometimes a possibility - permission is usually needed from Water Catchment Authorities to take water from such sources and it is wise to make certain the supply is not going to run dry in drought conditions. The source should be free of injurious pollution and soft water is preferable (in other words, lime-free).

The available water pressure should be between 1.4 and 4.2 kg/cm^2 (20-60 lb. per sq. in) for most manual types of watering equipment.

The simplest type of watering equipment, (apart from hand-held hoses which still have a place even where sophisticated automatic systems are operational to cover troublesome dry patches) is the rotating or oscillating sprinkler. The latter is usually preferable for bowling greens as a squarer watering pattern is obtainable - an advantage for a turf area which is itself square. Such sprinkers are inexpensive but have to be moved frequently and are hence labour intensive and can interfere with play to an irritating extent. Rotary sprinklers may be better than nothing but tend to over-water some areas and under-water others.

Perforated hoses, oscillating lines or fixed spraylines (water squares) are preferred by most clubs and are probably the most commonly encountered type of watering equipment for bowling green purposes. The latter have found particular favour and consist of a number of 16 ft. 6 in. (5 m) lengths of 1^1/4 in. (32 mm) diameter aluminium sprayline, fitted with brass nozzles in a carefully designed pattern to apply a gentle even 'rain' over a strip of up to 40 ft. (12 m) in width. Each length applies up to 120 gallons of water per hour (0.54 m^3/hr) at operating pressures of from 30 psi (2.1 kg/cm^2). The spraylines are connected by flexible quick-action couplers and mounted on swivel ball-carriages so that they can be moved in any direction without uncoupling and without damaging the turf. A standard bowling green set, to water an overall length of 126 ft. (38 m) consists of:

1 16 ft. 6 in. (5 m) sprayline with flexible coupler and hose adapter
6 16 ft. 6 in. (5 m) spraylines with flexible coupler
1 8 ft. 3 in. (2.5 m) sprayline with flexible coupler
1 1^1/4 in. (32 mm) end plug
9 Ball carriage assemblies with clamps.

For the flat rink game sprinklers of the spray-line variety have the advantage of allowing the whole surface of a single rink to be watered at the same time - the pipe-line should of course

PLATE 97. Spraylines, such as this Giant Watersquare from British Overhead Irrigation Ltd., are the most commonly encountered, and a very effective method of bowling green irrigation. (Photograph courtesy Borough of Brecknock.)

PLATE 98. Automatic pop-up watering systems allow night-time watering and minimise labour requirements. (Photograph courtesy Toro Irrigation Ltd.)

always be laid out along the current direction of play and not at right-angles to it. This maintains uniformity of pace along the rink as a whole - watering only sections of a rink or different sections at different times produces variations in green speed which affect the run of the bowl.

A number of the more affluent clubs have now installed automatic watering systems with fixed sprinkler heads buried in the green surround. Such systems are costly but permit efficient night time watering with no expenditure of extra labour and minimal interference with play. A typical system for a single green would consist of eight pop-up sprinklers, four in the green corners set for 90° operation and four in the centres of the sides set for 180° water throw. On cost grounds however, the corner sprinklers are often omitted except in the case of particularly open sites, where wind problems can affect the evenness of water distribution and hence make the four corner sprinklers mandatory. Each of these would come on automatically in turn. The advice of a specialised irrigation contractor with experience of bowling green watering is absolutely mandatory if the installation of a system of this kind is being contemplated.

In New Zealand it is quite common to find greens where either four or eight perimeter pop-up sprinklers are supplemented by an additional sprinkler positioned at the dead centre of the green. This extra, central sprinkler may be a portable head which has to be manually placed in position at the end of the day's play, connected by a length of hose to a suitable stop-cock at the side of the green, to be switched on later in the night by the time switch, which controls the other fixed, perimeter pop-ups. Five or nine sprinkler systems of this kind give rather more even coverage than perimeter heads alone. To overcome the necessity for manually positioning this centre sprinkler, some New Zealand clubs have opted for a buried pop-up centre sprinkler with the head disguised by a small circle of artificial turf laid flush with the green's surface. Alternatively, it is possible to fill a cup-shaped receptacle on the pop-up head with soil and hence grow grass or *Cotula* in that position - such heads are then virtually invisible when retracted and do not affect the run of a bowl passing over. An economical pop-up system might be envisaged, which consists of only one large central sprinkler set to throw water in a large circle extending out to the green's corners. This would mean that some water is wasted as it of necessity falls on surrounding banks and paths (particularly at the mid-point of each of the green's sides), and would necessitate a larger head in the centre of the green, disguised by a larger plug of artificial or natural turf. In practice, it would be impossible to achieve a sufficiently even distribution patern from a single central head and the necessity for perimeter sprinklers cannot therefore be avoided.

RENOVATION AND REPAIRS
Worn areas evident at the end of the bowling season will need renovating and thus the question arises should one seed or turf worn parts? Perhaps the general answer to this question is best expressed as follows:-

[1] If there are bare areas at rink ends - re-turf.

[2] If there are thin areas (as distinct from bare ground) at rink ends - overseeding could be undertaken if the work can be done early in the autumn.

There are, however, a number of important points to bear in mind when renovating.

Overseeding
Only use proven cultivars of Chewings fescue and browntop bent grass seed obtained from a reputable seed house. The thin turf should be adequately pricked or forked or maybe lightly raked to provide a suitable surface on which to overseed (the seed could perhaps be mixed with a little compost). The necessity to do this work early in the autumn cannot be overstressed if the technique is to prove successful. Make sure during the overseeding work that levels are not upset.

Turfing
If possible try and use turf which matches that already on the green - this is when a turf nursery on site can be so useful. If turf has to be imported make sure that the soil in which the turf is growing is not of a heavy nature, but a free-draining, sandy loam material.

PLATES 99 & 100. Turf repair tools make accurate patching much simpler. The 9 in. square Turf Doctor and 6 in. round Turf Plugger from Better Methods Europe of Poole, Dorset.

One of the most common mistakes made by amateur greenkeepers is obvious when inspecting their turfing. Turf introduced into worn parts is usually left proud to allow for settlement. The latter invariably never happens or at least not to the extent expected, consequently during the first close cut the next season the area is scalped and the problem begins all over again. When re-turfing worn patches one should:-

[a] Remove the turf to the thickness of the new turf being introduced.

[b] Thoroughly fork over underlying soil particularly if there are layers of sand, soil, peat, etc.

[c] Re-firm the cultivated soil perhaps by heeling and raking if possible to ensure an evenly firmed turf bed condition.

[d] Lay the new turf on to the prepared surface so that it is flush with surrounding ground, not proud in anticipation of settlement. Top dress lightly.

There should be no settlement problem if the turf bed is properly firmed, but if the odd turf does sink a little, levels could be made good with some top dressing.

Although turfing can proceed much later into the autumn than seeding, it is still good policy to try and finish the work as soon as possible, and certainly before the worst of the winter weather arrives. One final word about turfing particularly on rink ends; make sure the turf is mature and not one of the seedling types (the latter probably not having sufficient strength to stand up to heavy play the following season).

Levels
The advantages of obtaining an accurate survey of playing surface levels have been stressed earlier. This is of considerable help if remedial work on surface levels is being contemplated as a part of autumn renovation and repair work. With such information available contour lines can be drawn on to the plan and a clear indication of exactly where and how big low or high areas are. It is surprising how many times people have tried to fill in a 'valley' whereas in fact the correct course of action would have been to have lowered the 'hills'.

With an accurate survey exact remedial work can proceed. If level discrepancies are, say, ± 18 mm (³/₄ in.) then remedial top dressing work over a period of time could correct low spots whereas hollow tining (maybe on several occasions over 2-3 years) could lower high areas. If the low or high spots are in excess of ± 18 mm (³/₄ in.) it is worth contemplating more extensive work, i.e. removing the turf, adjusting soil levels as necessary and returning the turf. Such levelling work is of a specialist nature, and should only be undertaken by a skilled and confident greenkeeper if the area to be covered is of any size. Large-scale re-turfing of a major part of a bowling green's total area is probably best left to a specialised and experienced sportsground contractor. The major re-contouring of either flat or crown greens is a very skilled task and the inexperienced turfer could well end up with a surface even more uneven than the one he was attempting to correct.

Raising the edges
Besides general discrepancies within the body of the green a particular concern at many clubs is a situation where the edges of the green tend to fall away. In such instances the problem can be solved by cutting the turf into strips about 300 mm (1 ft.) wide at right angles to the green and carefully slicing under the turf with a turf float to create a turf which can be rolled back towards the centre of the green. The turf should obviously be rolled back a sufficient distance to allow levels to be made good. Extra sandy loam soil should be bought in to make up any deficiencies in levels ensuring that this imported material is properly firmed before unrolling and re-laying the turf to the required level. Again, it is important to be aware of the dangers of leaving the edges proud in anticipation of settlement.

If the actual edge of the green has to be raised 25-50 mm (1-2 in.) it is not a bad idea to lay a narrow inverted strip of turf with a heavy soil right on the edge of the green upon which to eventually re-lay the rolled up turf. This technique at least produces a very firm edge to the green (due to the heavy soil) - problems can be encountered with crumbling edges if there is any significant build up of sandy soil over the inner kerb edge.

Spring renovation

Autumn renovation work is always preferable as this leaves a longer period for establishment and recovery before play starts once again. Not infrequently, however, some renovation must also be completed in the spring - in a situation for example where a green has been vandalised or damaged by disease over the winter months. Winter moss control can also leave bare patches where dead moss has been raked out. (If moss control is carried out late in the off-season it can be wise to leave patches of dead moss undisturbed. These will slowly disappear and the grass grow in, causing less disruption of the playing surface than if the moss is raked out to leave bare spots at the start of the playing season.)

Great care must be taken if renovating in the spring to avoid adding to problems with disrupted surface levels. Success is also to a great extent dependent on the weather - in late springs no growth may occur before play starts and overseeded patches may not germinate and establish before they are overtaken by play. Spring renovation must therefore commence as early in the year as possible, as soon as the weather is at all reasonable. Light top dressing, at least of damaged patches and possibly of the whole surface can sometimes be appropriate at this time to speed germination of seeded patches and to maintain good levels.

Turfing can be most useful in the spring, particularly for the minor patching of small scars. Again, great care must be taken with levels, avoiding the practice of leaving new turves standing proud against the surrounding surface. Turf patching tools which cut square or circular turf plugs and which allow them to be fitted into identically sized holes cut in the green with the same tool, are particularly useful for spring work. Similar work may sometimes be necessary during the actual playing period but the need for playing surface renovation when play is proceeding should be avoided if at all possible. It is difficult to ensure that seed germinates satisfactorily or that turf establishes successfully when the green is being cut low and renovated areas disturbed by the players.

The success of renovation can sometimes be improved by confining play to healthy areas of the green while damaged patches are attended to. It is relatively easy to close one rink on a flat green early in the autumn or late in the spring to allow for renovation, but even on crown greens something similar can often be arranged if players co-operate.

RINK MANAGEMENT

It is hoped that the crown green fraternity (to whom of course the subject is of no interest) will bear with us for a moment so that the importance of rink changing in flat green management can be stressed. The subject has been touched upon earlier, but is worth considering in more detail as it is often the cause of argument in many clubs, with certain bowlers taking it as a personal affront that the greenkeeper has moved strings off a favourite rink position.

For a flat green the ideal to be aimed for is a completely uniform surface with constant playing characteristics over all parts. This theoretical ideal is probably never achieved in practice but it is essential to attempt to approach it as closely as possible. Any factor which tends to concentrate play and wear on certain areas of the green is hence undesirable and tends to work against surface uniformity. Where play is concentrated on popular rinks, very significant differences between used and unused parts of the green can appear in time. Worn areas tend to show a higher annual meadow-grass content, more soil compaction, shallower root growth and less surface fibre (although more sub-surface thatch) than areas not played upon which in contrast tend to become soft, mossy and matted. Surface uniformity of playing characteristics is hence lost and it is worth remembering that a uniform surface is a key factor in separating a good green from a poor one. Changes in surface level are also a result of concentrating on a limited number of rink positions, heavily used rinks becoming gutter-shaped in time with consequent deleterious effects on bias and the quality of the game.

For the long-term welfare of a flat green therefore, it is essential to move rink markers as much as possible and to encourage bowlers to use as high a proportion of the total available area as possible. It is impossible to give hard and fast rules as to exactly how this should be done in practice as greens vary in overall size. The permissible variation for both E.B.A. and Federation greens is between 40 x 40 yd. and 44 x 44 yd. (120 x 120 ft. and 132 x 132 ft), but there are of course many non-standard greens, some in the shape of narrow rectangles, where play is only possible in two directions rather than four. In the case of greens where the dimensions approach the 42 x 42 yd. (126 x 126 ft) which can be regarded as the norm however, variations in rink position can be achieved by:-

[a] Varying the width of rinks
For the game played under Association rules, rink width may be varied between 18 ft. and 19 ft. Federation rules are more flexible, the permitted variation in this case being 16 ft. to 21 ft. Narrower rinks are permissible for friendly play (14 ft. minimum) on EBA greens.

[b] Varying the position of rinks
Six rinks are normal for a standard sized green and fit well within the limits set by the 126 ft. length of the green sides (remember a margin of at least 2 ft. must be left between the string of the end rink and the adjacent parallel side of the green) so six 19 ft. rinks take up 6 x 19 = 114 ft. plus two 2 ft. margins = 118 ft. This leaves 8 ft. spare for varying string positions by increasing or decreasing the width of the side margins.

[c] Varying the number of rinks
The maximum number of rinks are a necessity when the green is busy, but in slacker periods it may be possible to reduce the number and hence vary positioning even further.

This question of varying playing positions can become extremely complex, so most clubs settle on a simplified system, having coloured marks along the inner ditch kerbing representing perhaps three alternative rink positions. Strings should be changed daily from one colour to another, on a rota system. In addition, wear should be further spread by changing the direction of play through 90° at least once a week, and preferably more than once a week in wet weather or periods of poor growth.

One can never entirely escape the problem that end rinks are unpopular as they run along the worn rink ends caused by play in the other direction. All that can be done is to minimise wear as far as possible on all rink ends, bringing us back to our basic argument that play must be as evenly spread over the green, as far as this is possible. The co-operation of players is a main requirement and all club members should be made aware of the long-term problems caused by the over-use of favourite rinks.

It is in fact possible on most greens approaching standard size, by the sensible positioning of full width rinks or by the use of narrower rinks for casual play, to maximize the size of spare areas of the green surface running between the outside string of the end rink in play and the ditch of the parallel side. This allows the greenkeeper to work on these spare areas, which of course include the worn heads of rinks running at right angles. Spiking, hand forking and surface pricking can all be performed without interfering with the area in play. During the playing season as a whole therefore, considerable extra work can be carried out on all rink ends and it is these areas where damage is concentrated in the flat rink game. Judicious rink positioning can also allow the centre of the green to be covered during such extra work but this part of a flat green takes far less wear than the ends so additional treatment is not often essential for the centre area of the green. This is a most important point in the maintenance of flat greens which is overlooked by many greenkeepers who do not realise how much of a green's surface is not actually being played over at any one time.

The use of mats can be very helpful in minimising wear. They are particularly appropriate for use at the end of the season (say early September onwards) when major competition play has usually ceased and when greens tend to be wetter and hence more easily scarred. The open-weave nylon mesh type of matting is to be preferred to denser textured materials.

THE CARE OF DITCHES, BANKS AND SURROUNDS
Although the highest proportion of the greenkeeper's time will obviously be spent on the actual playing surface itself, ancillary surrounding features of the green too need regular attention if they are to remain in satisfactory condition.

Ditches
To consider ditch maintenance first, EBA rules state that the surface of the ditch infilling

material should be no less than 2 in. (51 mm) or more than 8 in. (203 mm) below the level of the green itself - this should be checked periodically. (Requirements are much less rigid for the Crown or Federation codes.)

A variety of materials are currently available as ditch infilling. A list can be presented as follows, with the possible advantages and disadvantages of each. Remember that requirements are much more exacting in the case of the EBA game where a bowl is not necessarily dead when in the ditch and where any lateral movement of the bowl along the ditch must be prevented.

[a] Sand: grade is important - medium sands of even particle size are probably best. Coarse particles, if present, can scratch bowls whilst a proportion of silty fines can lead to packing and hence poorly drained ditches. Sand filled ditches are somewhat prone to weed growth. Total weedkiller may be used in such situations but great care must be taken during application to avoid contaminating the edge of the green and killing the grass. Non-residual weedkiller only should be used, either a contact material such as paraquat or preferably a systemic herbicide like glyphosate. Bowls or the soles of shoes may become contaminated with the material immediately after application and hence transferred to the playing surface - the work is therefore best done when play is not taking place. In wet conditions after rain or irrigation, sand tends to adhere to bowls causing some annoyance to players. Sand is reasonably effective at killing the motion of a bowl, providing it is kept reasonably loose and not allowed to pack down too hard.

[b] Pebbles: the most commonly encountered ditch infilling material is smooth, rounded pepples, usually between 1/2 in (12 mm) and 3/4 in. (18 mm) in diameter. Such pebbles are usually considered suitable for the purpose, although they are by no means perfect as some scratching of bowls can occur. An alterntive material is Lytag of 10-12 mm grade. Pebbles are effective at preventing lateral bowl travel, but vandals can throw handfulls onto the green perhaps causing damage to mowing equipment etc.

[c] Corks: old wine-bottle corks can be obtained cheaply in some localities. They are excellent at preventing damage to bowls and kill motion quite well. Their main disadvantage is that they can float out onto the green in very wet conditions, or even occasionally blow out of the ditch in very high wind.

[d] Wood chips: advantages and disadvantages are similar to those for corks.

[e] Rubber chips: nodules of hard rubber are excellent ditch fill material, killing bowl motion very effectively and being heavy enough to stay in position. It is interesting to note that in trials comparing various ditch materials held at Worthing in preparation for the 1992 World Bowls Championships, rubber chips were preferred by players and officials. A cheap source of supply are sporting-goods manufacturers - mis-shapen reject shuttlecock heads are ideal for the purpose, and apparently available in quantity.

The above materials might all be described as loose aggregates - most become soiled in time and need to be removed and washed periodically, this being usually a winter taks for the greenkeeper. Our listing can be continued to cover more rigid ditch liners.

[f] Industrial belting: old mill pulley belts or strips of mine conveyor belt are traditional ditch topping for crown green ditches, usually laid as a cover over gravel or sand. Almost indestructable, such material remains popular but does not stop bowls moving along ditches and is hence unsuitable for EBA greens.

[g] Battens: ladder-like sections of wooden battens are commonly used for both crown and flat green ditches. As an alternative in recent years, a number of EBA clubs have used plastic duck-boarding as a final ditch surface with great success. This consists of a vinyl lattice of strips at right angles, actually manufactured as floor covering for changing rooms etc. It is available in vaious lengths 600 mm wide, so it has to be cut down into strips corresponding in width to the bowling green ditch width. The material is placed in the ditch so that the strips of the lattice, which are uppermost run across the width of the ditch, longitudinal strips being underneath. This ensures that woods falling into the ditch do not move laterally along the ditch,

183

s they are held in the groove between lattice strips running across the ditch. Use of this material appears to be an ideal method of eliminating scratching problems without creating any other disadvantages, and it is easy to lift for cleaning, but does not prevent weed growth in underlying sand or gravel.

[h] Wener ditchfill: a commercial product supplied by Wener Amenity Landscaping of Barnet, Herts., this is a dimpled black rubber material with a surface resembling an egg-box. It is easy to lift and hose down and eliminates damage to bowls. It may, however, allow some lateral movement of bowls on rare occasions, particularly if the bowl is spinning rapidly. Weed growth in underlying material is obviously eliminated, but the material is relatively expensive.

[i] Artificial turf: supplied commercially by a number of firms including the Sportsmark Group Ltd. Sportsmark supply Astroturf which resembles a long, loose-pile, green carpet. The only problem with such material hinges around whether they kill bowl travel along ditches completely effectively. Cost is also quite high.

Banks
As for the green itself, mowing is of course the most frequent operation for grass banks. The traditional hand shears are still used for this purpose, usually at weekly intervals during the growing season. Spinning filament mowers of the strimmer type are now also widely used, with a considerable saving of time and labour as compared to the use of hand clippers. Rotary mowers of this type must be used carefully, trying to cut at an even 12 mm (^{1}/$_2$ in.) or so. Over-close cutting on bank faces is all too easy and will in time weaken the grass and encourage bank erosion.

PLATE 101. Cleaning ditches with a purpose-made rake marketed by Better Methods Europe of Poole, Dorset.

Operations such as moss and weed control are sometimes necessary on banks and should be carried out using methods and materials advised earlier for the green itself. Weedy banks are not only unsightly but are also a source of infection, seed being easily transferred to the bowling surface. Bank renovation is usually required periodically as bank faces can erode or subside. Turfing is usually the best method of repair, pegging new turf in place as described earlier for initial green construction. Difficulties in maintaining a strong turf on bank faces is often the result of summer drought - banks tend to dry out very rapidly. Hand watering should therefore not be neglected if required; one usually finds that south and west facing banks dry out first.

Wall surrounds and high-backed purpose made ditch units (as discussed previously) minimise such maintenance work but such constructions are not completely maintenance-free. Striking boards and battens need replacement at times. If artificial turf is used as a facing it is very easy to damage it when mowing around the edge of the green. Adhesive should be kept in stock so that sections torn by the mower can be glued back or replaced. The Sportsmark Group Ltd. now market a hard rubber bumper as an alternative to wooden striking battens.

Surrounds
It is hardly necessary to say that, although a well kept playing surface is the heart of a bowling club, required maintenance work extends further than banks or ditches. Pavilions, flower-beds and other features also require regular attention and pleasant and well kept surroundings can add a great deal to the pleasure of the game.

Of perhaps more relevance here is the fact that some features of the green's surroundings can have a definite effect on the quality of the surface. Take the case of perimeter fencing, and particularly hedging, for example. Walls, solid fencing such as larch-lapp for instance and hedges should be at least 10 feet from the green to minimise shade effects. It should be remembered that shaded greens tend to be damper and this adds to problems with slow bowling surfaces, annual meadow-grass and fusarium patch disease. Ideally bowling greens should be on very open sites, but there is a conflict here between the needs of the green and the needs of the bowlers. Shelter makes playing conditions more pleasant on windy days and a strong wind across a green can make accurate bowls doubly difficult, if not impossible. A compromise must obviously be arrived at - windbreaks should be as far from the green as is practicable and should not be excessively high. Hedges should not be allowed to grow more than 5-6 feet high.

A further problem with hedges, particularly if they are too close, is root growth under the playing surface or into perimeter ditch drains. Turf weakness near the edge of a green can not uncommonly be attributed to this cause - strongly growing hedge plants like Cupressus and privet are paticularly troublesome. In certain circumstances it may prove necessary to sever roots - usually this involves trenching around the outer edge of the path surround and infilling with broken stone (plastic sheeting to create an unbroken physical root barrier may also be appropriate) to prevent re-growth.

Single trees near the green can create the same problem of drought-stricken and starved looking areas of turf. Again roots may have to be pruned and their growth blocked. Overhanging branches too should certainly be pruned to minimise shade and autumn leaf fall onto the green.

Path surrounds should be kept in good condition. As with banks, moss and weed growth can be a source of infection for the playing surface and suitable herbicides should be used if necessary.

A common query is whether foot baths of fungicide or disinfectant should be provided to prevent fusarium and other disease spores being carried from other outside turf areas onto the green. This on the face of it would seem a wise precaution but is in fact almost totally pointless. A cupful of soil from virtually every green in the country will contain millions of disease spores and these will develop to produce symptoms if conditions are favourable to the development of the fungus. Cross-infection from one green to another is not therefore a significant factor - disease can only be combatted by the methods outlined earlier, i.e. maintaining a healthy disease-resistant sward and using fungicide when applicable.

Other points in the general management of ancillary features of the green are to vary the point of entrance to the green if possible to spread the wear caused by players constantly stepping onto the green at the same point. Mowers and other equipment should also be taken onto the green by varied routes, usually by means of a moveable ramp over bank and ditch. One can also mention draining external pipework of irrigation systems to prevent winter frost damage, and examining silt pits and inspection chambers of the green's drainage system to ensure that water flow from drains is as it should be, clearing silt deposits and rodding drains etc. as necessary.

TURF NURSERIES

A well maintained nursery of suitable replacement turf is of great value for the repair of areas damaged by wear, disease, accident or vandalism. It is appreciated that a suitable space is not always available but wherever it is possible to have one the value of a turf nursery should not be overlooked.

The preferred position is one that is easily accessible and within reach of the hydrants, possibly adjacent to the storage sheds used for machinery and materials. The site should be well prepared and have a cover of stone-free soil (to facilitate lifting) matching the areas for which the turf is intended. Sometimes turf is used in constructing a new turf nursery but usually establishment is effected by sowing suitable grass seed, the mixture sown being selected to match the area being catered for. Initial preparation, fertilising, etc. should be on normal lines. In practice, preparing a turf nursery is a relatively straightforward matter but there is greater difficulty in ensuring the regular first-class maintenance which is so essential if the nursery is to serve its purpose of providing good replacement turf at short notice.

Usually nursery turf established from seed needs about two to three years before it is entirely satisfactory for replacement purposes so that a suitable size for a nursery is twice the estimated annual requirement plus an amount for emergencies. For a single green, a nursery of about 100 sq. yd. is probably adequate. Maintenance should involve at the very least, weekly cutting, spring fertilisation, occasional scarification and weed, worm and disease control as required. Most of the time one finds that nurseries tend to be rather neglected, but remember that a supply of suitable turf can be an invaluable resource at times.

APPENDIX A

Reprinted from the Journal of the Sports Turf Research Institute, Vol. 61, 1985

TECHNICAL NOTE
A SURVEY OF pH, PHOSPHATE AND POTASH LEVELS IN SOIL SAMPLES TAKEN FROM GOLF AND BOWLING GREENS

By D.M. STANSFIELD

The Sports Turf Research Institute, Bingley, West Yorkshire, BD16 1AU

SUMMARY

Results are presented of pH, phosphate and potash levels of some 1800 individual golf greens and 225 individual bowling greens sited throughout the United Kingdom and Ireland and sampled between 1978 and 1981. The summary of results shows 55% of golf greens and 25% of bowling greens have pH's less than 5.5. The phosphate levels show that 58% and 90% of all golf greens and bowling greens respectively have a P_2O_5 content of greater than 150 ppm. The potash levels show 28% and 20% of all golf greens and bowling greens respectively have a K_2O content greater than 150 ppm. In general the results show excessive amounts of potash and phosphate, particularly the latter, present in the rootzone material of golf and bowling greens.

INTRODUCTION

As a service to its subscribers, the Sports Turf Research Institute (STRI) undertakes chemical analysis of soil samples taken from turf areas used for sport. While a complete analysis can be made, as a routine mainly pH values, and the levels of extractable phosphate and potash, are measured. The results obtained are used as an aid to making recommendations for appropriate fertilizer programme(s) to clubs which subscribe to the STRI Advisory Service. The survey presented shows the results from tests on soils taken from 1800 individual golf greens and 225 individual bowling greens, sited throughout the U.K. and Ireland, between October 1978 and November 1981.

The clubs concerned receive advice on turf management from the STRI but all do not necessarily implement this fully with respect to fertilizer treatments. Also, some of the results have come from clubs which had only recently entered into membership of the STRI and in these cases the fertilizer programme applied prior to this will have affected the values obtained. No records are available which detail the various fertilizer programmes which have been applied and obviously this reduces the value of the results as a scientific survey. Similarly, there is no strict control over the sampling technique (samples are collected by individual clubs along guidelines provided) and as the timing of each sampling will vary within a given year means there are important variables which have not been controlled. The results presented here are simply to provide a record of the values obtained during routine soil analysis in recent years. In the future it is hoped to expand upon this work by carrying out more surveys of results obtained and thereby present a picture of the true value of the soil sample analysis to advisory work, that is the identification of trends in the availability of phosphate and potash, and changes in pH levels both within a given year and over a number of years.

MATERIALS AND METHODS

[1] Sampling technique.

Samples are usually collected by the club themselves. The recommended method is to randomly sub-sample a whole green where conditions are reasonably uniform, or to take separate bulk samples from each area where distinct differences in the turf are evident on a single green. Sub-samples are taken using a hollow tine fork and the cores raised bulked together to form a minimum 0.5 kg soil from a green or each area of a green. Sampling depth should be 100-125 mm.

Samples are air dried, crushed, then passed through a 2 mm mesh sieve prior to testing.

[2] pH determination.

20 g soil is mixed with 50 ml distilled water and allowed to stand for one hour with occasional stirring. pH is determined by means of a glass electrode and a direct reading meter.

[3] Extractable phosphate.

2.5 g soil is shaken with 100 ml N/2 acetic acid for one hour. The suspension is then filtered and diluted by a factor of ten. The phosphate content of the filtrate is determined by spectrophotometry using the molybdenum blue method, employing stannous chloride as the reducing agent.

[4] Extractable potash.

5 g soil is shaken with 25 ml Morgan's solution for one hour. The suspension is then filtered. The potash content of the filtrate is determined by flame photometer.

RESULTS

To give definition to the results presented, a soil reaction value of less than pH 5.5 is considered significantly acid, i.e. sufficiently acid for this to have some effect on the quality of the turf. For extractable phosphate and potash the dividing lines are at levels of 60 ppm and 150 ppm. Below 60 ppm there may be a theoretical deficiency of either of these nutrients. While above 150 ppm there is considered to be an unnecessarily high supply of phosphate and potash. Without further dilution, the maximum readings are: P2O5, 330 ppm; K2O, 210 ppm.

Categorization within the above groups is given in Table 1 and the overall findings are presented as histograms in Figures 1 and 2.

TABLE 1

Groupings of the percentage number of golf and bowling greens above or below "significant" dividing categories.

Category	Percentage No. of golf greens	Percentage No. of bowling greens
(i) pH less than 5.5	55.2	24.7
(ii) P_2O_5 less than 60 ppm	5.2	2.9
(iii) P_2O_5 greater than 150 ppm	57.6	90.3
(iv) P_2O_5 greater than 330 ppm but included in (iii)	25.4	75.0
(v) K_2O less than 60 ppm	6.9	17.5
(vi) K_2O greater than 150 ppm	27.6	19.5
(vii) K_2O greater than 210 ppm but included in (vi)	9.4	8.9

DISCUSSION

The primary aim of soil analysis is to be an aid to advisory work and the analysis was not intended to be part of a scientific survey as such. Hence, while individual advisory officers (who interpret the data) will have been aware of the condition of the turf, soil type, the timing of the sampling, previous fertilizer treatments, etc., these have not been recorded for posterity, but just used as tools when offering practical advice. So a meaningful interpretation in chemical or biological terms cannot be presented because there are so many unknowns. For example, the extractable P_2O_5 greater than 330 ppm and extractable K_2O greater than 210 ppm groupings may represent heavily skewed distributions or those clubs who unthinkingly have applied complete fertilizer just before taking samples. Further work is now in progress which may assist with better interpretation of this data, but, again, the main intention here is to provide a record which can be used for the identification of trends when comparable results become available in the future.

The information presented here is indicative of frequency of the occurrence of situations which are thought to have a bearing on the condition of fine turf, in particular the type of fine turf one would wish to find on golf greens and bowling greens, i.e. composed predominantly of species of Agrostis and Festuca, and suffering with a minimum of weed invasion and worm casting. For example, it is generally considered that, on the majority of inland sites, an acid soil favours these desirable grasses. This is by no means the only factor involved, but only 55% of golf greens and 25% of bowling greens are on soils which could be considered significantly acid, i.e. less than pH 5.5 . Further to this, only 1% of soils from bowling greens are at a pH level which may be detrimental to good turf growth, while a more evident proportion of golf green soils, 7%, have been found in this very acid state. The number of areas within these two small groupings which may require some corrective measures as a last resort will be even smaller because the overall condition of the turf and the general trend of pH readings are more important than one reading at one point in time.

It is at the low end of the range of results for extractable phosphate where the values obtained could give advisory officers useful information for recommended fertilizer programmes, and it will be noted that in only 5% of golf green soils and 3% of bowling green soils, amongst those sampled, there is even a theoretical deficiency of this nutrient. The chances are that a level of deficiency of phosphate for fine turf grasses in a heavy wear situation is far lower than the 60 ppm extractable phosphate quoted, but there is no general agreement on a particular figure, and in very acid soils where availability of phosphate is very low, there is the possibility that the soil could be deficient in available phosphate even though the extractable phosphate level is above 60 ppm. Even so, widespread, routine use of phosphatic fertilizer on fine turf in the United Kingdom and Ireland appears to be a questionable procedure in terms of actual plant needs. A similar survey of golf greens in West Germany also concludes that phosphate fertilizer has been over supplied during the period 1973-1982 (Büring 1984).

The results for extractable potash show levels which are more depressed at the lower end of the range in comparison with available phosphate. This may reflect lower application rates, the effects of more rapid leaching, the effects of luxury uptake, or most likely a combination of these factors. However, in the absence of more information, one possible interpretation on the practical use of these figures is that potash should continue to be a relatively important part of the sphere of fertilization of fine turf grasses (dependent, of course, upon individual soil analysis and an assessment of site conditions in each case, particularly soil type and drainage) given the important interrelationship between potash availability and nitrogen uptake, along with its effects on disease and drought susceptibilities in turfgrasses.

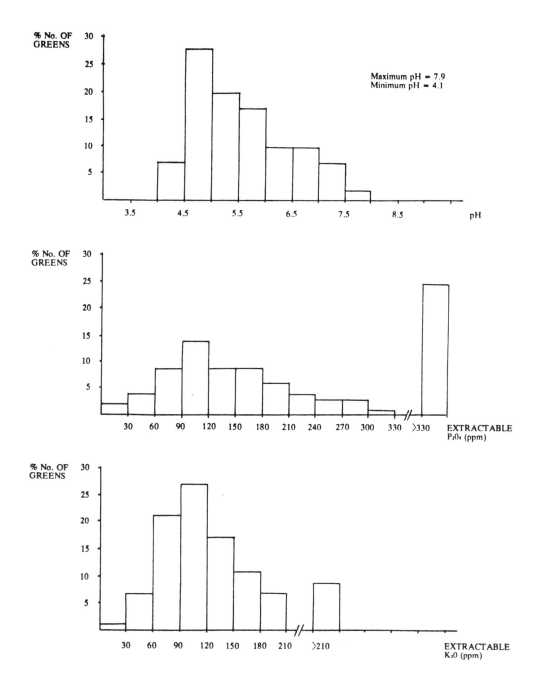

FIGURE 1.   Distribution of pH, extractable phosphate and extractable potash in soil samples taken from golf greens.

III

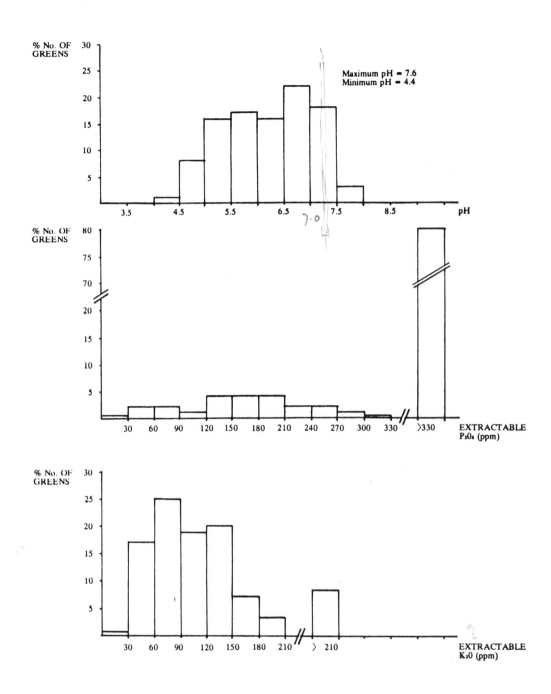

FIGURE 2. Distributions of pH, extractable phosphate and extractable potash in soil samples taken from bowling greens.

REFERENCES

Büring, W. (1984). Nutrient status of sports turf soil in the German Federal Republic, 1973-1982. *Zeitschrift für Vegetationstechnik* **7**, 45-55.

IV

APPENDIX B

Reprinted from the Journal of the Sports Turf Research Institute, Vol. 62, 1986

THE PLAYING QUALITY OF LEVEL BOWLING GREENS

By G. Holmes & M.J. Bell

The Sports Turf Research Institute, Bingley, West Yorkshire, BD16 1AU

INTRODUCTION

Four criteria are often cited in popular bowling literature as being indicative of the ideal level bowling green: a level surface, fast green speed, an even draw on both backhand and forehand and a good cover of fine turfgrasses, yet rarely are all these criteria met in an objective sense. Robinson (1977) suggested that although bowling can be enjoyed at a recreational level on a "less than perfect" green, as the standard of play increases, so the requirements of the players become more stringent and greater emphasis is placed on the above criteria. Indeed, Robinson ventured to suggest that a green should be of such quality that the result of a competitive game is solely dependent on the relative skills of the players and is not a matter left to chance.

The purpose of this work was to: (i) identify the playing characteristics of level bowling greens that are most important to bowlers; (ii) measure the playing quality of a sample of bowling greens and (iii) propose test methods and standards for playing quality.

In order to develop standards for bowling greens, data on surface levels and green speed were collected over a three year period between 1985 and 1987. Seventy-four bowling clubs from most regions of Great Britain agreed to take part in the survey. The bowling clubs included members of the English, Scottish and Welsh Bowling Associations and the English Bowling Federation. Of this sample, 54 (73%) were members of the Sports Turf Research Institute. Although the Clubs were selected randomly from County Handbooks with an equal split of members and non-members, it appears that members of the Institute were most willing to co-operate with the research. Ten of the greens were maintained by Local Authorities, the remainder by the clubs themselves.

MATERIALS AND METHODS

Measurement of surface levels

An automatic surveyor's level was used to survey the 74 bowling greens and surface height was measured to an accuracy of 1mm. Thirty-four greens were surveyed with spot heights at 2m centres, 29 at 3m centres, two at 4m centres and nine at 5m centres. Measurements of surface height were made around the edges of the greens as well as on the main playing area of each green. The statistical analyses of the data were restricted to the measurements taken on the main playing area of the green although the measurements around green edges proved to be useful in the proposal of standards.

Four statistics were used to assess the variation of surface levels within a green: (i) the range or difference between the highest and lowest points on the green; (ii) the maximum gradient between contiguous spot heights; which allows for the different sampling grids used; (iii) the standard deviation of the spot heights and (iv) the kurtosis of the spot heights (see below). The surface levels of a bowling green are best described using a group of statistics as, individually, none of the above measures adequately describes the variations in surface levels.

Although it was intended to keep the tests of playing quality simple, with the objective that they could be easily understood and employed by the 'lay-person', it soon became obvious that simple measures were poor descriptors of surface evenness. Hence, statistical measures such as standard deviation and kurtosis have been employed with the justification that they summarise sets of data but retain descriptive power.

Kurtosis is a measure of the 'peakedness' of a frequency distribution. A positive kurtosis value indicates that the distribution of spot heights is narrower and more peaked than a normal distribution while a negative kurtosis value indicates that the distribution of spot heights is wider and flatter than the normal distribution. A normal distribution of spot heights would give a kurtosis of zero (see Equation 1). The ideal situation for a bowling green surface is a high and positive kurtosis value which would indicate that most of the spot heights are very similar.

The kurtosis is calculated from:

$$k = \frac{\sum_{i=1}^{N}[(X_i - \bar{X})/s]^4}{N} - 3 \qquad \textbf{Equation 1}$$

where: k = kurtosis; N = number of spot heights; X_i = value of the ith spot height; X = mean value of the spot heights; s = standard deviation of the spot heights.

Tests were also made of the surface evenness of greens over 2m lengths using a profile gauge (Holmes & Bell 1986b). Four sets of ten measurements were taken on each rink, the evenness of a rink being expressed as the average of the sample standard deviation for the four sets of ten measurements.

Measurement of green speed
Green speeds were measured in two ways: (a) the average distance rolled by ten non-biased bowls (five observations from each end of a rink) when released from 1m height down a ramp and (b) recording by stopwatch the time taken for a biased bowl to travel from the bowler's hand and stop within 0.15m of a jack sited 27.4m (30 yards) from the front edge of the bowling mat. The second measure of speed gives a time in seconds and is the definition of green speed given in the Laws of the Game (English Bowling Association 1986). Only bowls that stopped within 0.15m of the jack were used to measure green speed. Twenty bowling clubs assisted by recording the speed of one or more rinks on their greens during the 1985 season, using the second method described above. The number of green speed measures varied from one per week to two per season.

The correlation between green speed (method b) and the distance rolled test (method a) was studied using 62 pairs of green speed/distance rolled values collected in 1985. All the green speed tests above 13 seconds were measured on synthetic bowling greens. Linear regression was used to predict green speed from the mean distance rolled by ten non-biased bowls.

Bowlers' perceptions of playing quality
Bowlers were asked to complete a questionnaire that asked their opinion of the surface levels, the uniformity of bowl bias on each hand and the speed of the green they had just played on. Seventy-nine questionnaires were collected in 1985, 366 in 1986 and 329 in 1987, a total of 774. The basic data set consisted of coded responses to the questionnaires with the values for green speed (if measured) and the different measures of surface evenness for each record. Each record also contained the playing quality measurements for the rink on which the individual played.

Uneven surface levels can prove disruptive to a game if they occur in the vicinity of the jack, usually between 25m and 32m from the mat. Within this area bowls generally roll slowly making them susceptible to uneven levels. Knowing the directions of play and rinks upon which bowlers detected a difference in the reaction to bias on left and right hand draw, the green evenness data was used to test if local gradients at rink ends influenced the reaction to the bias of a bowl (Holmes & Bell 1986a).

If there is an even decline in surface levels from a relatively high left hand edge of a rink towards its right hand edge, then a bowl released down the left hand side of the rink will need to be drawn wider than one sent down the right hand side, in order to stop in the rink centre. Following this supposition, the replies given by bowlers to the question concerning the reaction to bowl bias on each hand were coded according to those responses that would be predicted by analysis of the surface geometry at the rink end and those that would not (Holmes & Bell 1986a). The surface evenness data were analysed by subtracting the spot heights R1 and R2 from the spot heights L1 and L2, respectively (Figure 4.1) and using the criteria shown in Figure 4.2, the expected response to the bias of a bowl was compared with the responses as perceived by players. In Figure 4.1, C denotes the centre of the rink.

Other data
The surface hardness of five greens was measured by a Clegg Impact Soil Tester in 3m x 3m test plots covering the whole green. A 0.5kg hammer was dropped from a height of 0.3m and five observations were made in each test plot. Tests of surface hardness were also combined with green speed measurements at 33 rinks to ascertain if green speed was affected by the hardness of the bowling surface.

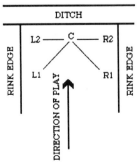

FIGURE 4.1: The position of spot heights used to calculate the gradient of rink ends

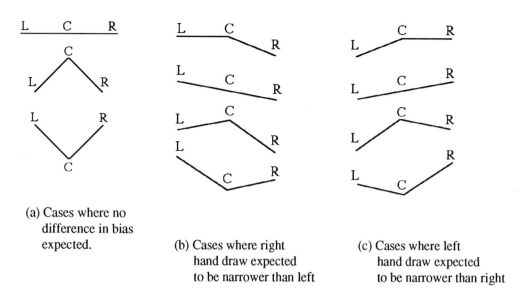

(a) Cases where no difference in bias expected.

(b) Cases where right hand draw expected to be narrower than left

(c) Cases where left hand draw expected to be narrower than right

FIGURE 4.2: Schematic view of the criteria used for determining expectedvariations in the draw of bowls

The clubs that co-operated with the work in 1985 were asked to record the number of hours use each rink received per day and the time spent on different maintenance jobs each day. The hours of green usage were expressed as the sum of the total number of hours of use each rink received. Of the 50 clubs that agreed to keep these records, 19 returned usage data for the full season and 21 recorded the maintenance carried out during the season. In addition, 15 clubs completed a questionnaire that asked for more details of the maintenance procedures carried out and for an estimate of the total expenditure on maintenance.

RESULTS
Variation of heights within the sample of bowling greens
Figure 4.3 shows the frequency of height ranges found on the 74 surveyed bowling greens and for individual rinks where questionnaire responses were obtained.

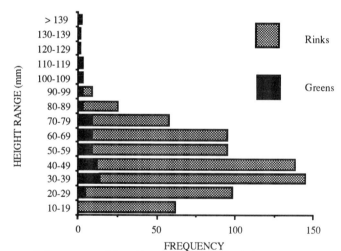

FIGURE 4.3: Height ranges of the surveyed bowling greens and individual rinks

Both frequency distributions have a modal height range of 30-39mm. For the main playing areas of greens, the lowest height range of 23mm was found on a newly-constructed green. The largest height range for the main playing area of a green of 226mm was for a green thought to be over 200 years old. The average height range for the main playing areas was 65mm. The maximum height range for individual rinks was 96mm and the minimum was 12mm. The standard deviation of the spot heights for the main playing areas of greens varied from 4.4mm to 60.7mm. The maximum standard deviation recorded for a rink was 25.7mm and the minimum was 3.4mm. Maximum slopes between adjacent spot heights ranged from 0.17° to 1.06° with a mean of 0.50°. The kurtosis values ranged from -1.36 to 2.67, the mean being -0.13.

Figure 4.4 shows the distribution of spot heights on two greens, one with comparitively good surface levels (kurtosis = 2.67), the other with relatively poor levels (kurtosis = -1.03).

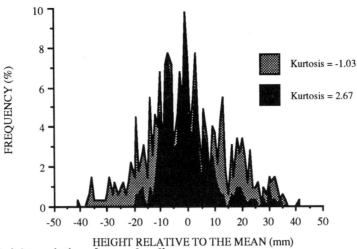

FIGURE 4.4: Surface height variations for two bowling greens

Figure 4.5 shows the variability in the surface evenness of rinks for which questionnaire data were collected and for the 74 greens surveyed. 32% of the rink standard deviations occurred in the range 10-14mm and 29% in the range 5-9mm.

The frequency of rink standard deviations as measured using the profile gauge is given in Figure 4.6. The distribution is symmetrical with 52.3% of the rinks occurring in the range 1.5-1.999mm.

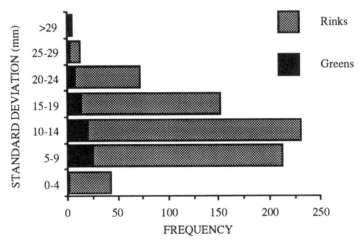

FIGURE 4.5: Rink and green standard deviations in surface evenness

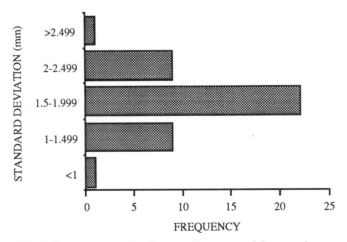

FIGURE 4.6: Rink standard deviations measured using profile gauge. Measured green speeds

Figure 4.7 shows the relationship between green speed as measured by the 30 yard test and the distance rolled by a non-biased bowl. The distance rolled and green speed are strongly correlated (r = 0.98***) so that green speed can be predicted from the distance rolled using the equation:

VIII

$$Gs = 6.01 + 0.36Dr \quad (\pm 0.34) \qquad \textbf{Equation 2}$$

where: Gs = green speed (s); Dr = the distance rolled (m) by a non-biased bowl released from 1m down a ramp.

Figure 4.8 shows the frequency of green speeds measured during the project. The figure consists of 262 measures made by the authors and co-operating clubs in 1985 using the 30 yard test and 75 measures of distance rolled by non-biased bowls in 1987 that have been converted to a green speed in seconds using Equation 2. These data are not averages for greens but mean values recorded for individual rinks. The majority of green speed measures were between 10s and 12s, with an average speed of 11.0s.

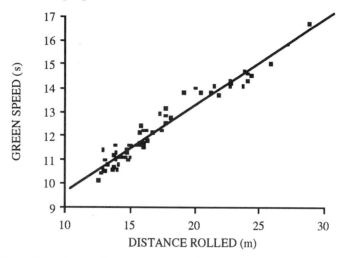

FIGURE 4.7: The relationship between distance rolled and green speed

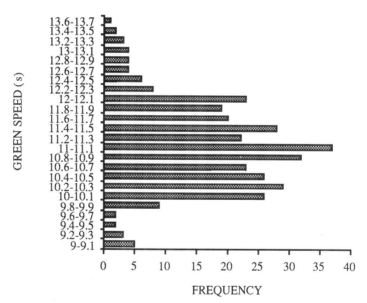

FIGURE 4.8: Green speeds recorded during the survey

The speeds of different rinks on the same green were found to vary by as much as 3.7s at the same time of day, although the mean variation in green speed between rinks on the same day (67 cases) was 0.67s.

Players often speak of a rink speeding up during a game. To examine the effect of successive bowl roll along the same track, a non-biased bowl was released 16 times along the same line using a ramp with a release height of 1m (so ensuring that the bowl was released with constant initial velocity) on a green with a measured green speed of 10.9s. Figure 4.9 shows that the distance rolled by the bowl increased by almost 2m during the test, an estimated increase in green speed of c. 0.5s.

Surface hardness
Figure 4.10 illustrates the variability in surface hardness of one bowling green. As expected, the rink ends were among the hardest areas of the green and softer areas occurred nearer the green centre. Although players continually walk between rink ends and down the centre of rinks, most wear and compaction occur at the rink ends where the

players congregate. The relatively lower amount of pedestrian traffic walking over the centre of the green may allow an increased accumulation of dead plant material known as "thatch" in the centre of bowling rinks. Thatch often causes a soft, sponge-like playing surface.

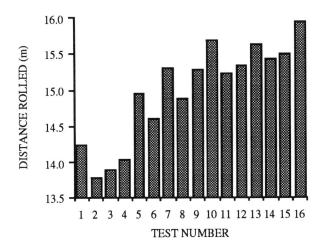

FIGURE 4.9: Progressive increase in the distance rolled by a bowl

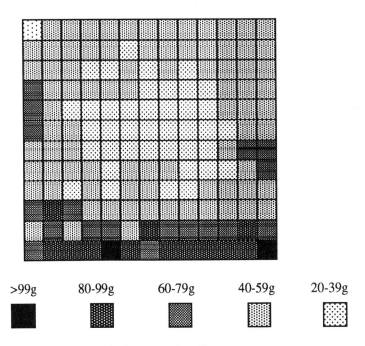

FIGURE 4.10: Surface hardness variations within a level bowling green

Lush (1985) reasoned that surface hardness should be positively correlated with green speed. She inferred that a bowl would deform the surface less on a hard green than on a soft green and consequently the deceleration of a rolling bowl would be smaller. This hypothesis is confirmed by the positive relationship between green speed and Clegg Impact hardness ($r = 0.47***$) found in this study.

It is clear from Figure 4.10, however, that considerable variations in surface hardness can be found within one bowling rink. This suggests that the deceleration of a bowl may vary along its course in response to changes in the hardness of the playing surface. The deceleration of a bowl may also vary because of differences in sward characteristics (see section on green speeds).

DISCUSSION
Surface evenness
The four measurements of surface evenness show that the levels of bowling greens vary greatly. Gooch & Escritt (1975) recommended that the levels of a newly constructed green should be within ±6mm of the average height of the green. Sports Turf Research Institute (1985, 1987) suggested that if levels were within ±18mm from the green average (i.e. a range of 36mm) then the surface could be improved by selective top-dressing and hollow-tining.

However, if the discrepancy was greater than this figure, more extensive work such as returfing was recommended. None of the 74 greens surveyed during the study would satisfy Gooch & Escritt's recommendation and only 13 (17.6%) would not require the extensive remedial action suggested by Sports Turf Research Institute (1985, 1987).

The surveys revealed that local gradients between adjacent spot heights were up to 1.06° with an average of 0.50°. For comparison, the British Crown Green Bowling Association (1983) recommends that a new *c*. 37m x 37m green should have a crown height of 0.305m, giving average gradients of 0.62° from the crown to the corner of the green and 0.95° for the shortest distance between the crown and the ditch. Thus, many level greens have local gradients similar to the overall slopes found on crown greens.

Green speeds
The English Bowling Association (EBA) considers that the ideal speed for a level bowling green is 12-13s, and that speeds of less than 10s "should not occur" (J.F. Elms *pers. comm.*). The green speed results show that of the 337 speed tests carried out, only 13.3% fell within the EBA's ideal range and that 6.2% were below 10s.

There was little difference found between the speeds of different rinks on the same green when recorded at the same time of day, with a difference of 3.7s at one green being the largest variation. The latter difference cannot be easily explained, as the rinks had received similar amounts of play in the week preceding the test and on other occasions throughout the season the speeds had been similar or their rank order had been reversed. A possible explanation is that popular rinks may be more compacted because of greater pedestrian traffic and, given the relationship found between green speed and surface hardness, the surface of a rink that is less favoured may become relatively softer and slower.

The average club player may not be greatly concerned about the speeds of adjacent rinks being dissimilar, but in competitions, when bowlers may play consecutive games on different rinks, the effect could be important.

Variability of speed within a bowling green has long been thought to be caused by differences in grass species composition. As part of the project, a trial was set up in June 1986 at the Sports Turf Research Institute's trial ground to assess the influence of species composition on the rolling resistance of bowls (Canaway, Baker & Pye unpublished). Five turfgrass species were used: *Festuca rubra* ssp. *commutata* 'Frida', *Festuca rubra* ssp. *litoralis* 'Dawson', *Agrostis castellana* 'Highland', *Agrostis tenuis* 'Bardot' and *Poa annua* "Commercial". Each species was replicated four times in randomised blocks. Three non-biased bowls were released down a ramp from a height of 0.5m in opposing directions on each plot, giving 24 measurements for each species. The tests were made on 27 July 1987 when the turfgrass had been cut at a mowing height of 5mm.

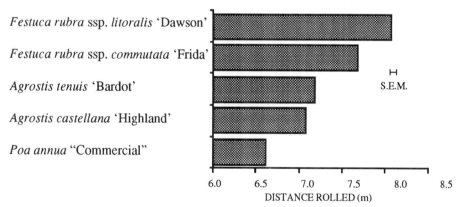

FIGURE 4.11: Distance rolled by a non-biased bowl on five turfgrass species

The data shown in Figure 4.11 are the distances rolled on each grass species. The average distance rolled on the *Poa annua* was 6.62m whereas the *Festuca rubra* ssp. *litoralis* produced the longest distance rolled of 8.07m. All the 'fine' turfgrasses gave longer rolling distances than the annual meadowgrass, with the two fescue species having the longest rolling distances. Canaway *et al.* also examined the influence of cutting height on green speed but surprisingly found smaller differences in speed between cutting heights than between grass species.

Bowlers often speak of a rink becoming faster during the day and on one occasion the speed of one rink was found to increase by 0.6s in three hours. Thus there are likely to be diurnal variations in green speed as well as longer term changes. The experiment described earlier in which ten bowls were released down the same track highlights the changes in green speed that may occur throughout a day. The successive tracking of bowls is thought to have flattened the grass so reducing its rolling resistance. This point is important as the green speed before a game is likely to be different to that recorded during the game's final stages.

Brearley & Bolt (1958) measured the distance rolled by biased bowls and the duration of rolling on three greens in Australia that were considered to be "fast", "medium" and "slow". The minimum, maximum and mean values of R/T^2 for each green and the corresponding green speeds are shown in Table 4.1.

TABLE 4.1
Minimum and maximum values of R/T^2 for "fast", "medium" and "slow" greens
(adapted from Brearley & Bolt 1958)

Green	Minimum value of R/T^2	Distance of minimum R/T^2(ft)	Corresponding green speed (s)	Maximum value of R/T^2	Distance of maximum R/T^2(ft)	Corresponding green speed (s)
"Fast"	0.41	57.7 64.4 89.4	14.8	0.46	47.7	14.0
"Medium"	0.48	11.5	13.7	0.56	43.9 91.2	12.7
"Slow"	0.57	55.4	12.6	0.67	21.9	11.6

Table 4.1 also gives an indication of the spatial variability of speed within a green. The fact that different length bowls produced different values of the ratio R/T^2 means that the speeds of the greens were not constant over the whole green. Using the method described in Section 2, however, the mean value of R/T^2 gives a good estimate of the green speed to within about ±0.5s. It is interesting to note that a "medium" green speed in Australia (12.7-13.7s, Table 4.1) would probably be considered relatively fast in the UK.

THE QUESTIONNAIRE SURVEY
For the purposes of comparing the data from the questionnaires with the playing quality test results, each test has been categorised into arbitrary classes (e.g. for the green speed test: 10-10.4s, 10.5-10.9s *etc.*) and the number of responses to each question given in the form of cells. The columns shown in Figures 4.12 and 4.13 are the categories for the test results and the rows record the different responses to each question. The cells are shaded to indicate the proportion of responses within each cell expressed as a percentage of each column e.g. what proportion of the players that played on a surface with a green speed between 10.0s and 10.4s thought that the speed was "slow" or "satisfactory".

Bowlers' perceptions of surface evenness
Of the 713 bowlers who replied to the question "Does the green undulate ? ", 258 (36.2%) answered "yes" and 455 (63.8%) answered "no". In response to the question asking if the surface of the green was bumpy, 530 bowlers (82.0%) said that the surfaces were "satisfactory". These responses suggest a general satisfaction with surface levels among bowlers although there appears to be a higher level of dissatisfaction expressed about the larger scale variations in surface evenness (undulations) than smaller scale variations (bumpiness).

The standard deviations of spot heights within rinks show that the majority of bowlers thought that the rinks did not undulate at standard deviations between 0-25mm (Figure 4.12). At standard deviations between 25mm and 30mm the majority of bowlers (53%) thought that the rinks undulated. The highest proportion of bowlers who considered that the rinks did not undulate was 88% in the standard deviations category of <5mm (Fig. 4.12). A standard deviation for a rink of less than 5mm would appear to be ideal but players still find standard deviations greater than 5mm acceptable.

Of bowlers who had played on rinks with green speeds over 11.5s, 84% thought that the rinks were "fast". 77% of the bowlers who said that the speeds were "unacceptably slow" had played on rinks with speeds below 10.5s. The survey showed that 85% of the bowlers stating that the green speed was "satisfactory" had played on rinks with speeds between 10.5s and 12s and that none thought the speed to be "satisfactory" below 10s. The highest proportion of "satisfactory" responses (77%) occurred for green speeds between 11s and 11.4s. At 12-12.4s, 65% thought that the speed was "fast".

The distribution of responses to the question regarding the smaller-scale variations (bumpiness) of the green showed that the majority of the bowlers stated that the surfaces were "satisfactory" at standard deviations of less than 3mm, as measured by the profile gauge. At standard deviations between 0.5mm and 1mm none of the bowlers thought that the rinks were "bumpy" or "unacceptably bumpy". At standard deviations between 1mm and 2.5mm, however, the proportion of bowlers that described the green surfaces as "bumpy" was 22%. A standard deviation for this test of ≤1.5mm may be appropriate for the average bowler.

X11

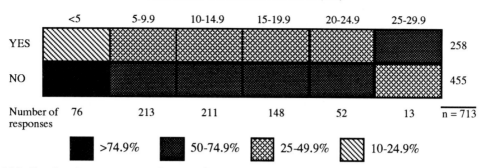

FIGURE 4.12: Bowlers' responses to the question "Does the rink undulate?" by standard deviation of rink spot heights

A sample of 612 bowlers replied to the question asking if the rink they had just played on gave an equal reaction to bias on both hands. Of these, 372 (60.8%) said the reaction to bias was not equal, although only about half of these responses were as predicted for the L1/R1 and L2/R2 slopes using the criteria given in Figure 4.2.

A total of 240 bowlers stated that there was no difference in reaction to bias on the rink thay had just played on. The only cases where such responses would be predicted are if the slopes either side of the rink centre are equal or if the rink is perfectly flat (i.e. L1-R1=0 and L2-R2=0) or that any difference in slope is negligible. However, this rarely occurred on the greens surveyed in this study but approximately 50% of the total number of bowlers who detected no difference in bias did so at L-R values of 8mm or less. This may be an indication of the difference in levels at the rink end below which the majority of bowlers do not detect a difference in the reaction to bias.

Bowlers' perceptions of green speed
Of the 405 players who answered the question concerning the speed of the rink they had just played on, 29 (7.2%) stated that the rinks were "fast", 283 (69.9%) said that the speeds were "satisfactory", 75 (18.5%) said they were "slow" and 18 (4.4%) said they were "unacceptably slow". No bowlers were of the opinion that the rinks were "unacceptably fast".

A total of 326 questionnaires was completed for occasions when a green speed test had been carried out immediately before matches. Figure 4.13 shows the relationship between bowlers' opinions of green speed and the green speed measurements in these cases. There is good agreement between green speeds recorded before matches and players' opinions (Figure 4.13). The chi-square test was used to test for equality in the distribution of responses by cells. Chi-square equalled 187.8***, indicating that the responses were not equally distributed within the cells.

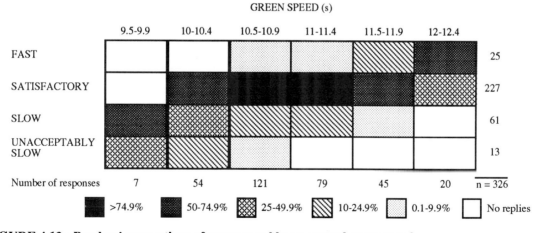

FIGURE 4.13: Bowlers' perceptions of green speed by measured green speed.

The responses regarding green speed were probably influenced by the playing characteristics of the greens the bowlers had played on most recently. In a hot and dry summer, similar green speeds to those found during the survey would probably result in more "slow" and "unacceptably slow" responses. In the summer of 1985 and during June 1987, when most of the questionnaires were collected, the EBA's "ideal" speed may have been regarded as "fast" by the average club player.

It is suggested that the perception of a "fast" green speed is a positive comment rather than a statement of a green's

XIII

poor performance. The interpretation of the data presented in Figure 4.13 therefore presumes that "fast" equates with the ideal speed and that "satisfactory" should be the minimum desirable speed. Thus it is concluded that a green speed in excess of 12s would be considered ideal by the average player.

STANDARDS FOR LEVEL BOWLING GREENS

Existing recommendations

Qualitative standards have been applied by turf specialists to evaluate the playing quality of bowling greens. For instance, by rolling bowls over a green the experienced adviser could get an impression both of the quality of surface evenness and the speed of the green. Judgements on the evenness of bowling greens are often based on the spacing and range of contours shown on survey plans.

Few formal standards exist for surface levels though Gooch & Escritt (1975) recommended that a newly constructed bowling green should have surface levels within ±6mm from the mean. With regard to green speeds, the English Bowling Association suggested that the ideal speed is between 12s and 13s and that speeds below 10s are unacceptable. Escritt (1978) gave two categories of green speed using the 30 yard test: a "slow" green, he suggested, would have a green speed of 10s and a "good fast green" would have a speed of 15s.

Sports Turf Research Institute (1983) measured the time taken for a bowl to just reach or just topple into the ditch when delivered from the opposite ditch. Using this test, a time of 18s was considered to be "very fast by average club standards", 14s was considered "satisfactory" and 12s was "excessively slow". The R/T^2 test (Holmes & Bell 1986a) can be used to convert these figures to equivalent speeds using the 30 yard test. Assuming that the figures were based on times for greens of the average dimension of 38m x 38m, they equate with speeds of 15.3s, 11.9s and 10.2s, respectively for the 30 yard test.

Proposal of standards

The questionnaire survey was mainly conducted at local club competitions and matches and although some County and International representatives completed questionnaires, the standards proposed are directed at local leagues and competitions and are given as "Preferred" and "Acceptable" values. The preferred values for surface evenness were determined by taking the category of surface evenness where the highest proportion of the players stated that the surface was "satisfactory". For green speed the preferred minimum speed was set by taking the category where the majority of players thought that green speed was "fast".

It is recognised that certain important competitions are played on specific rinks on a green that are known to be of high quality and the proposed standards attempt to account for this. It is recommended that at least three of the rinks on any green should meet the specified requirements.

Recommended test procedures and test conditions

Surface evenness

A survey of surface levels should be made with a surveyor's level to an accuracy of 1mm. Spot heights should be measured at 2m centres over the whole of the green and related to a permanent benchmark. All heights should be given in millimetres and the following tests refer to heights in millimetres. Surface heights should also be measured around the edges of the bowling green and a horizontal distance of 6m has been found suitable for the spacing of these spot heights. Unless otherwise stated, the proposed limits for green evenness refer to the spot heights measured within the main playing area of the green and the heights recorded around the edges of greens should not be included in the analyses.

The profile gauge can be used to determine the maximum variation in surface levels over a 2m length of the green surface. This instrument may be particularly useful where areas of a green have been returfed or there is an area where poor levels are suspected.

Green speed

(i) *The 30 yard test*: A jack is placed 30 yards (27.4m) from the front edge of the bowling mat. The time taken (measured to the nearest tenth of a second) for the bowl to roll from the bowler's hand and stop within 0.15m of the jack is recorded by stopwatch. The average of three tests in each direction is taken as the speed of the rink.

(ii) *The distance rolled test*: A non-biased bowl is released from a vertical height of 1m down a ramp inclined at 30° to the horizontal. The distance the bowl rolls along the ground is measured to the nearest centimetre from the end of the ramp to the centre of the bowl. Five tests are conducted in each direction on a rink and the average of the ten measures is used in Equation 2 to give the equivalent time for the 30 yard test.

(iii) *The R/T^2 test*: Three bowls are delivered corresponding to 'long', 'medium' and 'short' lengths and the travel time (T) for each bowl is recorded by stopwatch to the nearest tenth of a second. The distance travelled (R) by each wood from the front edge of the bowling mat is also recorded. This procedure is then repeated from the opposite end of the rink. R/T² is calculated for each of the six bowls. The average R/T² value (X) can then be used in Equation 4 to give the equivalent time for the 30 yard test.

$$\text{Green speed} = \sqrt{\frac{D}{X}}$$ **Equation 4** $= T\sqrt{\frac{D}{R}}$

where: D = 27.4m, 30 yards or 90 feet, depending on the units used to measure R.

Climatic variables
There are problems in setting maximum levels of rainfall prior to testing. The problem is particularly relevant to bowls as summer rainfall can be intense and the rainfall total for one day may exceed the total for the remainder of the month. The following conditions are suggested only as guidelines and in most circumstances it will be the duty of the test organisation or club to decide if the weather conditions are typical.

Prior to testing the rainfall shall not exceed any of the following: 5mm in the last hour; 10mm in the last 5 hours; 15mm in the last 10 hours and 25mm in the last 24 hours.

Playing surface conditions
Before testing is undertaken, the playing surface must be prepared as it would be before play. For instance, if the green is usually mown or brushed before play, the same conditions must apply for testing. The test of green speed should be made in the early afternoon once any dew has evaporated.

PROPOSED STANDARDS FOR SURFACE EVENNESS

TABLE 4.2
Proposed standards of surface evenness for individual rinks

	Differences between adjacent spot heights (mm)	Standard deviation of heights (mm)	Standard deviation using profile gauge (mm)
PREFERRED MAXIMUM	6	10	1.5
ACCEPTABLE MAXIMUM	10	15	2

It is recommended that the limits for the difference between adjacent spot heights should apply to the outer 2m around the edge of the bowling green as well as the main playing area. It is therefore suggested, for instance, that a decline or incline of more than 10mm over the outer 2m of a bowling green is unacceptable.

PROPOSED STANDARDS FOR GREEN SPEED

TABLE 4.3
Proposed standards for the speed of individual rinks

PREFERRED MINIMUM SPEED (s)	12
ACCEPTABLE MINIMUM SPEED (s)	10

It is further recommended that all the rinks on a green that will be played during a competition should meet the above requirements and, in addition, should have green speeds within 0.5s of one another.

No upper limits have been set for green speed. The justification for this is that 'quicker' greens are generally thought to demand a greater level of skill from the player. It is therefore thought inappropriate to propose upper limits for green speed. It is also worth noting that synthetic greens are already providing the average player with some experience of fast green conditions (i.e. 13-15s).

A green speed approaching 18s, however, may cause problems during competitions because the bowl will tend to draw right up to and possibly over the rink boundaries for a 'full length jack' with the consequent danger that bowls from adjacent rinks may collide.

REFERENCES

Brearley, M.N. (1961). The motion of a biased bowl with perturbing projection conditions. *Camb. Phil. Soc. Proc.*, **57**, 131-151.

Brearley, M.N. & Bolt, B.A. (1958). The dynamics of a bowl. *Q.J. Mech. Appl. Math.*, **11**, 351-363.

British Crown Green Bowling Association (1983). *Official Handbook*, Graphic Press, Coventry, 76 pp.

Clegg, B. (1976). An impact testing device for *in situ* base course evaluation. *Australian Road Res. Bur. Proc.*, **8**, 1-6.

Dury, P. & Dury, P.L.K. (1983). *A study of natural materials (dynamic/particulate) in the provision of synthetic non-turf sports facilities, particularly for soccer and other winter games.* Nottinghamshire County Council Education Department, Playing Fields Service, 78 pp.

English Bowling Association (1984). *Official Year Book*, Dotesion, Bradford-on-Avon, 296 pp.

Escritt, J.R. (1978). *ABC of Turf Culture*, Kaye & Ward Ltd., London, 239 pp.

Gooch, R.B. & Escritt, J.R. (1975). *Sports Ground Construction - Specifications*, 2nd Ed., National Playing Fields Association, London, 126 pp.

Holmes, G.H. & Bell, M.J. (1986a). The playing quality of level bowling greens: A survey. *J. Sports Turf Res. Inst.*, **62**, 50-65.

Holmes, G.H. & Bell, M.J. (1986b). A pilot study of the playing quality of football pitches. *J. Sports Turf Res. Inst.* **62**, 74-91.

Langvad, B. (1968). Sambandet mellan fotbollens studshöjd och klipphöjden på sportturf. *Weibulls Gräs-tips*, **10-11**, 355-357.

Lush, W.M. (1985). Objective assessment of turf cricket pitches using an impact hammer. *J. Sports Turf Res. Inst.*, **61**, 71-79.

Robinson, G.S. (1977). What the bowler wants in a bowling green. *N.Z.I.T.C. Sports Turf Review*, **112**, 171.

Sports Turf Research Institute (1985). Special problems concerned with the maintenance of flat greens. *Sports Turf Bulletin*, No. 149, April-June, 8-11.

BALL ROLL CHARACTERISTICS OF FIVE TURFGRASSES USED FOR GOLF AND BOWLING GREENS

By P.M. CANAWAY & S.W. BAKER

The Sports Turf Research Institute, Bingley, West Yorkshire, BD16 1AU

SUMMARY

Ball roll tests were carried out to determine the green speed on five turfgrasses: *Festuca rubra* ssp. *litoralis* 'Dawson', *F. rubra* ssp. *commutata* 'Frida', *Agrostis capillaris* 'Bardot', *A. castellana* 'Highland' and *Poa annua*. Measurements were made on four occasions for bowls and three for golf under variations in mowing height and surface moisture. Averaged over all assessment dates *F. rubra* ssp. *litoralis* provided the fastest surface for both golf and bowls, and *P. annua* was consistently the slowest. *Agrostis* species did not provide the fastest playing surface on any occasion, although 'Highland' ranked second overall for bowls. Surface moisture decreased green speed and a reduction in cutting height generally increased it, although there were some inconsistencies. In view of the differences found it is suggested that further research should be carried out on playing quality of grass species and cultivars.

INTRODUCTION

For sports played on fine turf such as golf and bowls, ball roll characteristics of the surface are of great importance. A ball decelerates as it moves across the playing surface because of the effects of rolling resistance, which can be considered as a force acting at the point of contact between the ball and the surface in a direction opposing that of forward motion (Bell *et al.* 1985). The effects of rolling resistance are referred to by players in terms of green "speed", the "faster" is the surface, the lower is its rolling resistance and *vice versa*. Although bowlers and golfers would both agree on what is a fast green the means of characterising the surface have developed in different directions in the two sports. In flat green bowls the method which has been developed and generally used has been to record the *time taken in seconds* for a biased bowl to travel from the bowler's hand and come to rest within 0.15 m of a jack (target ball) sited 27.4 m (30 yards) away. Because on a fast surface the bowl decelerates more slowly it can be released at a lower initial velocity and it also travels in a wider arc, this leads to the seemingly paradoxical situation where a fast green has a higher value, e.g. 15 s, than a slow green, e.g. 12 s. Bell & Holmes (1988) studied the speed of 74 bowling greens and obtained questionnaires from 774 bowlers to determine minimum standards for green speed and these, together with earlier standards, are given in Table 1. No upper limits were proposed for green speeds, players generally equating faster greens with a demand for a greater level of skill.

In golf the approach has been to measure the *distance rolled* by a golf ball when released from a standard ramp known as the stimpmeter (Stimpson 1974). Because of the importance of green speed in tournament conditions, a green speed test comparison table was proposed by the United States Golf Association (USGA) as long ago as 1977 (Radko 1977). This is reproduced in its metric equivalent in Table 2 (note the figures given by Bell *et al.* (1985) were converted inexactly).

TABLE 1
Standards for green speeds on bowling greens

Source of reference	Green speed (s)	Subjective description
Escritt (1978)	15	Fast
	10	Slow
Anon. (1983)	15	Very fast
(Converted by Bell	12	Satisfactory
& Holmes 1988)	10	Slow
Bell & Holmes (1988)	12	Preferred minimum speed
	10	Acceptable minimum speed

TABLE 2
USGA green speed test comparison table (Radko (1977) after conversion to SI units)

	Distance rolled (m)	Green speed
Regular membership play	2.59	Fast
	2.29	Medium-fast
	1.98	Medium
	1.68	Medium-slow
	1.37	Slow
Tournament play	3.20	Fast
	2.90	Medium-fast
	2.59	Medium
	2.29	Medium-slow
	1.98	Slow

Because of its ease of operation the stimpmeter has been widely used in the USA, both in preparation of courses for tournaments (Thomas 1978) and in research studies, for example, the effects of mowing (Engel *et al.* 1981), cultivars of ryegrass for overseeded greens (Batten *et al.* 1981, Dudeck & Peacock 1981). In the UK Lodge & Baker (1991) studied the effects of irrigation, construction and fertiliser nutrition on golf green speed. However, there have been no systematic studies of green speed of different grasses used for fine turf. The objective of the work therefore was to study the green speed for both bowls and golf of some grass species commonly used for fine turf in the UK.

MATERIALS AND METHODS
Trial construction and management
The trial was conducted on a loamy sand soil (9% clay, 10% silt, 81% sand) at the Sports Turf Research Institute, Bingley (NGR SE 095 391). The average slope in the direction of roll was <0.01%. The trial was laid out in four randomised blocks with the plots of the different grasses being 7.5 m in length by 1 m width. The five grasses included in the work and their sowing rates were as follows:

Festuca rubra L. ssp. *litoralis*
(G.F.W. Meyer) Auquier 'Dawson' (slender creeping red fescue)   35 g m⁻²
Festuca rubra L. ssp. *commutata*
Gaud. 'Frida' (Chewings fescue)   35 g m⁻²
Agrostis capillaris L. 'Bardot'
(browntop bent)   10 g m⁻²
Agrostis castellana Boiss. & Reuter
'Highland' (Highland browntop bent)   10 g m⁻²
Poa annua L. "Commercial"
(annual meadow-grass)   35 g m⁻²

The seedbed fertiliser was a 15:9:15 (N:P$_2$O$_5$:K$_2$O) material containing IBDU and 2% MgO, which was applied at a rate of 50 g m⁻². Both seed and fertiliser were applied on 20 June 1986 and the subsequent maintenance treatments are given in Table 3.

Measurement techniques
For bowls, green speed was obtained by releasing an unbiased bowl from a height of 0.5 m down a standard ramp (Bell & Holmes 1988) inclined at an angle of 30° to the horizontal. Six measurements were made on each plot with three tests in opposite directions. The distance

travelled (R, in metres) and the time taken before the ball stopped (T, in seconds) were recorded. Green speed (in seconds) was calculated using an equation given by Bell & Holmes (1988).

Green speed

$$\sqrt{\frac{27.4}{R/T^2}}$$

For golf the speed of the surface was assessed using a stimpmeter (Radko 1977) and the distance rolled was measured. A total of six measurements were made per plot, with three readings in opposite directions. The measurement dates, cutting heights and antecedent rainfall conditions are given in Table 4.

The initial measurements were recorded as either dry or moist, depending whether there had been recent rainfall. The surface was subsequently irrigated using a watering can immediately before measurement on each plot, adding a depth of water equivalent to 1.2 mm.

Statistical analysis
Analysis of variance was used to examine differences in ball roll behaviour of the grass species and subspecies (simply referred to as 'species' hereafter). In the tables and diagrams the least significant difference (LSD) at p = 0.05 is given to allow comparison of the treatment means. The effect of irrigation was examined using paired t-tests, again using a significance level of p <0.05.

RESULTS
Bowls
Green speed values for the individual measurement dates are given in Table 5 and mean values over all dates in relation to species composition are given in Fig. 1.

Grass species caused a significant difference in green

TABLE 3
Maintenance treatments

Mowing	First cut on 30 July 1986 at 50 mm and the cutting height was gradually reduced through the first year of growth reaching 10 mm on 1 December 1986. The cutting height was further reduced in 1987, down to 8 mm on 3 April, 6 mm on 1 June and 5 mm on 22 June.
Fertiliser	The total fertiliser inputs (kg ha⁻¹) were:

	N	P$_2$O$_5$	K$_2$O	
1986	170	45	107	in three applications including seedbed fertiliser
1987	155	0	64	

	The 1986 fertiliser programme included compound granular fertilisers plus ammonium sulphate. The 1987 programme included ammonium sulphate, potassium sulphate, sulphate of iron and dried blood.
Irrigation	During seedling establishment and until 24 July 1986 the trial was watered on a total of ten occasions to ensure that the seedbed remained moist. Thereafter no irrigation was applied, except for the light applications to wet the surface during monitoring work (see main text).
Top dressing	One light application of a 3:1 mix of sand and sterilised compost in 1986 and two applications of 1.5 kg m⁻² in 1987.
Mechanical treatments	The trial was verticut on six occasions between 29 July 1987 and 5 October 1987 and spiked on eight occasions between 3 April 1987 and 24 December 1987.

TABLE 4
Measurement dates, cutting height and antecedent rainfall

Date (1987)	Bowls	Golf	Cutting height mm	Antecedent rainfall (mm) Previous day	Previous 3 days	Previous week
29 May	✓		8	1.6	1.6	5.2
1 June	✓		6	0.7	1.7	3.3
5 June		✓	6	0.1*	22.0	27.2
27 July	✓		5	10.3	10.3	11.9
30 July		✓	5	12.5	13.6	25.0
31 July		✓	5	0.2	13.8	24.1
23 Oct.	✓	✓	5	<0.1	16.0	33.5

TABLE 5
Effect of grass species and moisture conditions on bowls green speed (s) (all dates 1987)

	29 May Dry	Wet	1 June Dry	Wet	27 July Dry	Wet	23 Oct. Moist
F. rubra ssp. *litoralis*	11.3	11.2	11.4	11.3	11.7	11.9	11.2
F. rubra ssp. *commutata*	10.8	10.5	10.3	10.4	11.6	11.6	10.9
Agrostis capillaris	10.7	10.2	10.8	10.4	11.2	11.4	10.7

speed on all sampling occasions, except on 27 July following irrigation. Green speed was greatest on *F. rubra* ssp. *litoralis*, averaging 11.45 over all sampling dates, whilst *P. annua* gave the slowest surface with an average green speed of 10.45.

Green speed appeared to increase as the cutting height was lowered and was greatest on 27 July 1987 at a cutting height of 5 mm. The effect was, however, not entirely consistent and, for example, there was no difference in ball roll values at the 8 mm and 6 mm cutting heights.

The effect of irrigation was also inconsistent. On 29 May and 1 June 1987 green speed decreased after irrigation but on 27 June 1987 there was a significant increase in green speed (p <0.05) after irrigation.

Golf
The pattern for ball roll for golf was similar to that for bowls (Fig. 2, Table 6). Averaged over all dates the rolling distance was greatest for *F. rubra* ssp. *litoralis*, i.e. 1.96 m and least for *P. annua*, averaging only 1.57 m.

There was a significant difference in ball roll (p <0.001) following irrigation, averaging 1.87 m when dry and 1.76 m when wet. Ball roll values were greatest under dry conditions at a cutting height of 5 mm on 30 July 1987 when ball roll for all the grasses except *P. annua* was greater than 2 m.

Over all dates, ball roll ranged from 1.37 m for *P. annua* on 5 June 1987 at a cutting height of 6 mm and after irrigation to 2.21 m for *F. rubra* ssp. *litoralis* under dry conditions on 30 July 1987 (5 mm cutting height).

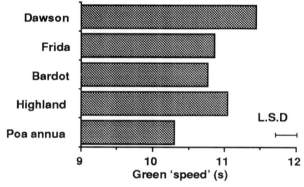

FIGURE 1. Green speed for bowls for the different grass species averaged over all sampling dates. (In both figures Dawson = *F. rubra* ssp. *litoralis*, Frida = *F. rubra* ssp. *commutata*, Bardot = *A. capillaris* and Highland = *A. castellana*.)

DISCUSSION
Considering first the results for bowls, none of the measurements reached the preferred minimum speed of 12 s given by Bell & Holmes (1988). However, only one species (*P. annua*) failed to reach the acceptable minimum speed of 10 s on one occasion of measurement. Overall, *F. rubra* ssp. *litoralis* 'Dawson' always gave the fastest surface and *P. annua* always gave the slowest surface. The two *Agrostis spp.* and *F. rubra* ssp. *commutata* were intermediate in performance and not statistically different from one another except on 1 June when *A. castellana* was significantly faster than *F. rubra* ssp. *commutata*. Overall, it would be fair to state that these three species were comparable in performance. Evans (1988) stated "long experience indicates that the most common causes of excessive slowness are the dominance of annual meadow-grass in the sward and the presence of a sub-

TABLE 6
Effect of grass species and moisture conditions on distance rolled (m) for golf (all dates 1987)

	5 June		30/31 July		23 Oct.
	Moist	Wet	Dry	Wet	Moist
F. rubra ssp. *litoralis*	1.87	1.78	2.21	2.01	1.93
F. rubra ssp. *commutata*	1.72	1.69	2.10	1.95	2.05
Agrostis capillaris	1.69	1.67	2.10	1.92	1.91
Agrostis castellana	1.73	1.66	2.09	1.93	1.71
Poa annua	1.49	1.37	1.72	1.64	1.62
LSD (5%)	0.182	0.140	0.232	0.185	0.131

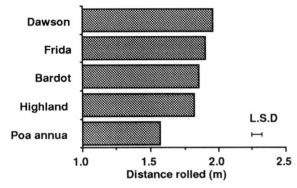

FIGURE 2. Distance rolled by a golf ball for the different grass species averaged over all sampling dates.

surface thatch or fibre layer". The trial certainly confirmed this long held view of *P. annua*. Evans (1988) also stated "fescue produces a tough wiry type of turf and a fast bowling surface". The trial also bore out this comment although clearly the type of fescue which is chosen could have a large bearing on the speed of the green. Newell & Gooding (1990) demonstrated a considerable range of values for: shoot density, leaf width, leaf numbers, shoot phytomass and thatch depth for a number of species and sub-species of *Festuca* and hence there could be a large, undiscovered source of variation in green speed among different fescues.

For golf, during the trial no attempt had been made to emulate tournament preparation and hence the trial would equate with regular club greens. The figures given in Table 2 for golf green speeds should not necessarily be equated with those given for "minimum standards" for green speed of bowling greens in Table 1. The purpose of the USGA green speed comparison table was not to propose minimum standards for different categories of green speed, but rather to provide an objective test of green speed to enable superintendents to work towards more uniform putting conditions over 18 greens (Engel *et al.* 1980). Indeed, it is not stated whether the figures given refer to the minimum value for each category or its mid-point. Furthermore, the inference is that such precision was not intended. However, some general comparisons can be made. The *P. annua* gave consistently the slowest surface and would have corresponded with slow to medium-slow in the USGA table. Only the *F. rubra* ssp. *litoralis* would have been rated medium-fast on 30 July (dry). All of the remaining data fell into the

medium or medium-slow categories.

The effect of moisture was generally to decrease green speed for both bowls and golf as would be expected, although it apparently increased for bowls on one occasion of measurement. Results of t-tests carried out on the pooled data for wet versus dry showed significant differences for both bowls (t = 2.23, p = 0.04) and for golf (t = 5.61, p = 0.0003). The effect of moisture was greater for the smaller golf ball than for the relatively massive bowl. Only 1.5% reduction in green speed due to wetness was observed for bowls, whereas the reduction was 6% for golf (calculated as (dry – wet/dry) x 100).

Overall, the trial showed interesting species differences in ball roll characteristics, which suggests that a wider screening of species and cultivars, for use on UK golf greens, for green speed could yield fruitful results, especially for seed companies marketing cultivars for the golf course market. It was originally intended to continue the trial for a further year, however, significant amounts of *P. annua* invaded the plots of the other species (12% overall on the worst affected species, with some plots having individual amounts up to 35%). It was felt that this *P. annua* contamination would undoubtedly mask species differences and therefore the trial was ended.

ACKNOWLEDGEMENTS
The authors wish to thank the Sports Council (London) for support for work on bowls, Messrs Pye, Smithies and Birtle for technical assistance and Mrs D.S. Hill for preparation of the manuscript.

REFERENCES
Anon. (1983). The speed of golf and bowling greens. *Sports Turf Bulletin* 143, Oct.-Dec., pp. 11-12.

Batten, S.M., Beard, J.B., Johns, D., Almodares, A. & Eckhardt, J. (1981). Characterisations of cool season turfgrasses for winter overseeding of dormant bermudagrass. In: *Proc. 4th Int. Turfgrass Res. Conf.* (Ed. R.W. Sheard), University of Guelph, Canada, pp. 83-94.

Bell, M.J., Baker, S.W. & Canaway, P.M. (1985). Playing quality of sports surfaces : a review. *J. Sports Turf Res. Inst.* **61**, 26-45.

Bell, M.J. & Holmes, G. (1988). Playing quality standards

for level bowling greens. *J. Sports Turf Res. Inst.* **64**, 48-62.

Dudeck, A.E. & Peacock, C.H. (1981). Effects of several overseeded ryegrasses on turf quality, traffic tolerance and ball roll. In: *Proc. 4th Int. Turfgrass Res. Conf.* (Ed. R.W. Sheard), University of Guelph, Canada, pp. 75-81.

Engel, R.E., Radko, A.M. & Trout, J.R. (1980). Influence of mowing procedures on roll speed of putting greens. *USGA Green Section Record* **18**, 1, 7-9.

Escritt, J.R. (1978). *ABC of Turf Culture*, Kaye & Ward Ltd, London, 239 pp.

Evans, R.D.C. (1988). *Bowling Greens Their History, Construction and Maintenance.* The Sports Turf Research Institute, Bingley, 196 pp.

Lodge, T.A. & Baker, S.W. (1991). The construction, irrigation and fertiliser nutrition of golf greens. II. Playing quality assessments after establishment and during the first year of differential irrigation and nutrition treatments. *J. Sports Turf Res. Inst.* **67**, 44-52.

Newell, A.J. & Gooding, M.J. (1990). The performance of fine-leaved *Festuca* spp. in close-mown turf. *J. Sports Turf Res. Inst.* **66**, 120-132.

Radko, A.M. (1977). How fast are your greens? *USGA Green Section Record* **15**, 5, 10-11.

Thomas, F. (1978). The stimpmeter and the Open. *USGA Green Section Record* **16**, 6, 7-9.

Stimpson, E.S. (1974). Putting greens - how fast? *USGA Golf J.* **27**, 2, 28-29.

BIBLIOGRAPHY AND REFERENCES

History of the game

Anon. (c. 1934). *Encyclopaedia of Sports Games & Pastimes.* Fleetway House, London, pp. 93-99.

Arlott, J. (Ed.) (1975). *Oxford Companion to Sports & Games.* Oxford University Press, London, pp. 89-106.

Brasch, R. (1972). *How Did Sports Begin?* Longman Group Ltd, London, pp. 163-166.

Brougham, R.W. (1990). Bowls - Brazilian style. *NZ Turf Management J.* **4**, 1, February, 23.

Bryant, D. (1990). *Bryant on Bowls.* Pelham Books - Stephen Green Press, London, 223 pp.

Foulis, D. (1986). Bowling in the good old days. *World Bowls,* February, p. 19.

Hawkes, K. & Lindley, G. (1974). *Encyclopaedia of Bowls.* R. Hale & Co, London, 254 pp.

Henry, J.M. (1977). Introduction to Lawn Bowling. *California Turfgrass Culture* **27**, 3, 17-19.

Hotchkiss, F. (1937). *The Game of Bowls.* William Heinemann Ltd, London, 144 pp.

John, G. (1991). *Flat Green Bowls : The Skills of the Game.* The Crowood Press Ltd, Swindon, Wilts, 121 pp.

Jones, C.M. (Ed.) (1965). *Winning Bowls.* Stanley Paul & Co, London, 144 pp.

Johnson, C. (1974). *Beginner's Guide to Bowls.* Pelham Books, London.

King, N. (1959). *Tackle Bowls this Way.* Stanley Paul & Co Ltd, London, 128 pp.

Linney, E.J. (1933). *A History of the Game of Bowls.* T. Werner Laurie.

Mills, C. (1983). *Winning Bowls : An Introduction to Crown Green Bowls.* W. Foulsham & Co Ltd, Slough, Berks.

Moore, R. (Ed.) (1982). *Official Rules of Sports & Games 1982-83.* Kay & Ward, Tadworth, Surrey, pp. 141-166.

Newby, D. (1987). Indoor bowls. *Leisure Management* **7**, No. 1 January.

Sullivan, P. (1986). *Bowls : the Records.* Guinness Superlatives, Enfield, Middlesex.

Viney, N. and Grant N. (1978). *An Illustrated History of Ball Games.* William Heinemann Ltd, London, pp. 161-179.

Vose, J.D. (1969). *Corner to Corner (and Over the Crown).* The Strule Press, Omagh, N. Ireland, 191 pp.

Wakelam, M. (1988). *Crown Green Bowls.* Haygrove Pub. Ltd., Surrey, 112 pp.

Greenkeeping : historical

Anon. (undated, c. 1930). *Bowling Greens : Advice to Groundsmen.* Issued by Miners' Welfare Commission, London, 24 pp.

Anon. (undated, c. 1935?). *Notes on the Maintenance of Bowling Greens.* Maxwell M. Hart, London, 23 pp.

Beale, R. (1931). *The Book of the Lawn.* Cassell & Co. Ltd, London, 151 pp.

Beale, R. (1924). *Lawns for Sports : Their Construction & Upkeep.* Simpkin Marshall Hamilton Kent & Co. Ltd., London, 276 pp.

Cave, L.W. (1967). *Cave's Guide to Turf Culture.* Pelham Books Ltd, London, 181 pp.

Cherry, C.E. (1947). The maintenance & management of sea-washed turf bowling greens. *J. Bd. of Greenkeeping Research* **7**, 23, 70-79.

Clouston, D. (1937). *The Establishment & Care of Fine Turf for Lawns and Sportsgrounds.* Wyllie & Son, Aberdeen, Scotland, 121 pp.

Dawson, R.B. (1933). Report to the London & Southern Counties Bowling Association. *J. Bd. of Greenkeeping Research* **3**, 8, 19-22.

Dawson, R.B. (1939). *Practical Lawncraft.* First Edition. Crosby Lockwood & Son Ltd, London, 300 pp.

"EX GREEN RANGER" (1936). Bowling green investigations - a plea for more support. *J. Bd. of Greenkeeping Research* **4**, 14, 217-219 .

Faulkner, R.P. (1950). *The Science of Turf Cultivation.* Technical Press Ltd., Surrey, 64 pp.

Fittis, R.S. (1975). *Sports & Pastimes of Scotland.* Alex Gardner 1891. Reprint by E.P. Publishing, Wakefield, pp. 200-203.

Garelick, P. (1987). Salt of the earth (turf growing in Cumbria). *Horticulture Week* May 22, p. 20.

Halford, D.G. (1982). Old lawnmowers. *Shire Album No. 91.* Shire Publications Ltd, Aylesbury, Bucks, 32 pp.

Howell, W. (1967). Bowling greens in Australia. *Parks & Sportsgrounds*, September, pp. 1071-1073.

Howell, W. (1968). *Bowling Greens : Construction and Maintenance.* Published by Journal of Park Administration Ltd, London, 172 pp.

Lawfield, W.N. (1959). *Lawns & Sports Greens.* W.H. & L. Collingridge Ltd, London, 84 pp.

Lewis, I.G. (undated, c. 1950?). *Succeeding with New Greens from Sea-Washed Turf.* Issued by J. Brailsford (Turf Supplier), 12 pp.

MacDonald, J. (1923). *Lawns, Links and Sportsfields.* Country Life Ltd, London and George Newnes, London, 78 pp.

Macself, A.J. (1924). Bowling greens. *Grass ..... for Ornamental Lawns and All Purposes of Sports and Games.* Cecil Palmer, London, pp. 158-165.

Manson, J.A. (1919). *The Complete Bowler.* A. & C. Black Ltd, London, 248 pp.

Paul, W. (c. 1920). *Digging Up a Bowling Green by Paul's Process.* Privately published by the author, Paisley, Scotland.

Paul, W. (c. 1920). *The Care and Upkeep of Bowling Greens.* Privately published by the author, Paisley, Scotland, 4 pp.

Pettigrew, V.M.H. (1937). *Municipal Parks : Layout, Management & Administration.* Published by The Journal of Parks Administration, London, 279 pp.

Pilley, P. (Ed.) (1987). From Drake to Bryant. *The Story of Bowls.* Stanley Paul, London, 301 pp.

Robertson, T. (1934). The construction and maintenance of bowling greens. *Official Year Book of the E.B.A.*

Rohde, E.S. (1927). *Garden-craft in The Bible and other Essays.* Herbert Jenkins Ltd, London, 242 pp.

Rohde, E.S. (1932). *The Story of the Garden.* The Medici Society, London, 326 pp.

Sanders, T.W. (1920). *Lawns and Greens.* W. H. and L. Collingridge, London, 138 pp.

Smith, P.W. (1950). *The Planning, Construction & Maintenance of Playing Fields.* Oxford University Press, London, 224 pp.

Sutton & Sons. (1931). *Lawns : Garden Lawns, Tennis Courts, Croquet Grounds etc.* Sutton & Sons, Reading, Berks, 64 pp.

Suttons of Reading (1948). *Lawns and Sportsgrounds.* 16th Edn. Sutton & Sons, Reading, Berk, 79 pp.

Sutton, M.A.F. (1962). *Lawns and Sportsgrounds.* 17th Edn. Sutton & Sons, Reading, Berks, 248 pp.

Various Authors (1948). The green manual : the construction of bowling greens and their maintenance. *Official Handbook of the Johannesburg and Southern Transvaal S.D.B.A. Greens Advisory Committee.* Walters & Powell, Johannesburg, South Africa, 123 pp.

Construction

Anon. (1962). *Bowls, Flat & Crown Green.* Know the Game Series. EP Publishing Ltd, Wakefield, West Yorkshire, 41 pp.

Baker, S.W. (1990). *Sands for Sports Turf Construction and Maintenance.* Sports Turf Research Institute, 67 pp.

Gooch, R.B. & Escritt, J.R. (1975). *Sportsground Construction Specifications.* N.P.F.A., London 2nd Edn, 126 pp.

Sports Council (undated, c. 1983). *A New Bias : A Report on the Future Provision for Bowls.* The Sports Council, London, 46 pp.

STRI (1979). Organising fine turf construction d) bowling green. In: *Sports Turf Bulletin No. 124*, Jan-Mar, p. 7, Bingley, West Yorkshire.

STRI (1982/3). Bowling greens : construction & maintenance of flat & crown greens. *Sports Turf Bulletin Nos. 137, 138, 139, 140* (in four parts), April-March, Bingley, West Yorkshire.

Maintenance

Anon. (1988). Playing quality for natural turf sports surfaces : level bowling greens. *Sports Turf Bulletin*, STRI, **160**, 11-12.

Anon. (1989). *Sports Ground Maintenance. An Elementary Guide for Club Committees & Their Groundstaff.* National Playing Fields Association, London, pp. 21-28.

Baldwin, N.A. (1990). *Turfgrass Pests and Diseases*. Sports Turf Research Institute, Bingley, 57 pp.

Bladon, M.J. (1990). Maintenance of bowling greens. *Sports Turf Newsletter (Canada)* **3**, 4, 3-5.

De Malmanche, M. (1991). Beam me up - laser levelling available in New Zealand. *NZ Turf Management J.* **5**, 3, 8.

Escritt, J.R. (1978). *ABC of Turf Culture*. Kaye & Ward Ltd, London, 239 pp.

Evans, R.D.C. (1984). Spring work on the bowling green. *Parks Golf Courses and Sportsgrounds* **49**, 6, 22-23.

Evans, R.D.C. (1989). The care of bowling green ditches, banks and surrounds. *Sports Turf Bulletin*, STRI, **167**, 9.

Evans, R.D.C. (1990). Bowling green maintenance. *Sports Turf Bulletin*, STRI, Bingley, **171**, 2.

Evans, R.D.C. (1990). Green matters. *World Bowls Magazine* (in 5 parts), June, p. 13, July, p. 16, August, p. 19, September-October, p. 33, November, p. 22.

Evans, R.D.C. (1991). Autumn bowling green maintenance. *Parks Golf Courses & Sportsgrounds* **57**, 1, 28.

Holmes, G. & Bell, M.J. (1985). Is your green fast or slow? *World Bowls Magazine*, March, p. 25.

Holmes, G. & Bell, M.J. (1986). Help keep our greens level. *World Bowls Magazine*, August, pp. 14-15.

Holmes, G. & Bell, M.J. (1986). The playing quality of level bowling greens : a survey. *J. Sports Turf Res. Inst.* **62**, p. 50.

Holmes, G. & Bell, M.J. (1987). *Standards of Playing Quality for Natural Turf*. Sports Council/STRI, pp. 36-49.

Hope, F. (1990). *Turf Culture : A Manual for the Groundsman* (2nd Edn.). Cassell Publications Ltd, London, 293 pp.

Laird, E. (1990). Laser levelling (of bowling greens) - caution!. *Turf Topics*, TRAI, Victoria, Australia **32**, 7-8.

Lawson, D.M. (1991). *Fertilisers for Turf*. Sports Turf Research Institute, Bingley, 47 pp.

Mulder, J.E.V. & Walmsley, W.H. Monitoring bowling green levels. *NZ Turf Management J.* **3**, 2, 7.

Perris, J. (1988). Getting bowling greens back into condition. *Parks Golf Courses & Sportsgrounds* **53**, 5, 4-5.

Reed, A. (1992). Care of bowling greens in the playing season. *The Groundsman* **45**, 3, 20.

Smith, J.D., Jackson, N., Woolhouse, A.R. (1989). *Fungal Diseases of Amenity Turf Grasses*. E. & F.N. Spon, London, 401 pp.

Squires, N.R.W. (1992). Autumn maintenance of bowling greens. *Sports Turf Bulletin*, STRI, Bingley, **179**, 2-4.

Stansfield, D.M. (1983). Flat rink bowling green problems. *Parks Golf Courses & Sportsgrounds* **48**, 12, 809.

Stansfield, D.M. (1985). Technical note - survey of pH, phosphate and potash levels in soil samples taken from golf and bowling greens. *J. Sports Turf Res. Inst.* **61**, 136.

STRI (1985). Special number on bowling greens. *Sports Turf Bulletin No. 149*, April - June, Bingley, West Yorkshire.

STRI (1987). Special number of bowling greens. *Sports Turf Bulletin No. 158*, July-September, Bingley, W. Yorks.

Walmsley, W.H. (1989). Interpreting bowling green level survey plans. *NZ Turf Management J.* **3**, 3, 7.

Walmsley, W.H. (1990). Centre pop-up sprinklers for bowling greens. *NZ Turf Management J.* **4**, 4, 26.

New Zealand *Cotula* greens
Davies, B. (1991). The origins of *Cotula*. *NZ Turf Management J.* **5**, 3, 8.

Escritt, J.R. (1978). *Cotula* bowling greens. In: *ABC of Turf Culture*. Kay & Ward, London, p.21

Evans, P.S. (1984). The Use of Cotula for Bowling Greens in New Zealand. *J. Sports Turf Res. Inst.* **60**, 37.

Evans, P.S. (Ed.) (1990). Bowls. In: *Proc. Third NZ Sports Turf Convention*. Palmerston North, pp. 32-81.

Grant, A. (1991). *Cotula* lawns : a case study. *NZ Turf Management J.* **5**, 2, 25.

Laughton, P. (1991). Planing your bowling green. *NZ Turf Management J.* **5**, 4, 29.

Levy, E.B. (undated, c. 1950). Construction, renovation & care of the bowling green. *N.Z. Greenkeeping Research Committee.*

Murphy, J.W. (Ed.) (1985). Bowls section. In: *Proc. Fourth NZ Sports Turf Convention.* Palmerston North, pp. 32-81.

Richards, C.W. (1991). *Feasibility Study on the Establishment and Playing Quality of Cotula Species for Level Green Bowls in the United Kingdom.* STRI Document 5004/2, unpublished, 3 pp.

Robinson, G.S. (1977). What the bowler wants in a bowling green. *N.Z.I.T.C. Sports Turf Review* **122**, 171.

Stockdill, S.M.J. (1961). Weed greens. In: *Turf Culture.* N.Z. Institute for Turf Culture. Palmerston North, New Zealand, p.77.

Walker, C. (1971). The bowling green. In: *Turf Culture.* New Zealand Institute for Turf Culture, p. 234.

Walmsley, W.H. (1989). Bowling green mower adjustment and renovation. *NZ Turf Management J.* **3**, 1, 8.

Way, B. (1991). Part 1 : bowling surfaces : *Dioica* vs *Maniototo. NZ Turf Management J.* **5**, 2, 9.

Way, B. (1991). Bowls tournament preparation. *NZ Turf Management J.* **5**, 4, 14.

Wrigley, M.P. (Ed.) (1980). Bowls. In: *Proc. of the First New Zealand Sports Turf Convention* May, pp. 36-66.